Contributors

Beth R Crisp, Department of Social Policy and Social Work, University of Glasgow, Lilybank House, Bute Gardens, Glasgow G12 8RT, Scotland

John Pinkerton and **Jim Campbell**, School of Social Work, Queens University Belfast

Pat Petrie, Thomas Coram Research Unit Institute of Education, University of London

Juha Hamalainen, University of Kuopio, Finland

Kieron Hatton, University of Portsmouth

CONTENTS   PAGE

Chapter 1   **1**
Introduction
Brian Littlechild and Karen Lyons

Chapter 2   **3**
Similar but not the same:
    social work education in Britain from an Australian perspective
Beth R Crisp

Chapter 3.   **11**
Coming to terms with 'pedagogy':
    Reconceptualising work with children
Pat Petrie

Chapter 4.   **17**
Social Care Service and Social Work in Transition
Juha Hamalainen

Chapter 5   **23**
Social Work & the 'Troubles' in Northern Ireland:
    Reconfiguring Occupational Space
John Pinkerton and JimCampbell

Chapter 6   **31**
Valuing Difference:
    making sense of different value bases
Kieron Hatton

CHAPTER 1
INTRODUCTION

What is the future of social work? Where is it to find its occupational space in the changing landscape of social service provision, with pressures of globalisation, managerialism and performance based, audited and cost controlled cultures?

The papers presented in this collection, originally presented to the attempt to a seminar organised by the UK's Joint University Council Social Work Education's International sub-committee Locating the Occupational Space for Social Work: International Perspectives in November 2001, attempt to answer these and other challenges to the way forward for social work, from an international perspective, and to develop strategies for the development of social work. It provides critical and novel insights into current formulations of social work at national and international levels, and how different values, political and economic drivers are affecting the development of social work, and how the social work community can attempt to affect these.

Pat Petrie from the Thomas Coram Research Unit, Institute of Education, University of London, presents the findings of her research in Europe concerning social pedagogy, and considers the relevance of this unique approach to the United Kingdom. Petrie explores the different meanings of the term pedagogy, and explores its place in several European countries using qualitative approaches, and national reviews of policy and practice.

Juha Hamalainen, University of Kuopio, Finland, explores what he sees as the three predominant models of social work service provision in Europe: the Nordic or institutional model, based on social security and national insurance, rooted in market socialism; the middle European model, based on a corporate model of the welfare state, where the social market predominates; and the Anglo-American model, which is based on a liberal view of social policy, with individual freedoms based on rights set out in legislation, with minimal state intervention.

Hamalainen suggests that the Anglo-American model is set to dominate the international stage, with globalisation and free market ideology becoming the major forces which social work must contend with in practice, training, education and social work's value and skills base. The particaular threats to social work's capacity to promote democracy, social change and social justice are explored.

Continuing with the theme of social justice, John Pinkerton presents a piece prepared by himself and Jim Campbell, both of the School of Social Work, Queens University Belfast, concerning how global theoretical frameworks affect the development and practice of social work in Northern Ireland, where the fractured civil society and problematic issues of State legitimacy have given rise to the 'post technocratic option' compared to the situation in the 1970s and 1980s when social work was a profession in the ascendancy and seen as part of the British solution to the problems of sectarianism and conflict in Northern Ireland.

The status of social work is seen by Pinkerton to have been enhanced by its inclusion in the unique- in the UK- situation where it is integrated within health and social care services, which were seen as non-sectarian and technocratic. However the onset of Thatcherism and managerialism worked against integrated services, which had major implications for those form social work backgrounds managing such services. He suggests that social work may split into two separate occupational groups- the highly skilled therapists, and the low paid operatives.

Pinkerton emphasises the need for community social work, challenging sectarianism, working with minority groups, and user empowerment of a re-invigorated social work in Northern Ireland.

Kieron Hatton of the University of Portsmouth draws on his research in Britain, Denmark and Ireland, and suggests that is little evidence of a developing European social work. He argues that the International Federation of Social Workers definition of social work does not address the importance of social control functions in social work, although social work is about the dialectic between empowerment and regulation. Hatton explores how different formulations of social work within different ideological and political systems, based on different views of human nature, affect the values and delivery of services within the different countries. Issues of anti-discriminatory practice are examined by Hatton as touchstones of such differences.

Beth R Crisp of the Department of Social Policy and Social Work, University of Glasgow, examines some of the differences between social work education in Australia and the United Kingdom based on her experiences of teaching social work in Scotland. These concern the definition of social work, the organisation, regualtion and role of social work education, and placement offerings. Notwithstanding these differences, the paper concludes that social work education is largely the same between Australia and the UK. Nevertheless, at a time when British employers are increasingly attempting to recruit Australian social workers, some recognition of differences is essential, and she explores what the issues are for employers who wish to employ workers who have qualified in another country. Crisp argues that radical social work still has some currency in Australia while the UK model emphasises expectations on state social workers, with particular emphasis on legal responsibilities and organisational issues, as emphasised by CCETSW (now the GSSC).

NOTES

1.   At the time of writing the Scottish Executive's paper was not yet available.

CHAPTER 2
SIMILAR BUT NOT THE SAME: SOCIAL WORK EDUCATION IN BRITAIN FROM AN AUSTRALIAN PERSPECTIVE
Beth R Crisp

INTRODUCTION

In recent years I have come to expect mailings to members from the Australian Association of Social Workers [ASS] to include a number of advertisements for UK recruiting companies. Nevertheless, I was surprised to find seven such advertisements in the September 2001 edition of *Australian Social Work*, and given the current shortages of social workers in many parts of Britain, expect the recruitment of overseas trained staff to remain integral to the employment strategies of some local authorities. The implicit assumption is that social work (and hence social work training) in Australia is the same as, or similar enough to, social work in the UK. While my task is to compare social work education between our nations, one by-product may be that you find yourselves reflecting on the product that is acquired when foreign trained social workers are employed.

As social work education varies considerably within both Australia and the UK, my starting point for considering differences in social work education between these countries has been the various documents which contain the parameters and minimum standards required of programme providers and candidates for an entry-level qualification in social work. In Australia, such documentation is produced by the Australian Association of Social Workers (2000). While recognising that the Central Council for Education and Training for Social Work (CCETSW) has recently been superseded by the four new councils in Scotland, England, Wales and Northern Ireland, and that discussion papers for the future of social work education have been issued in England, Wales and Northern Ireland[1], fundamental principles in the CCETSW (1995a; 1995b) documentation largely remain (or at least in relation to the issues which I will focus on in this paper).

WHAT IS SOCIAL WORK?

In both Britain (Jones, 1998) and Australia (Dickey, 1987) social work has its origins in the Charity Organisation Societies and other philanthropic attempts to aid the poor. Statutory responsibilities such as child protection were later additions to the realms of social work. The current extent to which some Australian social work texts are adopted in the UK and vice versa reflects many ongoing similarities between social work in these geographically diverse arenas. Yet despite the many similarities, differences in conceptions and the practice of social work exist have emerged in recent decades as Australia has moved on from importing British and American versions of social work (Napier and George, 2001) and has developed an Australian version of social work which reflects our distinctive national history, health and welfare systems, economic and social policies, as well as the experiences and expectations of social workers (McCallum, 2001). Sharon McCallum, in a recent edition of *Australian Social Work* makes this point cogently when reflecting on her experiences in Canada:

> *When I was studying in Canada in the early nineties I was surprised at how conservative social work was in that country as it quite closely follows a psychodynamic line of development. In comparison, I was often told that social work in Australia was socialist. This was news to me: social work at home was social work... And it was not until I had*

lived, studied and worked in another country that I could see just how the actions of the professions differ from place to place. (McCallum, 2001: 2)

In its *Policy and Procedures for Establishing Eligibility for Membership of AASW*, the document which outlines the requirements for accrediting social work courses in Australia, the AASW (2000) has developed the following definition of social work:

> *Social work is the profession committed to the pursuit of social justice, to the enhancement of the quality of life, and the development of the full potential of each individual, group and community in society.*
>
> *Social workers pursue these goals by working to address the barriers, inequalities and injustices that exist in society, and by active involvement in situations of personal distress and crisis. This is done by working with individuals towards the realisation of their intellectual, physical and emotional potential, and by working with individuals, groups and communities in the pursuit and achievement of equitable access to social, economic and political resources. Social workers also pursue their goals through involvement in research, policy development and analysis, management and consultancy.*
>
> *Social workers:*
> *Work with individuals, groups and communities to shape and change the conditions in which they live.*
> *Advocate for disadvantaged members of society.*
> *Work towards the elimination of social inequalities in society to facilitate a more equitable distribution of resources.*
> *Engage in research to build our knowledge-base and understanding of society.*
> *Analyse, challenge and develop social policies.*
> *Social work practice is informed by professional education based on an analysis and understanding of human development and behaviour and of complex social processes. It accepts a commitment to working within a stated value position and code of ethics. An integral part of the education of each social worker is the demonstration in practice settings of this analysis, understanding and commitment.* (AASW, 2000: 4)

This Australian definition of social work encompasses both sides of the social work/ social administration divide which is much more apparent in the UK. By comparison, the equivalent CCETSW (1995a) document provides a much more circumscribed view of the purpose of social work, with a greater emphasis on direct service provision. Rather than contributing to social policy development, the CCETSW perspective emphasises the requirement for social workers to work within established policy and legislative guidelines. CCETSW balances the potential for empowerment with notions of social control, which are missing from the Australian definition of social work (although not from social work practice in Australia):

> *The purpose of social work is to enable children, adults, families, groups and communities to function, participate and develop in society. Social workers practice in a society of complexity, change and diversity, and the majority of people to whom they provide services, are amongst the most vulnerable and disadvantaged in that society. Social workers are employed by a range of statutory, voluntary and private organizations, and work in collaboration with colleagues from allied professions and departments, as part of a network of welfare, health, housing, education and criminal justice provision.*

Social work and criminal justice agencies are given specific responsibilities and powers through statute, and social workers and probation officers have to practice within legislative frameworks and organizational policies and procedures. They have to balance the needs, rights, responsibilities and resources of people with those of the wider community, and provide appropriate levels of support, advocacy, care, protection and control. (CCETSW, 1995a: 16)

Chris Jones' (1998) paraphrase of the CCETSW definition of social work provides an even starker contrast with how social work has been defined in Australia:

... in recent years it would appear that, for some, social work is best described as that activity undertaken by those people employed as social workers by state social service departments. This is the position taken for example by the CCETSW in its national curriculum for social work education. It is not a helpful definition in that it captures nothing of the history of social work or its essence independent of a specific context and suggests that social work can be almost anything if it is called such by a state agency. (Jones, 1998: 34)

These differences in the definition of social work manifest themselves in a range of issues pertaining to qualifying social work programmes including the questions of what is the role of social work education, and the curriculum for courses leading to qualification as a social worker. However, before considering these questions, we should first detour via a discussion of the organisation of social work education, which also impinges on each of these.

ORGANISATION OF SOCIAL WORK EDUCATION

In Australia the Bachelor of Social Work (BSW) degree is the qualifying award for entry into professional social work. The BSW can only be awarded to candidates who have completed a minimum of four full-time years of tertiary education, of which at least two years have been dedicated to social work. Hence most BSW courses are either four year undergraduate degrees or two year courses of study which require applicants to be graduates or to have already completed two years tertiary study which should have included studies into human behaviour (e.g. psychology) and society (e.g. sociology or another social science). Included in the BSW programme must be at least 140 days of supervised practice, in a minimum of two contrasting settings.

The BSW must be taught by a recognised university, with the programme headed by a senior academic who is eligible for AASW membership and preferably of at least the rank of associate professor (or reader). With increasing numbers of Australian social workers holding doctorates or currently undertaking doctoral degrees, some schools of social work are now requiring a doctorate even for junior lectureships.

Universities apply to have their courses accredited by the AASW, and once accredited undergo five-yearly reviews for re-accreditation, the BSW is an academic degree of the awarding university. It is thus the university authorities which have the sole determining power as to whether candidates meet the requirements for the qualification, despite a recognition that "social work education must be provided in a manner that acknowledges the partnership between university and human service organisation" (AASW, 2000: 5). For example, in relation to placements, the AASW guidelines note:

The assessment process should include contributions from all parties involved in the student's placement and should be carried out in an equitable and collaborative manner.

The final decision about whether the student has achieved the identified educational out-comes and has passed the field education subject is to be made by the school after con-sideration of material submitted by all parties. (AASW, 2000: 9-10)

The primacy of the universities as the providers of social work education in Australia is a far cry from the organisation of social work in the UK, where *'The DipSW is a CCETSW award'* (CCETSW, 1995a: 56) which can be awarded to successful candidates who may be sub-graduates, post-graduates or anywhere in between. While the DipSW must be taught by an educational institution, there is no requirement that this be a university. Nor is there a specific requirement for course providers to have staff who have attained qualifications of a minimum level (e.g. Bachelors, Masters or Doctoral), or hold positions of or equivalent to a senior academic. Rather CCETSW spelt out a requirement for programme providers to have *'Staff with relevant qualifications and experience to meet students learning and assess-ment needs'* (CCETSW, 1995b: 14). Furthermore, decisions about educational outcomes are made not just by the educational institution, but must take into account the views of external parties who are members of Practice Assessment Panels and Programme Assessment Boards.

Apart from quite different relationships between the universities and other key stakeholders such as employers, the parameters in which academics work differ considerably between Australia and the UK. At the University of Glasgow, we have five full-time social work aca-demics and a total of approximately 45 DipSW students over the two years of the programme. Compared to my experiences of teaching social work in Australia, this staff-student ratio is incredibly luxurious. Large classes are increasingly the norm in Australian higher education and social work as a discipline is not exempt from the demands that high numbers of students are taught efficiently and effectively (Napier and George, 2001). Those of us who have taught a hundred or more students in a semester, with little overlap from the similar number we taught in the previous semester, are struggling to remember all the names and faces let alone be able to spend quality time individually with each student we teach. This leads to the situation where 'students are forced into self-directedness and independent learning by default, rather than acquiring those capacities in a nurturing environment' (Napier and George, 2001: 81).

THE ROLE OF SOCIAL WORK EDUCATION

Despite increasing recognition that social work education can provide a good generalist edu-cation and skills which can be applied in a broad range of careers both within and beyond the human services (Crawford, 2001; Parton, 2001), the overwhelming expectation of social work students in Britain is that at the conclusion of their training they will be employed in direct service work, predominantly in the statutory sector. This expectation is arguably not as widely held in Australia, which to some extent reflects the employment prospects for graduating social workers, the majority of whom who not take up posts with the title of 'social worker' (Hawkins *et al.*, 2000), although many in fact are employed in the human services sector.

It is perhaps not surprising that there is a greater emphasis in Britain on selecting students into courses who demonstrate potential for direct service work. The notion that applicants for social work courses in Britain are subject to police checks as part of determining their professional suit-ability would be against the principles of student selection in higher education in Australia where equal opportunities legislation imposes a duty on universities not to discriminate against students according to age, gender, race, disability, sexual orientation or criminal background (Shardlow, 2000). Indeed there have long been voices within Australian social work education who have argued for the inclusion in social work courses of students who are not necessarily destined for direct practice. For example, in a discussion about the student selection procedures at the University of Melbourne in the 1960s it was noted:

It would appear that academic brilliance is not the primary consideration-and yet the brilliant individual not suited to a casework role could perform valuable work in research. (Coleman, 1967: 18)

Consistent with the notion of the BSW being a university award, in most Australian schools of social work, academic grounds are the only reason that a university may terminate a student's training, although 'unsuitable' students (an issue for which there is no consensus) may be encouraged to drop out (Ryan, Habibis and Craft, 1997). Consequently, although one can be sure that holders of the BSW have completed the requirements for the degree, it is ultimately left to prospective employers to determine the professional suitability of new graduates.

As already noted, the employment prospects of social work graduates in Australia largely lie beyond positions titled 'social worker'. However, despite the declassification of many 'social worker' positions to more generic job titles over the last decade or so (Hawkins et al., 2000; Napier and George, 2001) social work education is at one level flourishing. In 1989 when the author completed her BSW there were 13 universities providing social work training in Australia, whereas a decade later there were 22 schools of social work, and many of the older schools are known to have much larger intakes than they did a decade ago. Furthermore, their graduates are highly employable, although this is due more to the skills and expertise of graduate social workers than because they are social workers *per se* (Ife, 1997).

Greater diversity in employment prospects of graduates to some extent also limits the extent to which Australian schools of social work can address the specific needs of employer groups. As one Australian social work academic has recently put it:

Employers are, and have been, concerned that practitioners can do 'the job'-the vagueness and uncertainty of what the job is, however makes the task difficult for academics. Employers have 'flirted' with specifying certain activities as needing social work knowledge and skills. Then on the other hand, employing individuals with other qualifications or none at all. (Camilleri, 2001: 18).

It is perhaps therefore unsurprising that in the absence of a coherent pathway to employment for social work graduates in Australia, social work academics see their role as developing human service professionals who are able to transfer skills and knowledge appropriately to both existing and emerging social problems in a range of employment contexts (e.g. Camilleri, 2001; Fook, 2001). While this may include preparing caseworkers for statutory social work settings, the role of social work education in Australia is somewhat different than in Britain.

CURRICULUM

The curriculum as a contested space with competing demands all seeking to be met within a confined timespan is familiar to social work educators in many countries:

Social work curricula have traditionally experienced intense competition for space between diverse fields including sociology and the political sciences, psychology, social work theory and practice, law and health subjects. (Wood, 1997: 8)

Consistent with its broad definition of social work, the AASW requires accredited social work programmes in Australia to teach in

... all areas of social work practice. These are group work, community work, social action, casework, research, social policy analysis and development, and administration. (AASW, 2000: 5)

Skills in this range of practice areas are also reflected in both the AASW's expectations as to the goals and outcomes of social work education (AASW, 2000) and the range of placement offerings considered appropriate for a BSW student. In relation to placements, La Trobe University advises students that

... at least one of a student's placements must contain a substantial direct practice component. At La Trobe we try to organise placements to emphasise casework and direct practice in first year, with the opportunity to apply and develop other skills, e.g. community work, research, program design and evaluation and policy development in the second placement. (La Trobe University, 1994: 1)

That students may undertake a placement in a non-direct service setting is widely accepted. Indeed the AASW itself has recently hosted the placement of a social work student on a policy placement.

While the social work knowledge required by DipSW students in Britain (CCETSW, 1995a) is similar to that required of their counterparts undertaking social work education in Australia, the practice requirements and core competencies which DipSW students are required to demonstrate in their placement learning seem to rule out (at least in practice) the potential for a social work placement in which the major emphasis is research or policy development. Indeed in the West of Scotland, placements are called 'Direct Practice Placements', as if to emphasise what aspects of social work are proper for student placements. This is a far cry from the Australian experience, where shortages of traditional social work placements increasingly require universities to be innovative and develop placements in other settings (Cleak, Hawkins and Hess, 2000).

CONCLUSION

In this paper, I set out to identify some key differences in social work education between Australia and the United Kingdom, and the issues identified in this paper are those which were most salient for me in my first few months of employment as a social work educator in Scotland, having previously taught in Australian BSW programmes. For me, these have been around the questions of what social work is, the organisation of social work education, the role of social work education and placement offerings. Others asked to undertake the same comparison may well have identified other differences, which may be equally valid. Notwithstanding the differences identified, DipSW programmes in the UK and Australian BSW programmes are largely alike, as is the range of tasks which both our employers and the wider profession expect Australian and British social work educators to be engaged in.

What, then, do Australian social workers bring with them to their work in Britain? Employers in Britain may want to consider the product they are obtaining when they employ Australian social workers in Britain. Overall, I would argue that they are getting a similar product, although with a potentially broader notion of what social work is. However on a more practical level, the main difference is that overseas-trained social workers may have developed their social work knowledge and expertise in a very differently organised health and welfare sector, and will need some induction into the organisation of social welfare programmes in this country. And as they struggle to come to terms with British social work, I would advise agencies to engage in dialogue with these workers, and just maybe they will not only gain a colleague or employee, but also someone from who they can learn some other perspectives on aspects of social work practice.

REFERENCES

Australian Association of Social Workers [AASW] (2000) *Policy and Procedures for Establishing Eligibility for Membership of AASW*. Canberra: AASW

Camilleri, P. (2001) Educating for social work: Facing the new century. *Australian Social Work*, **54** (1): 16-20

Central Council for Education and Training in Social Work [CCETSW] (1995a) *Assuring Quality in the Diploma of Social Work-1: Rules and Requirements for the DipSW*. London: CCETSW

Central Council for Education and Training in Social Work [CCETSW] (1995b) *Assuring Quality in the Diploma of Social Work-2: Approval, Review and Inspection of DipSW programmes*. London: CCETSW

Cleak, H., Hawkins, L. and Hess, L. (2000) 'Innovative field options' in Cooper, L and Briggs, L (eds.) *Fieldwork in the Human Services*. St Leonards: Allen and Unwin

Coleman, M. (1967) Satisfaction in social work. *Australian Journal of Social Work*, **20** (2): 18–9

Crawford, F. (2001) The aim of a Bachelor of Social Work? *Australian Social Work*, **54** (1): 13–6

Dickey, B. (1987) *No Charity There: A Short History of Social Welfare in Australia*. Sydney: Allen and Unwin

Fook, J. (2001) What is the aim of the Bachelor of Social Work? *Australian Social Work*, **54** (1): 20-23

Hawkins, L, Ryan, M, Murray, H, Grace, M, Hawkins, G, Hess, L, Mendes, P, and Chatley, B (2000) 'Supply and demand: A study of labour market trends and the employment of new social work graduates in Victoria' *Australian Social Work*, **53** (1): 35-42

Ife, J. (1997) *Rethinking Social Work: Towards Critical Practice*. South Melbourne: Addison Wesley Longman

Jones, C. (1998) 'Social work and society' in Adams,R, Dominelli, L and Payne, M (eds.) *Social Work: Themes, Issues and Critical Debates*. Basingstoke: Macmillan

La Trobe University (1994) *Social Work Practicum I & II 1994: Information Booklet*. Bundoora: Graduate School of Social Work, La Trobe University

McCallum, S. (2001) Editorial. *Australian Social Work*, **54** (3): 2

Napier, L. and George, J. (2001) 'Changing social work education in Australia' *Social Work Education*, **20**: 75–87

Parton, N. (2001) 'The current state of social work in UK universities: Some personal reflections' *Social Work Education*, **20**: 167–74

Ryan, M., Habibis, D. and Craft, C. (1997) 'Guarding the gates of the profession: Findings of a survey of gatekeeping mechanisms in Australian Bachelor of Social Work programs' *Australian Social Work*, **50** (3): 5–12

Shardlow, S. (2000) 'Legal responsibility and liability in fieldwork' in Cooper L and Briggs, L (eds.) *Fieldwork in the Human Services*. St Leonards: Allen and Unwin

Wood, A. (1997) 'The place of family therapy in the Australian undergraduate social work curricula: Literature and research findings' *Australian Social Work*, **50** (2): 3–11

CHAPTER 3
COMING TO TERMS WITH 'PEDAGOGY': RECONCEPTUALISING WORK WITH CHILDREN
Pat Petrie

INTRODUCTION

This paper draws on a presentation to a seminar organised by the International Sub-committee of the Joint University Council Social Work Education Committee, and on an article in Social Work in Europe (Petrie, 2001). It is based on a body of research conducted by the writer at the Thomas Coram Research Unit at the Institute of Education, University of London. The research includes: a survey of out-of-school services in the European Union (Meijvogel and Petrie, 1996); work on children's services in Sweden (Moss and Petrie, in press); a project on homework in six European countries; the changing role of the school (in integrating, for example, social work and health services) in Sweden, France and the USA (Moss, Petrie and Poland, 1999); a recently completed study of the part played by social pedagogy (or in France *éducation specialisée*) in work with looked-after children in Denmark, Belgium (Flanders), France, Germany and the Netherlands - where pedagogy/education, rather than social work or care, is the main approach used (report forthcoming). Ongoing work in the area includes a study of the incorporation of childcare into education in Sweden, Scotland and England. Methods used in these studies have included commissioning reports from national experts, and local fieldwork, involving interviews with policy makers and practitioners at all levels, in national and local governments and in a wide variety of services where pedagogues work face to face with children.

Comparative social research requires that the researcher develop a different way of looking so as to avoid translating the phenomena and institutions of other cultures into rough and ready equivalents of those to be found at home. The terms 'pedagogy' and 'social pedagogy', and the professional workers who engage in pedagogy are cases in point. At first sight it is too easy to see them as 'really' care workers, social workers, youth and community workers or nursery teachers - depending on the setting in which they work. Over the course of the studies listed above, I have developed understandings of what pedagogy can mean in one setting, but have gone on to find that it also refers to something that seems completely different, either within the same country, or as compared to its usage in a different country. In Britain - and other Anglophone countries - when we think of work with children we think, for example, in terms of formal education, care services and youth services. Our European colleagues share some of these understandings but, at the same time can see a link between work with children in different settings: this link is 'pedagogy'.

'Pedagogy' and 'social pedagogy' are terms that have aroused increasing interest in the UK over the last decade or so. Much English language literature on social pedagogy comes from academics with an interest in social work and social work training (Lorenz, 1991, Cannan, Berry and Lyons, 1992; Davies Jones, 1994; Crimmens, 1998; Higham, 2001) and, more specifically, in child care (e.g. Colton and Hellincx, 1993). The question often posed by this work is, in general terms, the extent to which the social pedagogy approach is preferable to that of social work. My own interest stems from a different background: that of a researcher into day care for preschool and school-age children and, more recently, into residential care.

This research has often focused on children's daily lives, including their relationships with staff. In cross-national work, it leads to questions such as the extent the social pedagogy approach is preferable to the care worker approach (or indeed to the approach of the teacher). In Britain, while much work with children is conceptualised as care work there are some suggestions of dissatisfaction with this term's adequacy or appropriateness. For example, 'children in care' became, with the Children Act 1989, 'looked after children'. Yet, child care (note, two words) continues to be the policy field relating to looked-after children who are the responsibility of the local authority. Somewhat confusingly, childcare (one word) denotes a different policy field. Childcare denotes services for children whose parents work and need alternatives to parental care, for preschool children and for school-age children, outside normal school hours. In this field, coinages such as 'educare', 'playcare' and 'early years services' seek to broaden the understanding of work with children, beyond the notions of responsibility and surveillance connected with 'care', in order to provide a more educative perspective - yet not placing the work purely in the educational domain. The relationship between care and education is long-standing (Davies Jones, 1994) and linked to systems of social control from the nineteenth century to the present day (Petrie, forthcoming). Clearly, a concept that relates to social work, childcare and education calls for exploration.

THE USE OF THE TERM 'PEGAGOGY'

A useful working definition of pedagogy is education-in-its-broadest-sense. The necessity to indicate whether education is being used in a broad or a narrow sense leads us to a central dilemma for English speakers. In English there is no single word that can stand for 'education-in-its-broadest sense' to distinguish it from 'education-associated-with-the academic-curriculum'. But it is 'education-in-its-broadest-sense' that many Europeans mean when they talk about pedagogy, a term capable of encompassing care and education as Davies Jones (1994) has pointed out. In Britain and other English speaking countries 'pedagogy' usually denotes the science of teaching and learning, and relates to the formal curriculum of school, college and university, what in Europe is sometimes referred to as 'didactics', rather than pedagogy. In Europe, 'pedagogy' has a much wider meaning and this very breadth of meaning can at first be perplexing for a British researcher. To add to the potential confusion, in French, and some other Romance languages, *éducation* (or its cognates) is used to designate what in Northern Europe is known as pedagogy, while words such as *scolarité* (schooling) and *enseignement* (teaching or instruction) are reserved for formal education. In what follows I shall refer to 'pedagogy' but using it as an umbrella to cover the more Latinate *éducation*.

Not only is 'pedagogy' used differently in the Anglophone world, it is a term that can disappear in translation. In papers that I have had translated from Dutch, German, Danish and Flemish into English, 'pedagogy' too often becomes 'education', and pedagogues appear as teachers. I have also seen similarly confusing translations in the official English language brochures of colleges and Universities. In France, on the other hand, *éducation* may also be mistranslated as 'education', *éducation specialisée* is translated as special education (when it relates much more to what we would call care or social work) and the *'éducateur'* becomes, misleadingly, a teacher. The problem is that there is no generally used English term for pedagogy (and its equivalent *éducation*) - we have not yet developed this concept. The nearest British equivalent is the use of 'social educator' to refer to youth workers – people who are interested in supporting young people's development, outside the formal education system

Further difficulties can arise because pedagogy is sometimes expanded into 'social pedagogy' (for example in Germany), while in Denmark the word 'pedagogy' is used without any qualification. The theory of social pedagogy (sozialpädagogik) was first defined in 1844 by Karl Mager, as the *"theory of all the personal, social and moral education in a given society, including the description of what has happened in practice"* (Winkler, 1988, page 41). Broadly speaking, 'social pedagogy' is used of services that are socially provided: parents play there part in educating children, in the broadest sense, society plays a part in providing pedagogic institutions, alongside or instead of parents. (Social may also be used to refer to the social or group dimension that is often an integral part of pedagogy).

In much of Europe, social pedagogy refers to the whole domain of social responsibility for children, for their well-being, learning and competence. As a field, social pedagogy can accommodate provision such as childcare, youth work, family support, youth justice services, secure units, residential care and play work– services that, to English eyes, appears somewhat disparate. The use of the term 'pedagogy' allows for a discourse that can rise above differences based on, for example, the age of those who use services or a service's immediate goals; it permits any particular provision to be located in the context of a wider social policy towards children.

THE FIELD OF PEDAGOGY

Pedagogy as a field has four important and connected levels: the development of theory, the formulation of policy, and the training and education of workers and daily practice with children (and sometimes adults). These four areas form an interactive system which each contributes to the other.

Pedagogic theory. The main site for the development of theory is the university and, sometimes, the school of higher education. Here, perhaps in faculties which combine pedagogy with other theoretical areas, such as psychology (as at the University of Ghent) or with *didactics* (as at the University of Gothenburg) research is undertaken and students are educated.

Training and Education. There is some variety as to training and education for work in the field of pedagogy. Students prepare for pedagogic work in universities and colleges. Their courses may take around 3 or 4 years, including practice placements. They study a range of theoretical subjects, in the behavioural and social sciences and are introduced to a body of skills that they will need in working with children. For example they learn how to work with groups, work with conflict and challenging behaviour, and teamwork (which is much emphasised). They also take courses, at their own level, in a range of creative and practical subjects, such as art, drama, woodwork, music, gardening. These are interests and skills that they will bring to their work with children and that will be one of the media through which they relate to children.

Pedagogic studies may also be undertaken in the last years of secondary school. These, too, lead to face-to-face work with children in a variety of settings and those who qualify in this way may later go on to higher education after working in the field.

Other pedagogic courses are more specialised and longer. In some Universities, students may take an initial five year course, resulting in a qualification that is the equivalent of an English masters degree (and includes practice placements). This prepares students for further academic work, for research and development posts in government and voluntary organisations, for management jobs, and consultancy and advisory positions connected to a range of provision. Some of those educated in this way choose to work directly with children in, for example, residential settings.

Work. In continental Europe, those who have trained in the field of pedagogy can have a variety of job titles relating to the setting in which they work. They may, for example, be called carers (or the local equivalent) or youth counsellors; nevertheless their work is seen as pedagogic, just as their training has been.

In Sweden, the pedagogue works alongside teachers in all school classes for children up to the age of 10 years (sometimes older). In addition, they provide the main workforce for out-of-school services. A pedagogue can be a school principal, or the principal of a cluster of schools. In interview, a pedagogue, herself a school principal, said that this was an obvious development for pedagogues who are, she said, professionals skilled in team work. The employment of pedagogues is central to recent educational reforms in Sweden, and emphasises a concern with the whole child, rather than the child as conceived in narrow educational terms (Moss and Petrie forthcoming). In Denmark, where the remit of the pedagogue is wider than in Sweden, pedagogues work as staff in nurseries, preschools, out-of-school services, children's residential establishments and in disability services with children or with adults. In spite of its etymological roots, in much of Europe, those trained in pedagogy work with adults as well as children, for example in residential and day care, in community development and in family support.

The pedagogic approach is to relate to the education of the whole person: body, mind, feelings, spirit, creativity and, crucially, the relationship of the individual to others. The domain of pedagogy is the social domain, and the work of the pedagogue is conducted via relationships, relationships in which the pedagogue is often the member of a group, of children, or of adults, but may sometimes work one-to-one. In their training, pedagogues are encouraged to be reflective practitioners and to draw on theory but not to be bound by it. Most importantly, and across all settings, their work is to support children's development.

PEDAGOGY AND THE UNITED KINGDOM

So, what might pedagogy have to offer to the UK? In a paper on training for residential child care workers (Crimmens, 1998, page 319), Crimmens cautions against 'a tendency to believe that the grass is always greener (in other parts of Europe)'. Nevertheless, recourse to 'pedagogy' and '*éducation*' has the potential for an inclusive, normalising approach, with the main focus on children as children, but also with an awareness that children can have special and additional needs (social pedagogy and terms such as *éducation spécialisée* are often reserved for work, for example, with disabled children, looked after children or children in secure units).

In English social and educational policy, there is currently no overarching concept that might help to bring coherence to work in the children's sector, such as that which pedagogy/ education might supply. Yet, for the sake of policy coherence, work with young people in whatever setting, needs to share the same overall aims – this would seem fundamental to the Government's policy of 'working together', on behalf of children across departments, overriding sectional interests. Also, there should, perhaps, be some unifying ethos across settings, whether secure units or playgrounds, some notion that workers in the children's sector would share values and have, fundamentally, the same approach towards children. Much of the UK's current approach to training, based on skills and competencies relating to the requirements of specific settings, blurs the similarities to be found across the whole area, and there seems little sense of commonality across the sector.

In part, this may be because the work has not usually been named as the children's sector or as pedagogy, so that addressing children and young people, and their relationship to society across settings, becomes difficult. There is little firm ground as a basis for public debate on children and childhood. It is interesting to contemplate how positioning- and being able to name - secure units for young offenders as both youth justice and pedagogic settings, might have informed recent discussions in the UK. Two young people had been found guilty of killing a young child. Seven years later, discussion as to their future centred, in the popular press, on their experience in the secure unit and what was seen by some commentators as their favourable treatment: for example, that they had pocket money and were taken shopping and to places of interest. This debate was hampered because it could not be conducted in terms of pedagogy, addressing questions such as how children should be brought up and the necessary requirements for this - whatever the setting, its constraints and other purposes.

While it may prove difficult to transfer whole systems of training and qualification from one country to another, perhaps the introduction of 'pedagogy' or 'social education' – or an equivalent term – has something to offer us in the UK. Such a term could address work with children across the board. It could have the potential to bring a greater coherence to policy development, to practice and to training. These are areas that, across settings and departments, may sometimes fail to focus on children as children, whatever their age, and whatever the type of service to be delivered. It could also provide a framework for discussing the place of children and young people in society as a whole. There are basic questions, such as what do we want for our children, what is a good childhood, what relationship would we wish to promote between children and children, and children and adults – pedagogic questions that cut across sectional interests. It should be stressed, however, that pedagogical practices and policies are only means to an end – the education, in its widest sense of children. Pedagogies are not value free; they can relate to systems of social control – but they also have the potential to be sites of resistance. Indeed, it is fair to say that the proponents of pedagogies, of whatever sort, have in mind a certain type of individual and a certain type of society. The Hitler Youth Movement is an example of one type of pedagogic approach, as were the settlements of Robert Owen and the Sure Start programmes in England, today (Petrie, forthcoming). The argument that I hope to have made in this paper is that, given that the values on which they are based are up for discussion, the concept of pedagogy and the pedagogic approach are potentially useful.

REFERENCES

Cannan, C. Berry, L. and Lyons, K. (1992) *Social work and Europe*, Basingstoke: BASW/Macmillan Press

Crimmens, D. (1998) Training for residential child care workers in Europe: comparing approaches in The Netherlands, Ireland and the United Kingdom, *Social Work Education*, **17** (3) pp 309–19

Colton, M. J. and Hellinckx, W. (1993) *Childcare in the EC: Country-specific guide to foster and residential care*, Cambridge: University Press

Davies Jones, H. (1994) 'The profession at work in contemporary society' in Courtioux, M *et al.* (eds) *The Social Pedagogue in Europe – Living with others as a profession*, Zurich: FICE

Higham, P. 2001, Changing practice and an emerging social pedagogue paradigm in England: The role of the personal adviser, *Social Work in Europe*, **8** (1) pp 21–9

Lorenz, W. (1994) *Social work in a changing Europe*, London: Routledge

Meijvogel, R., and Petrie, P. (1996) *School-age childcare in the European Union: A survey*, European Commission Network on Childcare and Other Measures to Reconcile Employment and Family Responsibilities of Men and Women: London

LOCATING THE OCCUPATIONAL SPACE FOR SOCIAL WORK: INTERNATIONAL PERSPECTIVES

Moss, P. and Petrie P. (2002) *From Children's Services to Children's Spaces*, London: Taylor and Francis

Moss P., Petrie, P. and Poland, G. (1999) *Rethinking School, Some International Comparisons*, Leicester: Youth Work Press

Petrie, P. (2001) The potential of pedagogy/education for work in the children's sector in the UK, *Social Work in Europe*, **8** (3) pp 23–6

Petrie, P. (in press) 'Social Pedagogy: An historical account of care and education as social control' in Moss, P and Brannen, J (eds) *Rethinking Children's Care*, Buckingham: Open University Press

Winkler, M. (1988) *Eine Theorie der Sozialpädagogik*. Stuttgart: Klett-Cotta

CHAPTER 4
SOCIAL CARE SERVICE AND SOCIAL WORK IN TRANSITION
Juha Hamalainen

INTRODUCTION

In this paper transcendental boundaries of and trends in social work and social care service are discussed from the point of view of changing circumstances. Attention is paid to factors such as globalisation, managerialism and increasingly complex mixed economy of welfare.

SOCIAL WORK STYLES IN THE KALEIDOSCOPE OF WELFARE STATE REGIMES

As in the arts, for example in architecture, where there are stylistic tendencies and trends, different styles can also be founded in social care service and social work. Following the conceptualisation of Pierre Bourdieu, you can call a style of social work as *habitus* being empirically understood through forms of practice. But you can speak about *paradigm* as well referring to a set of norms concerning social work's tasks, aims and methods.

The traditions and perspectives of social work are classified in many ways. They spring up from philosophical, psychological, sociological, educational, political and methodological analysis of social work. One sensible classification rests on the fact that the tasks and forms of the practice of social work are connected with the national welfare regimes, different state traditions and different approaches to citizenship (e.g. Lorenz 1994, 15-39). In theory and practice social work and social care service are closely connected to economical, social, political and cultural factors.

Generally, there are three main models of welfare states, i.e. three welfare ideologies and politics. From a geographical point of view they are called the Anglo-American, the Middle-European and the Scandinavian model of welfare state. These welfare state systems differ from each other ideologically and politically producing dissimilar systems of social security and welfare services (e.g. Niemela & Hamalainen 2001, 5-8). There are many sub-models with country-specific nuances in every main welfare regime and also the number of welfare regimes varies to some degree from classification to classification.

Social care has different character according to welfare state models. The Anglo-American social policies are traditionally based on the values of open capitalism, political liberalism, individualism and pragmatism producing problem solving oriented and method based habitus of social work. In the Middle-European countries social work is closely connected to the activities of civil society aiming at promotion of morals in and through families and communities, especially by help of ecclesiastical institutions. In the Nordic welfare states social work is primarily perceived as an instrument of the state-centred welfare policies with multitude of benefits based on national social insurance and a covering system of social and health services. It is public, bureaucratic and firmly based on social legislation. (See Figure1)

THE MIDDLE EUROPEAN MODEL

- social integration and opportunities for human development produced by a solidaristic civil society (corporations, communities) supported subsidiarily by the State

- Social Market Economy

▶

⇨ Social work:
- helping people to organise different kinds of self-help in their living world (*Lebenswelt*) in order to provide a setting for social integration arid human growth based on the idea of civilisation (*Bildung*)
- an expression of a solidaristic caring civil society

THE ANGLO-AMERICAN MODEL

- Managing and Solving problems of the poorest of the poor and very needy people in accordance with the principle of individual self-determination
- Open Capitalism
⇨ Social work:
- helping people to solve their every day problems by therapies, guidance and counselling
- entity of various problem-solving methods and techniques of guidance and counselling connected to the principles of human rights

THE NORDIC MODEL

- Social security for all people provided by the State through comprehensive systems of national insurance and welfare services
- State Capitalism/ Market Socialism
⇨ Social work:
- heIping people to use the complex systems of benefits and services according to their rights and needs
- an instrument of social policy in terms of promoting welfare equality and social security

Figure 1. Classical Models of Welfare State and the Role of Social Work Therein.

In all traditions social work is dealing with the problems between persons and society. In the Anglo-American model a great emphasis is placed on therapeutic methods and techniques which are directed at developing effective problem solving of clients under different circumstances. The Middle-European social work model creates traditionally the necessary conditions for human development in civil society by organising educational activities and self help. The German *Iebensweltorientierte SoziaIpedagogik* and the French *animatibn sociocultural* are modern expressions of this aspiration. The Nordic model of social work is directed to securing social security of all citizens. The traditions are obviously connected to Calvinistic, Catholic and Lutheran social doctrines and anthropologies.

LATE-MODERN SOCIAL WORK IN THE GLOBAL WORLD SCENARIO

All welfare state constructions are shaped by globalization processes which can no longer be steered by national policies. Free global movement of capital, information and political activities occur in an inter- and supranational context without recognising national borders. It influences social work theory and practice by bringing national traditions into interaction with each other and by raising common global problems and aims. Social work is challenged to be reformed in accordance with the fact that importance of national welfare regimes in social procedures has decreased.

Globalization is based on the ideas of free market global economy. It not only *"impacts upon understandings and constructions of client autonomy and the processes and procedures of risk assessment and management in respect of vulnerable children and adults with regard to both shared and conflicting of the concepts of free choice, informed choice, best interests, entitlement and preference"* (Adams 2000, 5), but also opens international markets of social care services as well. Social work is defined increasingly in terms of economy and business.

In brief, globalization means the extension of operations world wide as a result of international division of labour and free competition brought on between enterprises including the increase in capital, mobility of jobs and global job competition (e.g. Juntunen 2001). It is closely connected to world wide information revolution which changes the nature of entrepreneurship and economic strategies of industrialised countries changing significantly the content of working life as well (Castells 1998). One obvious consequence of globalization is the rising economical, political and daily life insecurity all over the industrialised countries.

Globalization tendencies are closely connected with neo-liberal economic policy which trusts in the blessing power of the invisible hand. According to this ideology, free competition is the best and most effective way to organise economic life. Also, that social work will achieve maximum efficacy and the best quality through competition. This also include the idea that social work can and must primarily be developed by means of developing methods and techniques based on empirical evidence of effectiveness. The organisations of social care service have to maintain their competitive capacity in local, national and international market by Research and Development.

The development of social work in various countries is not only a reflection of a certain welfare regime but also *"a response to how competing traditions of thought and knowledge forms, which in turn have affected the construction of theories, and practice methods have been received and adopted"* (Erath and Hamalainen 2001, 15). The role of social work in a global context is, as yet, unclear. Debate on it may require a radical reconsideration of the knowledge base, tasks and values of social work (Lyons 1999). In international social work new kinds of qualifications are needed.

Social work becomes necessarily superficial both anthropologically and morally by following post-modern individualism (Howe 1996, 88–92). Thus, there is a good reason to speak about ideological revolution or crisis of social work. Of course it is right to be critical towards the tendencies shaping society and social work therein, but without a black and white outlook based on combination of 'bad" society and "good" social work. Social work should not escape but face the vacuous and glance at the complexity of the modern world.

The increasing complexity of the post-industrial high-tech and pluralistic society brings new challenges of reflection in social policy and social work. The societal reality is only seen through theory. People's daily life as well as such social problems as poverty, criminality and domestic violence are increasingly influenced by the increasing complexity of society. Social work theory should deal with this complexity.

MANAGERIALISM AS AN EXPRESSION OF LATE-MODERN SOCIAL WORK IDEOLOGY

In late-modern free market -based societies, social work agencies are demanded to compete with and against each other according to the rules of economy. There is no place for the old welfare state ideologies in open world wide capitalism. Beside and instead of public welfare organisations commercial enterprises of social care service come into existence. Some of them are, and will be, inter- and supranational companies selling special welfare services – both to individual consumers and to authorities within state welfare systems. Economic and managerial issues play more and more fundamental roles in *habitus* and paradigms of social care service.

In accordance with the change of working life in real economic business, the work style of social work has also changed into a project-oriented system requiring know-how in information technology, co-operation and networking skills and ability to manage complex organisations. In the top enterprises of information societies *"work is done through teamwork and projects and by constantly learning and devouring novel ideas"* (Juntunen 2001:1). The organisations of social work are also changing their functional action and strategies in such a way.

Mixed economy is an essential part of the late-modern welfare system producing managerialism in social work (e.g. KIug 2001:74). New forms of expertise are needed in internationalising social work practices (e.g. Lyons 1999:1). These are primarily defined in terms of managerialism. In theory and practice, managerialism tends to emphasise technical points at the cost of moral issues (comp. Erath & Hamalainen 2001, 25). Uniting these two dimensions, technical and moral, is an enormous challenge to social work education. Both of them seem to be connected to quality of social work.

Social work tends to be increasingly based on economic interests and rationality. At the expense of other professional values it assimilates models known from economic business. Social work is more and more seen a system of organising and managing service parcels and chains in terms of care management including need and risk assessment, cost estimating and cost-benefit analysis (see Parton 1996: 10–3). The line management structure of social work has gradually been taken apart to make way for new managerial systems in which *"even senior social workers are being replaced by managers who may have social work backgrounds but have moved away from their professional base"* (Pinkerton 1998). Commercialisation of social work changes the professional identity of social workers and demands a reform social work training. Social work becomes a field of providers, managers and consumers of social services.

Economic measures of contemporary social work can be described in terms of market philosophy, budget orientation and management instruments and social political measures proportionately in terms of law-based social work, service orientation and consumerism (Erath, 2001). These are also dimensions of managerialism in social work, far away from the original values and identity of social work and there is a real tension between the past and contemporaneity. There is a strong belief that originated from neo-liberal social theory that the optimal quality of social services can be achieved through competition. Obviously, this belief at least as an universal principle is an illusion. It is reasonably evident that the importance of political steering can not be replaced by commercialisation and competition, political steering in promoting development and quality in the systems of social care service and in the fields of social work.

General management is influenced by the ethos of the market (Pinkerton, 1998). But social work has not lost its capacity to follow its original values, i.e. to promote equality, democracy and participation, to function as a force of socialchange and to help people living under the strain of social problems to achieve as satisfying a life as possible as members of society. However, the complexity of both people's daily life and the welfare systems demands social work to change its strategy. Economic and ideological preconditions of social work have changed and strategic questions of social work have become more complex and risk laden. Increasing complexity in society means necessarily increasing complexity in social work as well. Increasing complexity in social work means for your part increasing need to manage.

The complexity of late-modern societies is difficult to be analysed and comprehend. In welfare service care chains have become more and more difficult to be managed. The role and duties of social work are increasingly specified by care management ideology and quality standards. Thus, management skills have a great significance in helping and caring activities.

Organisations of social care service are demanded to show their necessity and effectiveness through systematic evaluation.

One dimension of the complexity is due to the 'digital' revolution facilitating the process of globalization and causing world-wide social inequality (Castells 1998). National social policies lose their legitimacy based on the ideas of economic, social and political stability. Alleviating social problems by social political mechanisms at national level is no longer of great importance. Instead of that the importance of local organisations has increased in terms of welfare mix. This means new configurations between statutory, independent and private actors in providing social services.

CONCLUSIONS

Preconditions of social work have rapidly changed. Processes of post-modernisation and globalization produce increasing complexity and uncertainty not only in people's everyday life but in social care service as well. In accordance with the rules of economy social care is characterised by competition, commercialisation and managerialism.

In a globalizing world, old traditions of social work connected to welfare regimes and welfare state models tend to lose their meanings. International tendencies in social policy and social work cross the borders of national traditions. National systems of social security and social care service are increasingly based on welfare mix. New strategies in social work are necessarily needed. Managerialism plays an increasingly important role therein.

Boundaries of traditions will be transited and banished through movement of information and ideas internationally. National identities of social work will be mixed. However, in the late-modern social work market the Anglo-American tradition based on liberal social theory seems to swallow the other traditions based on less pragmatic and utilitarian ideas. All over the world, social work is required to follow the rules of informational capitalism and requirements of globalization in designing its working style and defining its strategies.

However, from the point of view of social work it seems to be incorrect to claim that one of the three main welfare state models, the Liberal one, will win the ideological competition world wide and replace the two others, the Corporatist and the Social-Democratic models and forms of social work based on them. Whereas, completely new styles and strategies can endlessly be expected to crop up in social work.

REFERENCES

Adams, A (2000) 'The Challenge of Globalisation' in Adams, A, Erath, P and Shardlow, S (eds) *Fundamentals of Social Work in Selected European Countries* Trowbridge: Russell House Publishing, pp 1–8

Castells, M. (1998) *End of Millenium* Oxford: Blackwell

Erath, P. (2001). *Contemporary Social Work Theories and Practice in Germany* Unpublished paper presented at the University of Kuopio October 22 - 24

Erath, P. and Hamalainen, J. (2001) 'Theory in Social Work' in Adams, A, Erath, P and Shardlow, S (eds) *Key Themes in European Social Work. Theory, practice, perspectives* Bath: Russell House Publishing, 15– 25

Howe, D. (1996) 'Modernity, Postmodernity and Social Work' *British Journal of Social Work* **24** (5), 513–32

Juntunen, Esko, (2001) *Globalisation Process in Finland – The Strategy to Compete in the International Competition* Paper presented in the Inter University Centre, Dubrovnik, June 17–22

KIug, W. (2001) 'Social Work and the Third Sector: The Example of the German Welfare State' in: Adams, A, Erath, P and Shardlow, S (eds) *Key Themes in European Social Work. Theory, practice, perspectives* Bath: Russell House Publishing, pp 69 –75

Lorenz, W. (1994) *Social Work in a Changing Europe* London: Routledge

Lyons, K. (1991) *International Social Work. Themes and Perspectives* Aldershot: Ashgate

Niemela, P. and Hamalainen, J. (2001) 'The Role of Social Policy in Social Work' in Adams, A, Erath, P and Shardlow, S (eds) *Key Themes in European Work. Theory, practice, perspectives* Bath: Russell House Publishing, 5 - 13

Parton, N. (ed.) (1996) *Social Theory, Social Change and Social Work* London: Routledge

Pinkerton, J. (1998) 'Social Work and the Troubles: New Opportunities for Engagement' in *Social Work and Social Change in Northern Ireland. Issues for Contemporary Practice* Central Council for Education and Training in Social Work

CHAPTER 5
SOCIAL WORK & THE 'TROUBLES' IN NORTHERN IRELAND: RECONFIGURING OCCUPATIONAL SPACE
John Pinkerton and Jim Campbell

INTRODUCTION

I'm on a slow stumbling journey of discovery about myself and about the impact of the discriminating systems, including sectarianism, in our society. Vincent McAuley 1995

The aim of this paper is to share the present position of two social work academics in their journey to make sense of their experience of social work within Northern Ireland. In addressing how the circumstances of a social formation riven by sectarian division and political violence challenge and shape the occupational space available to, and created by, social work practice. The view presented concerns itself with the past, present and future of social work in Northern Ireland. As a starting point it will be argued that the social work profession needs to recognise that in the past it has benefited from the way in which the British state attempted to manage the political crisis that engulfed Northern Ireland society in the late 1960's and from which it is yet to successfully emerge. It will then be suggested that the situation has now changed to the detriment of social work and there is a need to radically re-vision the occupation. The present imperative for social work in Northern Ireland as it struggles to become a 'post conflict society' is to engage with those forces driving progressive social and political change through reconfiguring its occupational space in a manner that allows for a new relationship with both the state and civil society.

NORTHERN IRELAND AS CONTEXT

There is a strong tendency within social work in Northern Ireland to consider itself only in terms of the immediate contingencies of practice, thereby failing to address the societal context that both defines that practice and gives rise to the reluctance of the profession to consider the context, the 'space', in which it finds itself. One way of breaking this impasse is for social workers in Northern Ireland to look outside the borders of their own experience and consider what it is to be a social worker in other countries. From that enhanced view of social work it is possible to reflect afresh on the Northern Ireland experience. Cross country comparison not only encourages a sense of other possibilities but also requires a certain way of thinking about social work (Houston and Campbell 2001).

Lorenz in his seminal work on social work in Europe (Lorenz 1994) argues that cross national comparisons requires recognition that social workers everywhere are simultaneously the subjects and the objects of change. Describing and understanding that experience of change requires attention to the interaction of 'welfare models', academic discourses' and 'social movements'. A triangular social work occupational space is defined by the parameters of those three dimensions. Following Lorenz's lead and using the three parallel concepts of 'state', 'ideology' and 'civil society' allows the particular experience of social work in Northern Ireland to be understood as a variation on his theme of social work and change. The occupational space for social work within Northern Ireland is generated by the relationship between the 'state', 'civil society' and 'ideology' (Campbell and Pinkerton 1997). The following quotes provide dated but still useful working definitions of these three terms :

The state is a set of agencies claiming supreme authority for the co-ordination and continuity of the population within a particular territory, backed by a virtual monopoly of force (McLennan 1984)

Civil Society refers to all those social institutions and relationships which arise through voluntary association outside the sphere of direct state control, and which belong to the domain of 'society' rather than the state (McIntosh 1984)

The operation of ideology in human life basically involves the constitution and patterning of how human beings live their lives as conscious, reflecting initiators of acts in a structured, meaningful world (Thorburn 1984)

Using these three concepts as reference points to define the space occupied by social work in Northern Ireland draws attention to the contested legitimacy of the state, the fractured nature of civil society and the difficulty of finding adequate sets of ideas and cultural practices, that is to say ideology, to make a shared sense of how life is this troubled and troublesome part of Ireland and the United Kingdom. Recognition of those three aspects of the societal context within which social work functions leads to a particular view on social work's history during the last thirty years of political intransigence, state, communal and paramilitary violence which have cost some three and a half thousand lives and have left many more thousands physically and emotionally traumatised (Fay *et al.*, 1999). It can throw light on what direction social work might now take as a faltering peace process takes hold based on the paramilitary ceasefires of the mid 1990s and the political accommodation of the Belfast Agreement (NIO, 1998).

TECHNOCRATIC EXPANSION

The first part of the history of social work and the 'Troubles' as seen through the triangular lenses of state, civil society and ideology deals with the rise and fall of what can be termed the 'technocratic option'. During the 1970s and 1980s, following the restructuring of the state in Northern Ireland (O'Dowd et al. 1981), there was a major expansion in social work as a key profession within the integrated Health and Personal Social Services Board structures (Caul and Herron 1992). Although the early years of the Troubles were characterised by the intense violence which traumatised many individuals, families and communities (Fay *et al.*, 1999; Coogan, 1995), for social work the period marked a coming of age, as the occupation expanded in numbers, gained more access to resources and enhanced its professional authority within the new board structures. The occupation moved from its relatively minor and very traditional welfare function in local government and hospitals, to being a key young profession within the new state bureaucracies (Caul and Herron 1992; Kelly and Pinkerton, 1996).

Associated with the ascendancy of the technocratic tendency was a 'politics of silence' (Pinkerton 1983). In form, and to a considerable degree in practice, the Health and Social Services Boards very effectively achieved the aim of distancing statutory health and personal social services from discrimination and sectarianism. They provided an environment in which staff coming from both sides of the community could distance themselves from the sectarianism of the wider society and develop a non sectarian occupational identity which was silent in regard to communal, paramilitary and state violence that was characterising Northern Ireland in the eyes of the world. Social work's professional identity replaced, or at least in working hours overlaid, the divisive identities carried by staff from their positioning within the wider social and political networks of Northern Ireland society. Paradoxically through distancing themselves from a key aspect of their own social identities staff could work together and with all sections of the community. A taboo was operating that was functional but at what cost and for how long?

The cost of this 'politics of silence' was social work drawing back from engagement with civil society (Traynor 1998; Campbell and Healey 1999). With that went a loss of openness and accountability. The 'democratic deficit' associated with the replacement of the Stormont regional government by Direct Rule from Westminster, not only had implications for formal politics but also encouraged the closed professionalism based on expertise over clients and their problems that was taking hold within social work across the UK. During the 1980s efficiency and effectiveness became the watch words of an ascendant technocratic professional ideology. Management, practice and training all reflected this. Social work became increasingly routinised rather than creative, remedial rather than developmental and targeted on individuals rather than their social context.

MANAGERIALIST CONTRACTION

Ironically the characteristics of social work as a techno-profession which positioned it so well from the 1970s up to the late 1980s weakened its capacity to defend that position when the British Conservative Government under the leadership of Thatcher, decided to abandon Northern Ireland's 'special case' protection from its monetarist experiments (Gaffikin and Morrisey 1990). As elsewhere in the UK the attempt was then made to create market conditions for social care in Northern Ireland through the promotion of general management and Trusts as the basic administrative unit for personal social services. Although operating within the restraints of purchasing requirements laid down by the health and social services boards, the ethos of the market was what informed general management. The result, as predicted by some at the time (Ritchie 1994) was a fragmented range of services far removed from the integrated and planned public service which had driven the technocrats. Within the world of managerialism, with its language of the market and its purchasers, providers, costs and consumers, the power of techno-professional was significantly weakened. Although lines of professional accountability between the trusts and boards continued to an extent, power was increasingly moved away from the boards' towards the smaller operational units. The key players became the GP fundholders, managers of hospital trusts, and managers of health and personal social services community trusts. The social work professional line management structures were replaced by new managerial systems in which the powerful community trusts employed social work advisers but without giving them operational authority or responsibility. The middle ranking professional social work grades, and even senior social workers, were replaced by managers who may have had social work backgrounds but had moved away from their professional base. At the same time the direct practice of social work was undermined by case management, packages of care and skills mix. Social work staff competed with other professionals within the trusts and with employees from the voluntary and private sectors.

Within this context, that still dominates to-day (Campbell and McColgan 2001), the technocratic option as a means for social work to develop has become bankrupt and calls into question the occupations capacity to survive as a unified profession. As a practice ideology it has become displaced and subsumed into various levels and forms of 'managerialism'. There is now a real possibility of social work fragmenting as a unified occupation. Those unable or unwilling to join the flight from social work practice into management, or into training as agency trainers, academics or consultants, will find themselves as 'operatives'. They will have to locate themselves somewhere within the broad occupational field of social care, at some point along the qualification and skills continuum drawn up the newly established Northern Ireland Social Care Council - with wages and conditions that reflect their new status. No doubt some will find a specialist niche as highly skilled and well paid therapists, but it will be a minority. The occupational space is being dramatically reconfigured with social work struggling to respond and certainly not driving the change.

FINDING A NEW OCCUPATIONAL SPACE

There is however another option for social work in Northern Ireland to offset this bleak picture of a contracting professional occupational space resulting from the bankruptcy of the technocratic option and the ascendancy of managerialism. The opening out for social work may have come through its sponsorship by the state and its distancing from civil society but now it is timely to turn back to engagement with civil society as a way of regaining strength and confidence within the profession. To explore the opportunities for this it is again worth taking account of the three reference points of state, civil society and ideology.

As regards the state, the spectacular defeat of the Conservative government in 1997 suggested that there are limits to which an unbridled New Right agenda of rolling back the state can be pursued by a government within a democracy. Although New Labour, even in its second term of office, has shown little intention and less evidence of a dramatic departure from the social policies of its predecessors that position does make for political problems from within its own ranks and from an electorate who voted for improved public services. There are signs that a position more sympathetic to welfare goals, and thereby to social work, is emerging (Butler and Drakeford 2001)

Where New Labour has shown real initiative is in relation to constitutional reform to reflect the four national components of the UK. That is of particular importance to Northern Ireland as the advances made in the peace process through the creation of a local Assembly need to be seen in that broader context of UK devolution. Whilst it would be foolhardy to claim too much for the peace process and the new political arrangements, it is the case that as every new crisis is surmounted or plays itself out, a nervous optimism is growing. The Belfast Agreement, to a greater or lesser extent, has addressed a range of issues suggesting an openness to progressive reform and an emerging culture of human rights. The Unionist and Nationalist blocks look less monolithic and less relevant in a regionalising UK. In addition to the majority vote North and South for finding a new way forward through the Good Friday agreement, a range of small 'p' political initiatives, outside the formal arena of politics, have been emerging for some time on the back of experience built up over years of holding together the fabric of a society that so often seemed on the brink of tearing itself apart.

Despite, or perhaps because of, deepening poverty and sectarianism plus the challenging changes in family life and expectations about personal relationships and individual identities, it is within civil society that the dynamism necessary for progressive social change is visible. Young people, women, gay people, older people, people with disabilities, people from ethnic minorities, people from working class neighbourhoods on both sides of the community divide are now much more insistent on being recognised and respected for what they are (Horgan and Rodgers, 2000; Mann-Kier, 1997; McWilliams and McKiernan, 1993; Quiery, 2002).

For its own sake social work needs to connect with that energy within civil society - to hear the voices, play a role in getting them heard and be part of responding to them. If social work can effect the necessary shift in its practice ideology away from the controlling technocratic to that of an engaging empowerment it could be well placed to continue to play an important role in the development of personal social services. This must be as part of a larger movement that involves not just health or indeed just other statutory agencies but also the voluntary and in particular the community sectors. That requires opting for a more radical position than it has taken to date and developing appropriate types of practice; such as the rediscovery of community social work (McShane and O'Neill, 1999) and development of more culturally sensitive family therapy and mental health social work (Healey, 1996; Campbell and Healey, 1999).

Considerable work was carried out during the 1990s in Northern Ireland on developing resources to help practitioners work in a more empowering fashion (Logue, 1992; Leong and Huggins, 1996; Titterton *et al.*, 1996). For example *Difference, Diversity and Discrimination* (Bagnell *et al.*, 1995) was an initiative by the Northern Ireland Post Qualifying Education and Training Partnership to assist candidates in preparing portfolios for Post Qualifying and Advanced Award in Northern Ireland. It directly addresses sectarianism, recognising its particular challenge in Northern Ireland, but also stresses the importance of seeing sectarianism as one of a range of areas to be addressed through anti-discriminatory practice. The pack includes a "Levels of subordination/systems of subordination" model which unpacks the various levels, operations/practices and effects through which oppression is expressed and at which it needs to be countered. More recently the training pack *Getting off the Fence* seeks to help those working in the social care field and particularly in management overcome sectarianism (CCETSW, 1999). There have also been a number of local publications which have encouraged social workers to articulate, celebrate and critically reflect on their practice (Anderson (ed.), 1998; Anderson *et al.*, (eds.), 1998, Houston *et al.*, (eds.) 1999 , McShane and O'Neill, 1999).

Social workers need to draw on the values, knowledge and skills they developed during the technocratic period but use them critically to redefine the relationship of the profession to civil society and, as a necessary corollary to that, with the state. From that renegotiation a new occupational space could emerge based on a shared citizenship between social workers and service users. That space will be defined by a participatory civil society, a democratic state and an ideology of accommodation and celebration of diversity. Social work needs to both actively contribute to supporting the development of that space and draw sustenance from it as it emerges.

Conclusion

The political face of social change in Northern Ireland has been characterised by very real costs in human terms - pain, grief, frustration, destruction, death. But there are indications that there are now emerging opportunities for the *"Better Life For All"* called for by the Northern Ireland trades union slogan of the 1970s. Social work must engage these opportunities both as an expression of its professional responsibilities and for the sake of its own future. Just as maintaining the peace process in Northern Ireland depends on a capacity for dialogue, so too social work's necessary reorientation must be based on open negotiation of a new occupational space with both the State and civil society.

References

Anderson, M (ed.) (1998) *Challenge and Change: Celebrating good practice in social work in Northern Ireland* Belfast, CCETSW (NI)

Anderson, M, Bogues, S, Campbell, J, Douglas, H. and McColgan, M. (eds) (1998) *Social Work and Social Change in Northern Ireland*, London, CCETSW

Bagnall, A, Heery G, McConkey W, Pinkerton J and Smyth M (eds) (1995) *Difference, Diversity and Discrimination* Belfast: NIPQET Partnership

Butler, I and Drakeford, M (eds) (2001) 'Special Issue: Social Work and New Labour', *British Journal of Social Work* **1** (31) p 4

Campbell, J and Healey, A (1999) ' 'Whatever you say, say something': the education, training and practice of mental health social workers in Northern Ireland', *Social Work Education* **18** (4) pp 389–400

Campbell, J and Pinkerton, J (1997) 'Embracing change as opportunity: Reflections on social work from a Northern Ireland perspective' in Lesnik, B (ed) *Change in Social Work* Aldershot, Arena

Campbell, J and McColgan, M (2001) 'Social Work in Northern Ireland' in Payne, M and Shardlow, S (eds) *Social Work in the British Isles* London, Jessica Kingsley

Caul, B and Herron, S (1992) *A Service for People* Belfast: December

CCETSW (1999) *Getting Off the Fence: Challenging Sectarianism in Personal Social Services* London, CCETSW

Coogan, T P (1995) *The Troubles: Ireland's Ordeal 1966 – 1995 and the Search for Peace* London, Hutchinson

Fay, MT, Morrissey, M and Smyth, M (1999) *Northern Ireland's Troubles: The Human Costs* London, Pluto

Gaffikin, F and Morrisey, M (1990) *Northern Ireland: The Thatcher Years* London, Zed

Healey, A (1996) 'Systemic Therapy in a Culture of Conflict: Developing a Therapeutic Conversation' *Child Care in Practice* **3** (1) pp 68–86

Horgan G and Rodgers P (2000) 'Young People's Participation in a New Northern Ireland Society' *Youth and Society* **32** (1)

Houston, S and Campbell, J (2001) 'Using critical theory to develop a conceptual framework for comparative social work' *International Journal of Social Welfare* **10** (1) pp 66–73

Houston S, McConvey V, O'Rourke V and Leonard M (eds) *Social Work and innovation: An Anthology of Advanced Level Practice* Belfast: CCETSW

Kelly, G and Pinkerton, J (1996) 'The Children (NI) Order 1995: Prospects for Progress ?' in Hill, M and Aldgate, J (eds) *Child Welfare Services* London, Jessica Kingsley

Leong, F C and Huggins, D T (1996) *Anti-Racism Training in Northern Ireland – A manual for training personnel or those with responsibility for training* Belfast, MCRC

Logue, K (1992) *Anti-Sectarianism and the Voluntary and Community Sector* Belfast, CRC

Lorenz, W (1994) *Social Work in a Changing Europe* London, Routledge

McCauley V (1995 ' 'They're all the same' : Sectarianism and Social Work in Northern, Ireland in Bagnall, A, Heery G, McConkey W, Pinkerton J and Smyth M (eds) *Difference, Diversity and Discrimination* Belfast: NIPQET Partnership

McIntosh, M (1984) 'The family, regulation and the public sphere' in McLennan, G, Held, D and Hall, S (eds) *State and Society in Contemporary Britain* Cambridge, Polity Press

McLennan, G, Held, D and Hall, S (1984) 'Editors Introduction' in McLennan, G, Held, D and Hall, S (eds) *State and Society in Contemporary Britain* Cambridge, Polity Press

McShane, L and O'Neill, M (eds) (1999) *Community Development in Health and Social Services – The Craigavon and Banbridge Experience* Craigavon, Craigavon and Banbridge Community Health & Social Services Trust

McWilliams M and McKiernan J (1993) *Bringing it out in the Open: Domestic Violence in Northern Ireland* Belfast, HMSO

Mann-Kier D (1997) *Out of the Shadows: An action research report into families, racism and exclusion in Northern Ireland* Belfast, Barnardos/Save the Children Fund

Northern Ireland Office (1998) *The Agreement* (command Paper 3883) Belfast, NIO

Northern Ireland Office (1998) *We Will Remember Them: Report of the Northern Ireland Victims Commissioner, Sir Kenneth Bloomfield* Belfast, Northern Ireland Office

O'Dowd, L, Rolston, B and Tomlinson M (1981) *Northern Ireland: Between Civil Rights and Civil War* London, CSE Books

O'Hagan, K (ed.) *Competence in Social Work Practice* London, Jessica Kingsley

Pinkerton, J (1983) 'The Politics of Black' in Caul, B, Pinkerton, J and Powell F (eds) *The Juvenile Justice System in Northern Ireland* Jordanstown, Ulster Polytechnic

Quiery, M (2002) *A Mighty Silence – A Report on the Needs of Lesbians and Bisexual Women in Northern Ireland* Belfast, Lesbian Advocacy Services Initiative

Rawls, J (1972) *A Theory of Justice* Oxford, Oxford University Press

Ritchie, N (1994) *The Impact of trusts and the development of child care services* Belfast, CCNI

Smyth, M, Morrissey, M and Hamilton, J (2001) *Caring Through the Troubles: Health and Social Services in North and West Belfast* Belfast, North and West Belfast Health and Social Services Trust

Therborn, G (1980) *The Ideology of Power and the Power of Ideology* London, Verso

Titterton, M, Donaldson, T , Kavanagh, A, Houston, S and Stirling C (1996) *Theirs by Right: An Introduction to the UN Convention on the Rights of the Child* Training Resource Pack, Belfast, CCNI

Traynor, C (1998) 'Social Work in a Sectarian Society', in Anderson, M *et al.*, (eds) *Social Work and Social Change in Northern Ireland* London, CCETSW

CHAPTER 6
VALUING DIFFERENCE:
MAKING SENSE OF DIFFERENT VALUE BASES
Kieron Hatton

INTRODUCTION

This paper looks at the way in which the value bases underpinning their work condition the responses of social professionals. Tracing the values underpinning social professional practice in the three countries the paper explores how the values statements underlying the profession are translated into common principles in each country. Developing a framework which looks at issues around human nature, power and oppression, liberation and empowerment, praxis and equality and difference, the article suggests commonalities in the different value bases while arguing that important differences, particularly around the concepts of equality and difference, remain.

One of the major challenges facing social professionals in Europe involves developing strategies to tackle the increasing inequality, marginalisation and social exclusion facing minorities in all European states (Williams, C, 1999; Lorenz, 1998; Barry, 1998). Yet, there exists no common political or social language, which allows us to begin to work out ways of tackling these problems beyond the specific societies in which they occur. There is clearly a need for us to learn from each other, to engage in a dialogue about our practice and the values underpinning it. Such a dialogue may be difficult, fraught even, but it becomes increasingly necessary.

Attention is focusing on the way in which social work is internationalising (Lorenz, 1998; Hokenstad and Midgely, 1997). Johannesen (1997) has argued that, 'international social work cooperation is needed ... so that professional social workers around the world are effectively able to respond to the challenge posed by the internationalisation of social issues' (p.157). For social professionals and social work educators, this means responding in ways which demonstrate that they, in Taylor's words, could develop, 'a common core for social work education internationally (which) should reflect our dedication to helping people in interaction with their environments' (Taylor,1999: 315). This means exploring the potential for making the values and concepts with which we work intelligible in different social and cultural contexts, while retaining the meaning and specificity of these concepts in our national settings.

Not surprisingly, language and meanings are a constant source of debate, as are discussions and disagreements over the causes and the remedies for the discrimination/oppression faced by many of the service users with whom social professionals work. The challenge is that, instead of engaging in a process of cultural colonisation, (Cornwall, 1994) in which the truth is held to reside in one country vis a vis the others, there needs to be a genuine attempt to evoke dialogue around core ethical and value positions, particularly if, as Shardlow suggests in his review of social work values in the UK, '*no consensus exists about value questions in social work*' (Shardlow, 1998: 23). For example, in Britain, social workers bring with them perhaps a more explicit understanding of how discrimination/oppression manifest themselves in their society, particularly around issues such as racism, gender inequality, disability, sexuality and age. In Scandinavian countries, social workers/pedagogues bring a commitment to social solidarity and social cohesion which provides a useful counterpoint to the British experience. In Ireland, there is a distinct commitment towards developing empowering forms of intervention, particularly in the voluntary sector. The key is that people bring with them knowledge and skills from within their own cultural practice.

At Universities in Britain, various attempts have been made to respond to this challenge, including the development of courses at Bachelor and Masters level at the Universities of Portsmouth and East London. Not surprisingly, in such courses, language and meanings are again a constant source of debate, as are discussions and disagreements over the causes and the remedies for the discrimination/oppression faced by many service users (Horncastle and Brobeck, 1995; McNay, 1995; Lyons, 1998, 1999).

This article emerged from the dialogue which these contacts have engendered (Hatton, 2001). It attempts to explore the similarities and differences between Danish, Irish and British social work values. Its aim is to begin creating the preconditions for an international understanding of the values which underpin practice in these three contrasting welfare states. It seeks to demonstrate the connection between the British commitment to anti-discriminatory/anti-oppressive practice, (ADP)[1], an analysis of the key issues in Scandinavian, particularly Danish, social work/pedagogy (Davies Jones, 1994) and Irish social work (Powell, 1998; Skehill, 1999(a)(b)). It seeks to inform an analysis of the wider process of structural oppression with the understanding of humanistic and existentialist models of social work derived from a diverse range of writers such as Grundtvig, Kierkegaard, Friere, Arruda and with political theorists such as Foucault, Giddens, Memmi and Fanon.

To achieve this it integrates an understanding of power relations and the need to actively challenge discrimination/oppression through a form of practice which engages workers and service users, and which is equally of use to Danish, Irish and British practitioners. In particular, it seeks to integrate questions of difference and diversity (Williams and Pillinger, 1996; Yuval- Davis, 1998) within discourses around equality and solidarity (Spicker, 1991). However, at its core is an attempt to show that between the differing traditions there are similarities as well as differences. The recently agreed International Federation of Social Workers (IFSW) definition of social work includes the following statement about the values which should underpin social work internationally:

> *Social work grew out of humanitarian and democratic ideals, and its values are based on respect for equality, worth, and dignity of all people. Since its beginnings over a century ago, social work practice has focused on meeting human needs and developing human potential. Human rights and social justice serve as the motivation and justification for social work action. In solidarity with those who are disadvantaged, the profession strives to alleviate poverty and to liberate vulnerable and oppressed people in order to promote social inclusion. Social work values are embodied in the profession's national and international codes of ethics* (IFSW, Montreal, 2000).

While this is a clear reflection of the egalitarian principles which a large number of social professionals would suggest lie at the heart of their practice, the definition is interesting in its silence on the regulatory elements of social work practice, which lie at the heart of the paradox or dialectic of social work. This issue will be returned to below, but it is necessary to outline the core principles underpinning social work in the three countries before drawing on this analysis to delineate the commonalities and differences in the three traditions.

COMMON ETHICAL PRINCIPLES

The three countries have professional associations which lay down ethical standards for the conduct of social workers they represent. Social work performs different functions in each country – in Ireland, social workers are mainly employed by Health Boards, have a regulatory function in respect of child protection and are part of the framework of community care services. In Denmark, social workers (*social ardgivers*) have a statutory function, yet tend to work as part of multi-professional groupings and have a role in the assessment and provision of welfare benefits, social pedagogues work with individuals and groups in day care and residential settings. Social workers in Britain have a more diffuse professional identity, working in both statutory sectors and in a wider range of professional settings than their colleagues in either Ireland or Denmark.

The professional associations in each country, therefore, operate in slightly different ways. In Ireland, the Irish Association of Social Workers appears to represent primarily those people working in statutory settings and is relatively new. The Danish Association of Social Workers is a trade union as well as a professional association and claims to represent approximately 95 per cent of social workers in Denmark (*DASW factsheet*). The British Association of Social Workers represents a much smaller percentage of the social work workforce and has no trade union function (most British social workers would belong to a separate trade union). Allowing for these differences, there are similarities in the ethical base which underpins their work.

The *International Declaration of Ethical Principles of Social Work* of the International Federation of Social Workers suggests the following ethical principles should underpin social work:

2.2.4. *Social workers have a commitment to principles of social justice.*

2.2.5. *Social workers have the responsibility to devote objective and disciplined knowledge and skill to aid individuals, groups, communities, and societies in their development and resolution of personal-societal conflicts and their consequences.*

2.2.10. *Social workers generally expect clients to take responsibility, in collaboration with them, for determining courses of action affecting their lives. Compulsion which might be necessary to solve one party's problems at the expense of the interests of others involved should only take place after careful explicit evaluation of the claims of the conflicting parties. Social workers should minimise the use of legal compulsion.*

These principles clearly demonstrate the tension that lies at the centre of social work between regulation and empowerment. The code recognises this tension when it refers to:

__the fact that the social worker functions both as a helper and controller__. The relation between these two opposite aspects of social work demands a clarification based on an explicit choice of values in order to avoid a mixing-up of motives or a lack of clarity in motives, actions and consequences of actions. When social workers are expected to play a role in the state control of citizens they are obliged to clarify the ethical implications of this role and to what extent this role is acceptable in relation to the basic ethical principles of social work (IFSW - emphasis in original).

The Irish Association of Social Workers (IASW) code is much more explicitly client centred and in its value statement says that:

Social work asserts that with due regard to the rights of others:

– Every human being has a unique dignity and a right to self-expression and independence of action and lifestyle irrespective of nationality, ethnic background, social and economic status, ability, health, gender, sexual preference, age, belief, or contribution to society.

– Society regardless of its form has an obligation to pursue social justice, protect the human rights of all persons and support them in attaining their optimum potential.

The social worker has a professional responsibility to empower individuals, groups, communities and societies to act on their own behalf in so far as is possible. (IASW, Code of Ethics).

The British Association of Social Workers (BASW) code has an equally empowering agenda when it talks of the need for social workers to enhance well-being, facilitate self-realisation and relieve hardship:

6.   Basic to the profession of social work is the recognition of the value and dignity of every human being, irrespective of origin, race, status, sex, sexual orientation, age, disability, belief or contribution to society. The profession accepts a responsibility to encourage and facilitate the self- realisation of each individual person with due regard to the interest of others.

7.   Concerned with the enhancement of human well-being, social work attempts to relieve and prevent hardship and suffering. Social workers thus have a responsibility to help individuals, families, groups and communities through the provision and operation of appropriate services, and by contributing to social planning and action...

9.   The social worker's responsibility for relief and prevention of hardship and suffering is not always fully discharged by direct service to individual families and groups. The worker has the right and duty to bring to the attention of those in power, and of the general public, ways in which the activities of government, society or agencies create or contribute to hardship and suffering or militate against their relief. (BASW, 1996 - numbers in text).

It goes on to suggest that social workers '*will help their clients both individually and collectively to increase the range of choices open to them and their powers to make decisions, securing the participation, wherever possible, of clients in defining and obtaining services appropriate to their needs*'. (BASW, 1996).

COMMONALITIES AND DIFFERENCES

A number of common theoretical elements can be seen to inform social work values in the three countries. Briefly, these can be clustered under five headings:

- uncovering the reality of human nature,

- notions of power and oppression,

- a commitment to liberation through the development of strategies of empowerment

- the ways in which our ability to reflect on the social circumstances (context) in which we work impacts on and informs our practice.

- it is perhaps most strikingly around the notions of equality and difference that the similarities in theory and the differences in practice most clearly emerge.

The model in table 1 illustrates and conceptualises these processes.

TABLE 1. COMPARING SOCIAL WORK VALUES - DENMARK, IRELAND AND BRITAIN

	Danish values - Kierkegaard, Grundvitg, Freire	Irish values - regulation or empowerment	British values - ADP/AOP
Human nature	focus on individual, view of human nature distorted through process indoctrination, manipulation	Social authoritarianism of Catholic Church being replaced with new focus on non-deserving and 'dependent'	Experience tempered through ideological devices which legitimise those in power and marginalize powerless
Power/oppression	Knowledge compart-mentalis-ed, facts abstracted, whole picture denied oppressed	Dissonance between values statements recognising oppression and practice tending toward regulation	Looks at way power operates and is impacted upon by social divisions of race, gender etc, similarities in processes of oppression - different results
Liberation/ empowerment	Need to overcome dominant power inter-ests through liberatory pedagogy, creative process social transformation	Works on two levels - rejecting empowering perspectives in statutory work, promoting empowerment in community based work	Recognises that it is insufficient to create awareness/understanding, need for collective solutions recognising difference/diversity
Action + theory = praxis	Need for self-reflection, conscientization as guide to practice	Again tension between statutory and community approaches, emergence of 'ethnic intelligentsia' among Travellers exam-ple link theory/practice	Tackles forms of exclu-sion, suggests strategies to empower involving links theory to practice to expose oppression, create preconditions for change
Equality and difference	Promotion social soli-darity as means tackling inequality often denies difference	Strong equality agenda emerging promoted by community based organisations, some sign of recognition of differ-ence except around race	Recognition inequality, right to self-organisation, recognises difference within and between communities, lacks focus on social/political equality

HUMAN NATURE

As we can see, these sets of values provide the preconditions for a new expression of values which have the potential to be trans-European, but which respect the different traditions, national cultures and diverse populations of each country. In Grundtvig, Kierkegaard and Friere we see a focus on the individual as agent of change. The social milieu within which we operate constructs, they suggest, a distorted human nature through processes of indoctrination, manipulation and 'dominated consciousness' (Friere, 1972). People's behaviours become pathologised and their understanding of themselves and their world is fragmented. They lack the consciousness or understanding to decode their situations, to realise that their experience consists of interacting `constituent elements of the whole' (Friere, 1972). Thompson (1997) writes about the ways in which people's understanding of their situation is tempered through a series of ideological devices which presents inequality as somehow natural, as being the outcome of processes which ascribe negative evaluations to those without power and which seek to legitimise those in power. He argues that views of human nature are ideologically constructed to deny people the opportunity to realise the possibilities for change.

Skehill (1999) suggests that Irish social work, while moving away from the religious based morality which typified it until the 1970s is still very concerned with questions of moral regulation. She argues that, if families are not conforming to ascribed norms and morals, a more regulatory regime will ensue' (Skehill, 1999:188). Powell (1995) argues that this is accompanied by a reconceptualisation of the poor in terms of them receiving their just desserts and a concept of dependency, '*in which a less tolerant attitude is taken towards the unemployed and lone parents who have children born out of wedlock*' (Powell, 1995:29). Such negative stereotyping of the more marginalized sections of the community is, Powell asserts, most pronounced in relation to the Travelling community as a consequence of which, '*social prejudice re-enforces the administration of the vagrancy laws, creating a system of apartheid between the Travellers and the majority population*' (p.30).

POWER AND OPPRESSION

Grundtvig (Kohl, 1991) sought to critique existing power relations, particularly through the ways in which knowledge is compartmentalised, so that facts become abstracted and the whole picture becomes lost. Kierkegaard, in turn, questioned the ways in which the balance of power was constructed to protect dominant power interests. Friere (1972) points out these processes make the oppressed 'reluctant to resist' and lacking in the confidence to oppose their oppression.

Anti-discriminatory theory equally focuses on ways in which power operates. It points to the complex ways in which dominant interests operate at structural, institutional and individual levels to render the people powerless and passive. It attempts to show how this process is not accidental but is the outcome of processes of oppression which deny people equality, and that there are similarities in the ways in which these processes operate around social divisions of race and ethnicity, gender, sexuality, disability, age. However, anti-discriminatory theory goes further reflecting post-modernist conceptions of fragmentation and difference in its focus on the need to acknowledge the different experiences and outcomes within and between oppressed groups.

The IASW Code of Ethics, discussed above, clearly expects social workers to understand the structural nature of the oppression the clients of social work services face, and mirrors British social work's recognition that this may impact differentially on different client groups (Powell,

1998). Skehill criticises the IASW code precisely because it makes, '*no acknowledgement or reference to the regulatory nature of social work*' (Skehill, 1999: 190).

Grundtvig and Kierkegaard both recognise that to overcome these dominant power interests, the capabilities and resources of the people need to be liberated. Kierkegaard, however, recognises that the freedom of choice and resulting anxiety, which follow from them lead to 'the dizziness of freedom' (Macquirre, 1972, Gardiner, 1988). Gardiner suggests, therefore, that Kierkegaard sees the person as 'a*n active subject who can envisage and respond to possibilities and where there is nothing that objectively compels me to opt for one response as opposed to another - here I am the sole arbiter and what I do is entirely up to me*' (Gardiner, 1988: 107). Friere talks of the need to intervene in people's reality, to use education as a pedagogy of liberation, to awaken people through processes of conscientization (Freiere, 1972).

ADP/AOP theorists espouse similar approaches, talking of the need to build on people's experiences, of encouraging them to intervene in their own reality, through the development of collective solutions to their problems. This means developing methods of empowering people which encourage them to see the connections between their situations and that of others and resisting the establishment of hierarchies of oppression. It is about recognising the different realities people face, encouraging them to organise together with others and linking with people experiencing different kinds of oppression. If social transformation is the goal, it becomes necessary to build bridges within and between oppressed groups. Williams points to the way in which '*anti-oppressive practice implies a political role for social work. It confers on it an emancipatory interest*' (Williams, C 1999: 223).

In Ireland, as we have seen, there is a debate currently taking place about the potential of social work to contribute to an empowerment agenda. Not surprisingly, Skehill suggests that such possibilities, if examined along a continuum of regulation and empowerment, would position Irish social work '*within a traditional individualistic framework*' with a focus ' *on various aspects of individual casework*' (Skehill,1999: 184). Yet this is clearly only part of the picture. Leaving aside Powell's alternative analysis, there is enough evidence from other sources to indicate that the commitment to empowerment paradigms is still prevalent.

The Community Action Network (CAN) , one of the second tier agencies charged by the Department of Social and Community affairs with responsibility for implementing the department's community development strategy (XX from author's interview with M. Berry), organised a series of visits to Ireland by Marcus Arruda a Brazilain, social activist (and colleague of Paulo Freire) who described the potential of community development to counteract globalisation. Arruda (1999) spoke of the need to develop a praxis education '*as a means for empowering persons and communities to become subjects of their own development and education*' (Arruda, 1999: 6). These seminars were well attended by community activists and professional community workers. The Director of CAN describes an approach they have been developing which connects with the spirituality found in some of the Danish writing. She talks about:

'Soul work' - creative way of working, it is about focusing in on what sustains people in work and looking at how people who have been active over a long period of time can be nourished, what ways can we work differently...this means tapping into the resources people need to sustain them in their work, exploring themes such as change, conflict and hope...we look at ourselves, apply our personal learning to the work situation we are in.

What does this tell us about change at the community level or change organisationally, what do we need to sustain ourselves in a change process. (Director of CAN [interview with author, February 1998])

ACTION + THEORY = PRAXIS

How can such processes of social transformation occur? Again, there are similarities in the value bases in that they recognise the need for understanding to lead to action. Kierkegaard focuses on the need for self-reflection as a precondition for developing our understanding of the whole individual and social situation. Grundtvig's commitment to education for change and Friere's account of how education can be a liberatory mechanism, which not only creates understanding, `Conscientizacao', but leads to action for change, find clear echoes in anti-discriminatory practice.

ADP/AOP are essentially theories of action. It is not sufficient just to become aware, but to use this awareness to demonstrate that we are not alone in experiencing oppression and disempowerment. Our experiences are collective and our solutions must correspondingly be collective. They are about social transformation and are, therefore, forms of action, a praxis in which knowledge is used to facilitate change, tackle oppression and create the conditions for social transformation.

Thus, it is about linking an understanding of oppression to notions of action and empowerment (Ward and Mullender, 1991; Cornwall, 1993; Beresford and Croft, 1993). To some extent this is related to Giddens' notions of agency and structure. He refers to power as *'the transformative capacity of human action'* (Cassell, 1993: 109). This, he suggests, following Marx, is the key element in the notion of praxis. The creation of a radical practice based on notions of overcoming oppression, tackling discrimination/oppression and the creation of new co-operative social relationships is at the heart of any theory of social action.

We have seen in the debate between Skehill and Powell the tension in Irish social work between regulatory and liberatory discourses. Carmichael (1987) referred to the tension within Ireland caused by the way that, *'the role of the professional has particular power and significance'* (Carmichael, 1997: 21). These factors have played a role in cementing the status of Irish social work and reducing the capacity for empowering interventions. Yet within the voluntary sector there is clear evidence that the link between theory and action is well appreciated (Powell and Guerin, 1997). The emergence of the 'ethnic intelligentsia' among Travellers is the clearest expression of this process (McLaughlin, 1995).

EQUALITY AND DIFFERENCE

It is here that we see the biggest contrast between the Danish, Irish and British value systems. Danish social work has translated Grundtvig's, Kierkegaard's and Friere's commitment to tackling unequal power relations into a commitment to equality.

It has been suggested that this Danish commitment to equality comes about because they see, *'others behave democratically and create environments influenced by solidarity and trust in one another and each others abilities'* (FESET, 1999: 6).

Perhaps this is not surprising given the Danish welfare state's espousal of social solidarity as a policy goal. Goul Andersen has shown, that despite challenges to the legitimacy of the welfare state within Denmark, it remains true that 'welfare state support in Denmark has survived severe economic crises as well as sometimes quite aggressive (but verbal rather than institutional) attacks on the welfare state during more than ten years of bourgeois political rule' (Goul Andersen, 1997: 25).

However, this promotion of solidarity and equality is also a denial. It denies difference and assumes people have common interests regardless of their class, race, gender, age or sexuality. It results, for example, in processes in which the needs of black and ethnic minority communities are perceived as being the same, both within and between all minority ethnic groups, and to other Danish citizens. It accounts for the fact that in the words of one Danish anti-racist campaigner, `The only way to succeed in Denmark is to be Danish' (Quaraishy, 1994). The outcome is the development of policies of assimilation which minimise cultural difference. Birte Siim makes a similar point when discussing the challenges facing the Danish welfare state. She suggests that:

The old vocabulary of universalism and social equality had been favourable to the integration of women, but it is based upon a high degree of homogeneity among citizen's which made it difficult to integrate difference based on ethnicity (Siim, 1998: 391).

Powell (1995) when looking at trends in Irish society argued that Ireland was confronted with a choice between embracing the increasing inequality in British and American society or adopting the more egalitarian social policies found in Scandinavia. He left the option open. There are some signs that the move may be in a more egalitarian direction (see the recent enactment of the Equal Status Act and the establishment of the Equality Authority). However, despite the recent passage of the Equality Act 1999 Ireland still has some difficulty dealing with racism or recognising the necessity of allowing people to organise separately around anti-racist issues.

Yet Ireland is beginning to recognise an equality agenda. An official from the Department of Social, Community and Family Affairs described the way the department was beginning to tackle gender and inequality. She said, '*we have gender proofing. Gender proofing has been done and recently we got agreement that poverty proofing will be done and the next stage I suppose will be equality proofing*'. She defined poverty proofing as being 'when Government or major policies are being developed and major funding is being planned that the proposals would be assessed against criteria which will examine how they impact on people in poverty.' [2]

Not all groups in Irish society take such a sanguine view. One woman who is a member of the Travellers Visibility group in Cork argues that the Travellers, as a group, have been marginal in Irish society:

One of the difficulties has been because Travellers have not been named in the legislation to date. Travellers have been overlooked. It is presumed that everybody will need protection but not the Travelling community. People say that there was no such thing as racism in this country until the refugees arrived, that is crazy. The good thing about equal status legislation was the way that people combined to get it passed. We made a strategic decision that we would not support the Act until everybody – gays, lesbians, disabled people, refugees – everybody who needed to be protected was named in the legislation. Subsequently we got involved in lobbying with the Southern Justice Group. By us trying to create an alliance with other marginalised groups it strengthened our hand ... it has moved the debate on. It's about equality and action.

British social work values, on the other hand, centre precisely on the need to recognise differences. This is perhaps the outcome of nearly eighteen years of New-Right government, the development of social policies which promoted inequality and a welfare state, which, during this period, was configured by a lack of resources and a lack of commitment to social justice

(Johnson, 1990; Oppenheim, 1998). It may also be the outcome of Britain's need to deal with its post-colonial history, and the presence of a larger and more established minority ethnic community. However, it is also about recognising the unique way in which oppression structures people's lives. It is, for example, about saying that people with disabilities may have common experience but that this commonality is impacted upon by factors such as race, class, age, and sexuality. However, it is not about being different and unequal. It is about recognising difference within the context of struggles for equality. It is not enough to treat all people the same. Account should be taken of people's different needs and expectations. (Williams, 1996; Yuval-Davis, 1998).

Making connections

The above analysis demonstrates clearly the need for dialogue between social workers in different countries. It shows that we can learn from each other. British social work should encompass values of equality and solidarity, and Danish social work, the importance of difference within the context of an anti-discriminatory practice. Ireland is moving closer to the British experience, particularly if the new legislative environment is an accurate guide to potential changes in the social work environment. Yet it also has a vibrant voluntary sector where the values of empowerment and participation appear to be more central than in the British welfare mix.

It is not that these countries are far apart. The above discussion clearly demonstrates similarities between their value bases. Perhaps the time has come for each to respect each other's contribution to the debate, to learn from each other and to develop a form of praxis committed to social transformation and transferable to different national cultures and experiences.

Significantly, when we engage with people from other countries in co-operative or comparative work, we need to unpack the way in which the language we use carries with it particular cultural, social and political meanings, which we cannot simply read off through the process of translation. We need to understand how the concepts we discuss resonate with our colleagues - exactly what do we mean by discrimination, inequality, liberation, equality and difference. This article suggests that this process may allow us to see the similarities as well as the differences between us, to recognise that the truth does not reside in one set of culturally specific values, but that we often share ways of understanding, methods of working and commitments to social justice. Our countries may be at different stages, our experience is undoubtedly different but we may find that what we have in common allows us to transcend any differences and work co-operatively toward a fairer future.

References

Banks, S. (1995) *Ethics and Values in Social Work* Basingstoke, Macmillan

Barry, M. (1998) 'Social Exclusion and Social Work: an introduction' in Barry, M and Hallett ,C. *Social Exclusion and Social Work: Issues of Theory, Policy and Practice* Lyme Regis, Russell House Publishing

Beresford, P. and Croft, S. (1993) *Citizen Involvement: A practical Guide for Change* Basingstoke, Macmillan

Bjorgo, T. and Witte, R. (1993) *Racist Violence in Europe* Basingstoke, Macmillan

Cassell, P (1993) *The Giddens Reader* Basingstoke, Macmillan

Castles, F. G. (ed.) (1993) *Families of Nations: Patterns of Public Policy in Western Democracies* Aldershot, Dartmouth

Castles, F. G. (1998) *Comparative Public Policy: Patterns of Post-War Transformation* Cheltenham, Edward Elgar

Cornwall, N. (1993) From Understanding to Action: Developing and Assessing Anti-Racist / Anti-discriminatory Practice, *Issues in Social Work Education* **12** (2)

Cornwall, N. (1994) Social Work Education and Practice Sans Frontiers, *Issues in Social Work Education* **14** (1) pp 39–52

Davies Jones, H (1994) The Social pedagogues in Western Europe - some implications for European inter-professional care, *Journal of Interprofessional Care* **8** (1) pp 19–29

Dominelli, L. and Hoogvelt, A. (1996) Globalization and the Technocratization of Social Work, *Critical Social Policy* **16**

Esping-Andersen, G. (1990) *The Three Worlds of Welfare Capitalism* Cambridge, The Polity Press

Fekete, L. and Webber, F. (1994) *Inside Racist Europe* London, Institute of Race Relations

Freire, P. (1972) *Pedagogy of the Oppressed* London, Penguin

Gardiner, P. (1988) *Kierkegaard* Oxford, Oxford University Press

Gavalias, Y. (1994) Immigrants, refugees and asylum Seekers - who's who? *Etnica* **51**

Goul Andersen, J. (1997) The Scandinavian Welfare Model in Crisis? Achievements and Problems of the Danish Welfare State in an Age of Unemployment and Low Growth, *Scandinavian Political Studies* **20** (1)

Hannay, A and Marino, G. D. (1998) *The Cambridge Companion to Kierkegaard* Cambridge, Cambridge University Press

Hokenstad, M. C. and Midgely, J. (1998) *Issues in International Social Work: Global Challenges for a New Century* Washington, NASW Press

Humphries, B. (1996) *Critical Perspectives on Empowerment* Birmingham, Venture Press

Johannesen, T. (1997) 'Social Work as an International Profession: Opportunities and Challenges' in Hokenstad, M. C. and Midgely, J. (1998) *Issues in International Social Work: Global Challenges for a New Century* Washington, NASW Press

Kohl, H (1991) A Tradition of Radical Education: Highlander in Context *Social Policy*, Winter pp. 36–43

Lorenz, W. (1998) 'ECSPRESS: the Thematic Network in the Social Professions' *Social Work in Europe* **3** (3) pp 25–9

Macquarrie, J. (1972) *Existentialism: an introduction, guide and assessment* London, Penguin

McDonald, P. and Coleman, M. (1999) 'Deconstructing hierarchies of oppression and adopting a 'multiple model' approach to anti-oppressive practice' *Social Work Education* **18** (1) pp19–33

Melucci, A. (1989) 'Nomads of the Present: Social Movements and Individual Needs' in *Contemporary Society* Keane, J. and Mier, P. (eds.) London, Century Hutchinson

Midgely, M. (1997) 'Social work and International Social Development - Promoting a Developmental Perspective in the Profession' in Hokenstad, M. C. and Midgely, J. (1998) *Issues in International Social Work: Global Challenges for a New Century*, Washington, NASW Press pp11–26,

Oppenheim, C. (ed.) (1998) *An Inclusive Society: Strategies for Tackling Poverty* London, Institute for Public Policy Research

Oyen, E. (1990) 'Comparative Research as a Sociological Strategy - the Imperfection of Comparisons' in Oyen, E. *Comparative Methodology: Theory and Practice in International Social Research* London, SAGE/ISA

Quaraishy, B. (1994) Denmark from an Ethnic Angle, *Etnica* **51**

Relof, L. A. (1994) Freedom of Speech and Protection of Minorities, *Etnica* **51**

Shardlow, S. (1998) 'Values, Ethics and Social Work' in Adams, R, Dominelli, L. and Payne, M. *Social Work: Themes, Issues and Critical Debates* Basingstoke, Macmillan

Siim. B. (1998) - Vocabularies of citizenship and gender: Denmark, *Critical Social Policy* **58**

Sipilla, J. (1997) 'Comparative research on Social Care systems -How to Proceed' in Kautto, M. (ed.) *European Social Services - Policies and Priorities to the year 2000* pp 71–85, Helsinki, STAKES/ Ministry of Social Affairs and Health

Spicker, P. (1991) 'Solidarity' in Room, G. (ed.) *Towards a European welfare State?*, pp 17–37, Bristol, SAUS Publications

Svallfors, S. (1997) Worlds of Welfare and Attitudes to redistribution: A Comparison of Eight Western Nations, *European Sociological Review* **13** (3) pp 283–304

Taylor, Z. (1999) Values, theories and methods in social work education - a culturally transferable core? *International Social Work* **42** (3) 309–18

Thompson, N (1997) *Anti-Discriminatory Practice*, (2nd ed.) Basingstoke, Macmillan

Ward, D. and Mullender, A. (1991) Empowerment and Oppression: an indissoluble pairing for contemporary social work, *Critical Social Policy*

Weedon, C. (1987) *Feminist Practice and Poststructuralist Theory* Oxford, Basil Blackwell

Williams, C., Soydan, H. and Johnson, M. R. D. (eds.) (1998) *Social Work and Minorities: European Perspectives* London, Routledge

Williams, C. (1999) Connecting Anti-Racist and Anti-oppressive Theory and Practice: Retrenchment or Reappraisal? *British Journal of Social Work* **29** pp 211–30

Williams, F. (1996) 'Postmodernism, feminism and the question of difference' in Parton, N (ed.) *Social Theory, Social Change and Social Work* London, Routledge

Williams, F. and Pillinger, J. (1996) 'New Thinking on social policy research into inequality, social exclusion and poverty' in Millar, J. and Bradshaw, J. *Social Welfare Systems: towards a Research agenda* Bath, Centre for the Analysis of Social Policy in association with the ESRC, University of Bath

Yuval-Davis, N. (1997) 'Ethnicity, Gender Relations and Multi-Culturalism' in Werbner, P. and Modood, T. (eds) *Debating Cultural Hybridity: Multi-Cultural Identities and the Politics of Anti-Racism* London, Zed Books

NOTES

1   I am using the term ADP/AOP to indicate a broad consensus between the two positions around the need to be aware of the way discrimination and oppression operates and of the need to develop strategies to overcome them. The view of Dalrymple and Burke (1995) that ' if work with people who have limited power or who are marginalized is to be effective then it should link the personal realities of people's lives to the structural context in which they exist' (p.9) and the incorporation of power and oppression within that framework is not in my view that different from the position outlined by Thompson (1997) and more particularly Thompson (1998). This is particularly the case when considering Thompson's comment that discrimination and specific forms of oppression do not ' exist in isolation, separate from one another, (but) rather as parts of a complex matrix of multiple and interacting oppressions' (Thompson,1998:108).

2   A recent working group report has recommended the introduction of gender, poverty and equality proofing as part of the Partnership 2000 agreement between the Irish government and the social partners. The report defines equality proofing as, ' the (re)organisation, improvement, development and evaluation of policy processes, so that a(n)...equality perspective is incorporated in all policies at all levels and all stages, by the actors normally involved in policy-making' (Government of Ireland, 2000).

HENRY FIELDING

Born at Sharpham Park, Somerset, 22nd April 1707;
died at Lisbon, 8th October 1754.

HENRY FIELDING

Joseph Andrews

INTRODUCTION BY
A. R. HUMPHREYS
Professor of English in the
University of Leicester

DENT: LONDON
EVERYMAN'S LIBRARY
DUTTON: NEW YORK

NO. 467

BIOGRAPHICAL NOTE

HENRY FIELDING (1707–54); born at Sharpham Park, Somerset, seat of his maternal grandfather, Sir Henry Gould, judge of the King's Bench; his own father served under Marlborough, later becoming a general. 1719–24, at Eton, along with the elder Pitt, the elder Fox, Charles Hanbury (Williams), Thomas Arne and George Lyttelton, later a leading statesman, and Fielding's friend. 1728–9, studied literature at Leyden. 1729–37, wrote plays in London; the main surviving results are some songs (including 'The dusky night rides down the sky'), the burlesque *Tom Thumb*, two adaptations of Molière (*The Mock Doctor*; *The Miser*), and two political satires (*Pasquin*; *The Historical Register for 1736*). Walpole retaliated with the Licensing Act (1737). 1734, married Charlotte Cradock of Salisbury, commemorated in Sophia and Amelia. 1737, entered Middle Temple, and tried journalism in *The Champion* (1739–41) which reveals the wide reading and generous attitudes later displayed in the novels. Ridiculed Richardson's *Pamela* (1740) with a shrewd travesty, *Shamela* (1741), and with *Joseph Andrews* (1742). 1743, *Miscellanies* (3 vols., including *A Journey from This World to the Next* and *Jonathan Wild*). Severely harassed by poverty and family troubles; his wife died 1744. Anti-Stuart-and-Popery propaganda in *The True Patriot* (1745–6) and *The Jacobite's Journal* (1747–8). 1748, appointed Justice of the Peace for Westminster, later for Middlesex also; as Bow Street magistrate struggled with poverty, crime and corruption. 1749, *Tom Jones*. Despite failing health worked indefatigably, with his blind half-brother Sir John Fielding, to clean up legal malpractices and street violence. 1751, *Amelia* and *An Enquiry into the Causes of the Late Increase of Robbers*. 1752, *The Covent-Garden Journal*. 1753, *A Proposal for Making an Effectual Provision for the Poor*. 1754, fatally ill from his exertions and disease; sailed for Portugal, but died soon after arrival. 1755, *The Journal of a Voyage to Lisbon* published.

INTRODUCTION TO
'JOSEPH ANDREWS'

IN APRIL 1741, five months after *Pamela* appeared, Fielding
put on record what he thought of Richardson's book. *An Apology
for the Life of Mrs Shamela Andrews*, while directed mainly
against *Pamela*, purports, however, to be by 'Conny Keyber',
a pseudonym aiming jointly at Conyers Middleton and Colley
Cibber but hardly sufficing either then or now to conceal
Fielding's authorship. Middleton, librarian of Cambridge University, had aroused Fielding's levity with his *Life of Cicero*
(1741), obsequiously dedicated to the much-ridiculed Lord
Hervey (Pope's Sporus and, probably, the Didapper of *Joseph
Andrews*). Cibber's *Apology for the Life of Mr Colley Cibber*
(1740) had, like *Pamela*, been recently both acclaimed and
mocked. The vivacity with which Fielding derides all three
men (together with others touched in passing, like George
Whitefield) shows his invention at its most ruthless, his wit at
its gayest and strongest.

Joseph Andrews (1742) starts and finishes (even in its last
words) by parodying *Pamela*, and parody has often been taken
to be Fielding's whole initial intention, from which the growing
spell of the quixotic Abraham Adams diverted him. But why,
having finished *Shamela*, immediately embark on a second
travesty merely *as* a second travesty? More probably, wishing
to reduce the 'epidemical Phrenzy' over a questionable book
(not to have read which, the *Gentleman's Magazine* remarked
in January 1741, was '*as great a Sign of Want of Curiosity . . .
as not to have seen the* French *and* Italian *Dancers*'), he took the
same ingredients—high-placed lust, low-placed chastity and
a virtuous clergyman—and aimed from the beginning at an
opposed and healthier reading of life. The title-page calls the
book *The Adventures of Joseph Andrews and of his Friend Mr
Abraham Adams*; the Christian names are biblically significant.
'Joseph' is, of course, synonymous with the chaste man, dis-
cipliner of the passions (indiscipline being personified in Lady
Booby)—though discipline is not extermination; Adams himself, though he dissuades Joseph and Fanny from plunging headlong into marriage, has six children, and Mrs Adams has found
him 'a loving and cherishing husband' (IV. viii). 'Abraham',

the patriarchal name, symbolizes the servant of God, kindly
father of his flock, and is often so used in homiletic literature,
not least by the Latitudinarian divines Fielding so attentively
read.[1] Together, chastity and charity, the young disciple and
the guiding elder, they form a deeply felt moral theme. To
some readers Adams has seemed to take the whole book on
his own shoulders, yet in fact his character and values are
throughout held in admirable relationship with the others on
view.

The journey on which the book is organized has its symbolical
significances; the journey is not merely a journey. Starting
from London sophistication, it travels towards the bucolic
simplicity of the western parish. Homage to country life was,
indeed, an Augustan convention. But Fielding was too shrewd
simply to equate town high life with vice, country humble life
with virtue. His plays had shown vices and virtues in both
spheres and at all levels, and *Tom Jones* and *Amelia* were to do
so again. The town is, doubtless, more cynically corrupt, and the
country the place where happiness awaits Mr Wilson, Joseph
and Fanny, Tom and Sophia, Booth and Amelia, where Mr
Allworthy lives in Paradise Hall and Dr Harrison has his
contented benefice. (*Tom Jones* was to move the other way,
from human nature in the country's 'more plain and simple
manner' to the 'affectation and vice which courts and cities
afford'.) The rural virtues of Joseph, Fanny and Adams foil
the urban vices of Lady Booby's circle, and Mr Wilson's story
epitomizes the town/country contrast. Yet no naïve antithesis
can be sustained: Fielding's novel would be less rich than it is
if within the general potency of the town–vice/country–virtue
convention there were not a vigorous preparedness to recognize
vice and virtue wherever they appear. After all, to quote Pope:

> Honour and shame from no condition rise;
> Act well your part; there all the honour lies.

The symbolic journey, then, is enriched by its allusion to the
convention, but it does not assume simply that God made the
country and man made the town. Rather it tests varieties of
conduct by the standards of charity, and for this testing the
device of a journey through successive settings is eminently
suitable, serviceable equally for entertainment or for moral
example, and used through the whole Christian tradition to

[1] Martin C. Battestin's book, *The Moral Basis of Fielding's Art* (1959),
admirably brings out these points and Fielding's Latitudinarian inheritance.

symbolize man's pilgrimage through trials to the goal of virtue
or holiness. The journey has, too, its secular analogue. This
'comic epic poem in prose' hints at the *Odyssey*, the story of
the much-tried hero pursued on his homeward travels by
Poseidon's wrath. In Fénélon's version in *Télémaque*, referred
to in Fielding's preface, the jealous Venus replaces Poseidon
as the outraged deity, and in an essay in 1728 the critic Andrew
Michael Ramsay commented that 'the Hatred of *Venus*
against a young Prince, that despises Pleasure for the Sake of
Virtue, and subdues his Passions by the Assistance of Wisdom,
is a Fable drawn from Nature, and at the same Time includes
the sublimest Morality'.[1] Classically minded readers alerted
by the reference to *Télémaque*, Professor Butt observes, must
have relished the sublime morality of the handsome youth
pursued by the patrician dame, despising pleasure for the sake
of virtue, and subduing his passions by the example of his
sister Pamela.

Joseph Andrews has often been praised for its story, but
the praise has generally related to its plot mechanics. Fielding
takes care over these, it is true, and it is true also that events
which at first look like mere contrivance are entirely probable.
The main characters make their encounters not because Fielding
plays fast and loose with chance but because nothing is more
likely than that travellers on the same road, with particular
inns as staging-posts, will come across each other. The secrets
of Joseph's and Fanny's paternity are admittedly contrivances,
characteristic operations of traditional drama and story, such
as Aristotle places among the inferior means of solving plots.
But this matters little; as Mr Maynard Mack has well said:
'Comedy presents us with life apprehended in the form of
spectacle rather than in the form of experience,' and spectacle
can accept help from artifice. More important than plot-
mechanics is the organization by juxtaposed significances;
from this the modelling arises. Prefacing his sister's novel,
David Simple (1744), Fielding dropped a comment relevant
to his own book—'the fable consists of a series of separate
adventures, detached from and independent of each other,
yet all tending to one great end'. The great end being the opposition of integrity and Christian decency to corruption and
selfishness, most of the incidents bear upon it. The stories of
Leonora and of Mr Wilson, for example, are parables of the good

---

[1] Cited in John Butt, *Fielding*, 1954, page 17. Telemachus is guided
through his perils by Minerva in the guise of Mentor.

heart as against the mercenary. The smaller incidents, too, have their part to play. The famous stage-coach episode (I. xii) shows Joseph suffering first from physical and then from moral callousness, and saved only by the charitable postilion, to whom in turn society is to prove even more callous. Adams, modest and inoffensive, is introduced in the Tow-wouses' inn, and at once the cocksure surgeon is set up against him (I. xiv). No sooner have Adams and Joseph been seen kneeling in grateful prayer than the bookseller and Barnabas expose themselves as materialistic and bigoted (I. xvii). Trulliber's cupidity is contrasted with the poor pedlar's generosity (II. xiv–xv), and the Wilsons' happiness with the young squire's cruelty (III. iv). Vain of his schoolmastering, Adams lauds a private over a public education, and at once is 'roasted' by the privately educated fox-hunter (III. v–vii). This last juxtaposition is, indeed, almost too blatant; under the pressure of Fielding's feelings comedy gives way to ugly farce. *Joseph Andrews*, it must be remembered, falls in date just midway between *The Pilgrim's Progress* and *Pride and Prejudice*; not for sixty years was Jane Austen to subtilize the moral diagrams of the novel. In 1742 novel-readers needed explicit meanings rather than implicit, and indeed by nature Fielding was given to making things plain. But if now and then the story over-demonstrates, by that very fact it is not haphazard. And in many touches it makes an exquisite effect without over-demonstrating—in, for instance, its neat contrast between Lady Booby's shocking patrician manners and Mrs Adams's admirable plebeian ones (IV. ix).

The plot works, then, both fore and aft and laterally. It moves forward in the connections of the main characters and it spreads also, as a stream carries eddies, into illustrative episodes. The characters likewise are agents of the central narrative, or examples of conduct, or both. A Trulliber, Mrs Tow-wouse or Peter Pounce is only incidental to the story; all three, nevertheless, are intensely registered and have a powerful meaning. As for the main characters, Fanny, natural, affectionate, a good servant, an excellent wife, is Fielding's anti-Pamela, an object lesson in those virtues so ambiguously present in Richardson's heroine. Lady Booby is not only a satirical allusion to *Pamela's* amorous but outwitted Squire B——; she is the antithesis of the innocent raptures of Joseph and Fanny and of the Christian discipline counselled by Adams, her heartlessness equal to her self-indulgence. Melodramatic though her idiom is, she moves with a dangerous vitality, while yet remaining a figure of comedy as Lady Bellaston of *Tom Jones* does not—the scene in which she yearns towards a new husband and protests her modesty to the old one is wonderfully amusing (IV. vi). Her unscrupulousness is certainly felt to be formidable, though its total defeat by the mere 'kind of domestic' she takes Adams to be is central to Fielding's Christian egalitarianism.

Adams is above praise. Sublimely innocent, unshakably upright, he is the moral absolutist, yet charitable. *Joseph Andrews* was 'Written in Imitation of the Manner of Cervantes', and Adams like Quixote forms his ideas of life from the loftier realms of literature (very little of it contemporary), confident of finding in the world the virtues he finds in authors. Often deceived, he still asserts that 'books are the only way of travelling by which any knowledge is to be acquired'. His Christian principles leave him neither room nor inclination for compromise with wrong, though mere foolishness he tolerates philosophically. He takes the great words of faith and morals—truth, charity, forgiveness, eternity, God—to mean precisely what they say. Fielding enforces the reality of moral words throughout his writings; in the *Champion* (27th March 1740) he quotes Locke on the confusions of words and meanings (*Human Understanding*, III. x. 2–3); and he was to raise the same subject in the *Covent-Garden Journal* (14th January 1752), where he thinks it to be

an Office very worthy the Labour of a good Commentator to explain certain hard Words which frequently occur in the Works of Barrow, Tillotson, Clark, and others of this Kind. Such are Heaven, Hell, Judgment, Righteousness, Sin, *Etc*. All which, it is reasonable to believe, are at present very little understood.

As against Mrs Tow-wouse, or Leonora's aunt, or Trulliber, who think of themselves as Christians who 'know what charity is', or the rascally captain who will cut the throat of anyone disputing his 'imanity', Adams lives convinced that one is a Christian because Christian precepts are unblinkable realities. And earnest though he is in this, he is delightfully good-natured, 'with benevolence visible in his countenance'. One of the book's neatest juxtapositions occurs when he and Lady Booby arrive in the village. The villagers celebrate their lady's return, but from 'interest' only (their livelihood depends on it). Round Adams, welcoming him back, they

throng like affectionate children, and he himself glows with
'benevolence made happy by its objects' (IV. i).

Yet Adams has his dogmatisms and vanities, of which indeed
no one would propose to cure him; the great comic characters
of literature are not to be changed. But, while themselves
invulnerable, they may undergo a comic criticism in the
interests of good sense, and in this respect Joseph is allowed
an interesting function. An honest young jockey in Sir Thomas's
service, a handsome young footman in Lady Booby's, with a
melodious voice and excellent nature, eager to improve himself by good reading and good counsel, he grows from youthful
subjection to manly independence. He protects his beloved
Fanny with a courage and passion which in her gentler way she
fully reciprocates. His regard for Adams is unqualified. For
these very qualities, 'he is a good agent to comment upon
Adams's unworldliness'.[1] He emerges by degrees from his elder's
tutelage and even, at times, presides. He is superior in per-
spicacity; he sees through the false benefactor much sooner
than Adams does (II. xvi); his championship of public schools
is vindicated when the 'roasting' squire proves to be home-
bred (III. v). He praises charity with a power equal to Adams's
own, and thereby voices one of Fielding's leading themes:
'a Person void of Charity', the *Covent-Garden Journal* was to
proclaim (16th May 1752), 'is unworthy the Appellation of a
Christian'. And when Adams exhorts him to a stoicism Adams
himself cannot maintain (IV. viii), or invites the broken-
hearted lovers to rejoice at escaping the sin of incest (IV.
xiii), one's heart and mind are with Joseph against the doc-
trinaire, however good the latter's intentions. Fielding's
portrayals of goodness would increasingly credit the good man
with practical wisdom—Allworthy more so than Adams, Dr
Harrison more than Allworthy. This does not exalt these
later creations over Adams, but it suggests how his virtues can
be supplemented by Joseph's. Playing an increasingly valuable
part, by the end Joseph can hold his own with all comers, and
move into his higher station with ease.

Fielding's stage practice is apparent not only in the tricky
denouement but in the story's interplaying components and
lively conversation. With less improbability and more advantage of give and take, he achieves through speech the immediacy
Richardson managed by the epistolary method. The play of

---

[1] Dick Taylor, Jr, 'Joseph as Hero of *Joseph Andrews*', in *Tulane Studies
in English*, vii, 1957, page 98.

physical action may at first conceal how ample is the play of idea, but conceptions are ventilated through animated discourse around everything, conceptions revealed wittingly or unwittingly in argument and anecdote. What is said is indeed more important than what is done; everything, everyone, stands the test of dialogue.

The plot moves in depth, as well as length and breadth— the depth of social knowledge and moral valuation. The components of a real society are conveyed in their multitude and the moral reality is as insistent as the social, given with the full generosity of Fielding's nature. Remarks in the preface like 'Life everywhere furnishes an accurate observer with the ridiculous' and 'our Ben Jonson, who of all men understood the Ridiculous the best, hath chiefly used the hypocritical affectation' are rather misleading; they suggest that the novel is to be above all censorious—which, of course, predominantly it is not, though it includes censoriousness, and though the affectations assumed by conceit, greed, coarseness, prudery, ignorance and brutality are unmasked (detection has been called Fielding's guiding principle). Fielding certainly means to do good, and claims a serious value for prose fiction. In the *Champion* (3rd January 1740) he had written:

> When wit hath been used, like that of Addison or Steele, to propagate virtue and morality; when like that of Swift, to expose vice and folly; it is then only that these become commendable, and truly worthy of our praise and admiration.

In fact, the moral strength is a matter less of castigations than of attachments and admirations; the positive goodness displayed prevails warmly and engrossingly over its antitheses; and the great-hearted 'manner of Cervantes' is truly reproduced. Quixote and Adams, it has been said,

> combine a primal innocence and direct simplicity of judgment with dignity and learning, and with what one may call a rich inner resourcefulness. Who can deny that Don Quixote is a true knight, and Adams a true priest? [1]

In contrast to *Pamela*, the goodness is projected through characters quite unselfconscious about being good. One of Fielding's best qualities is that he can set down exactly the right thing, in the language of right-hearted, right-minded good sense; the chapter in which the travellers reach Mr Wilson's,

[1] A. C. McKillop, *Early Masters of English Fiction*, 1956, page 105.

for instance, is fresh and frank with decency (III. ii). Adams (and not he alone) can always when necessary speak the Christian and manly truth.

This force and clarity is its own kind of intensity, a concentration of mind and style. The style, indeed, can do as many things as it needs to do—sentimentality (for Horatio and Leonora), fulsome passion (for Lady Booby), garrulity (for Slipslop), Johnsonian strength (for Adams's address to the roasting squire), mock-heroic fun, Swiftian cogency and so forth. Its best ordinary quality is unaffected clarity and vigour; its best extraordinary quality is this same clarity and vigour heightened, as when it renders Adams's *apologia* (II. viii), or Trulliber's grossness (II. xiv), or Joseph's discourse on charity (III. vi), or Adams's defiance of Lady Booby (IV. ii). In *Unprofessional Essays* (1956), Middleton Murry observes that

Fielding's kind of moral intensity, not being laboured, does not lend itself to laborious analysis and critical expatiation. For that reason it can, apparently, pass entirely unrecognized, dismissed as 'the genial tolerance of the man-about-town', or as 'a simple attitude'. Nevertheless, it exists, and is pervasive.

It is this intensity, of moral grasp and art also, of engrossed and delighted attention to life and cleanness of writing, that makes the novel's great effect, an effect such that no one, Coleridge asserted, could rise from perusing it 'without feeling himself the better man—at least, without an intense conviction that *he* could not be guilty of a base act'. No praise could better testify that Fielding had triumphantly succeeded in doing wholly what he wished to do.

A. R. HUMPHREYS.

1962.

SELECT BIBLIOGRAPHY

THE best complete editions of Fielding's *Works* are those by Sir L. Stephen, 10 vols. (1882), and W. E. Henley and others, 16 vols. (New York, 1903). There are collected editions of the *Novels*, by G. R. Maynardier, 12 vols. (1903), G. Saintsbury, 12 vols. (1926), and the Oxford edition, 10 vols. (1926).

NOVELS. *The Adventures of Joseph Andrews, and of his Friend Mr Abraham Adams*, 2 vols., 1742; *The Life of Mr Jonathan Wild the Great* and *A Journey from This World to the Next* (in *Miscellanies*, 3 vols.), 1743; *Tom Jones*, 6 vols., 1749; *Amelia*, 4 vols., 1752.

PLAYS. *Love in Several Masques*, 1728; *The Temple Beau*, 1730; *The Author's Farce; and the Pleasures of the Town*, 1730 (revised 1734); *Tom Thumb*, 1730 (revised and enlarged as *The Tragedy of Tragedies*, 1731); *Rape upon Rape*, 1730 (reissued as *The Coffee-House Politician*, 1730); *The Welsh Opera*, 1731; *The Letter-Writers*, 1731; *The Lottery*, 1732; *The Modern Husband*, 1732; *The Covent-Garden Tragedy*, 1732; *The Old Debauchees* 1732; *The Mock Doctor*, 1732; *The Miser*, 1733; *Deborah*, 1733; *The Intriguing Chambermaid*, 1734; *Don Quixote in England*, 1734; *An Old Man Taught Wisdom*, 1735; *The Universal Gallant*, 1735; *Pasquin*, 1736; *Tumble-Down Dick: or, Phaeton in the Suds*, 1736; *Eurydice*, 1737; *The Historical Register, for the Year 1736*, 1737; *Eurydice Hiss'd*, 1737; *Miss Lucy in Town*, 1742; *The Wedding-Day*, 1743; *The Fathers: or, The Good-Natur'd Man*, 1778.

PERIODICALS. *The Champion: or, British Mercury*, 2 vols., 15 Nov. 1739-19 June 1741; *The True Patriot: and The History of our Own Times*, 5 Nov. 1745-17 June 1746; *The Jacobite's Journal*, 5 Dec. 1747-5 Nov. 1748; *The Covent-Garden Journal*, 4 Jan.-25 Nov. 1752.

OTHER WRITINGS. *The Masquerade, a Poem*, 1728; *Of True Greatness*, 1741; *The Vernoniad*, 1741; *An Apology for the Life of Mrs Shamela Andrews*, 1741; *The Crisis: A Sermon on Revel. xiv. 9-11*, 1741; *The Opposition, A Vision*, 1742; *A Full Vindication of the Dutchess Dowager of Marlborough*, 1742; *Plutus, the God of Riches* (translated from Aristophanes), 1742; *Concerning the Terrestrial Chrysippus*, 1743; *A Serious Address to the People of Great Britain*, 1745; *A Dialogue between the Devil, the Pope, and the Pretender*, 1745; *The History of the Present Rebellion in Scotland*, 1745; *A Dialogue between a gentleman of London . . . And an Honest Alderman of the Country Party*, 1747; *A Proper Answer to a Late Scurrilous Libel*, 1747; *Ovid's Art of Love paraphrased, and adapted to the present Time, Book i*, 1747; *A True State of the Case of Bosavern Penlez*, 1749; *A Charge delivered to the Grand Jury, at the Sessions, the 29th of June, 1749*, 1749; *An Enquiry into the Causes of the late Increase of Robbers*, 1751; *A Plan of the Universal Register Office*, 1752 (with John Fielding); *Examples of the Interposition of Providence in the Detection and Punishment of Murder*, 1752; *A Proposal for Making an Effectual Provision for the Poor*, 1753; *A Clear State of the Case of Elizabeth Canning*, 1753; *The Journal of a Voyage to Lisbon*, 1755.

BIOGRAPHY AND CRITICISM. Austin Dobson, *Fielding*, 1883; G. M. Godden, *Henry Fielding*, 1910; W. L. Cross, *The History of Henry Fielding*, 1918; A. Digeon, *The Novels of Fielding*, 1925; F. T. Blanchard, *Fielding the Novelist*, 1926; H. K. Banerji, *Henry Fielding*, 1929; E. M. Thornbury, *Fielding's Theory of the Comic Prose Epic*, 1930; F. O. Bissell, Jr, *Fielding's Theory of the Novel*, 1933; B. M. Jones, *Fielding, Novelist and Magistrate*, 1933; Elizabeth Jenkins, *Henry Fielding*, 1947; F. H. Dudden, *Henry Fielding, his Life, Works and Times*, 2 vols., 1952; John Butt, *Fielding*, 1954; M. Battestin, *The Moral Basis of Fielding's Art*, 1959; R. Paulson (ed.), *Fielding: A Collection of Critical Essays*, 1962.

The text is that prepared by George Saintsbury for the original Everyman's Library edition, following in the main that of the first collected edition of 1762. In a few evident misreadings the Saintsbury text has been corrected from that of the second edition, of August 1742. Some corrections of punctuation have been made, and an occasional editorial emendation appears, enclosed between square brackets.

AUTHOR'S PREFACE

As it is possible the mere English reader may have a different idea of romance from the author of these little [1] volumes, and may consequently expect a kind of entertainment not to be found, nor which was even intended, in the following pages, it may not be improper to premise a few words concerning this kind of writing, which I do not remember to have seen hitherto attempted in our language.

The EPIC, as well as the DRAMA, is divided into tragedy and comedy. HOMER, who was the father of this species of poetry, gave us a pattern of both these, though that of the latter kind is entirely lost; which Aristotle tells us, bore the same relation to comedy which his Iliad bears to tragedy. And perhaps, that we have no more instances of it among the writers of antiquity, is owing to the loss of this great pattern, which, had it survived, would have found its imitators equally with the other poems of this great original.

And farther, as this poetry may be tragic or comic, I will not scruple to say it may be likewise either in verse or prose: for though it wants one particular, which the critic enumerates in the constituent parts of an epic poem, namely metre; yet, when any kind of writing contains all its other parts, such as fable, action, characters, sentiments, and diction, and is deficient in metre only, it seems, I think, reasonable to refer it to the epic; at least, as no critic hath thought proper to range it under any other head, or to assign it a particular name to itself.

Thus the Telemachus of the archbishop of Cambray appears to me of the epic kind, as well as the Odyssey of Homer; indeed, it is much fairer and more reasonable to give it a name common with that species from which it differs only in a single instance, than to confound it with those which it resembles in no other. Such are those voluminous works, commonly called Romances, namely, Clelia, Cleopatra, Astræa, Cassandra, the Grand Cyrus, and innumerable others, which contain, as I apprehend, very little instruction or entertainment.

Now, a comic romance is a comic epic poem in prose; differing from comedy, as the serious epic from tragedy: its action being

[1] *Joseph Andrews* was originally published in 2 vols. 12 mo.

more extended and comprehensive; containing a much larger circle of incidents, and introducing a greater variety of characters. It differs from the serious romance in its fable and action, in this; that as in the one these are grave and solemn, so in the other they are light and ridiculous: it differs in its characters by introducing persons of inferior rank, and consequently, of inferior manners, whereas the grave romance sets the highest before us: lastly, in its sentiments and diction; by preserving the ludicrous instead of the sublime. In the diction, I think, burlesque itself may be sometimes admitted; of which many instances will occur in this work, as in the description of the battles, and some other places, not necessary to be pointed out to the classical reader, for whose entertainment those parodies or burlesque imitations are chiefly calculated.

But though we have sometimes admitted this in our diction, we have carefully excluded it from our sentiments and characters; for there it is never properly introduced, unless in writings of the burlesque kind, which this is not intended to be. Indeed, no two species of writing can differ more widely than the comic and the burlesque; for as the latter is ever the exhibition of what is monstrous and unnatural, and where our delight, if we examine it, arises from the surprising absurdity, as in appropriating the manners of the highest to the lowest, or *è converso*; so in the former we should ever confine ourselves strictly to nature, from the just imitation of which will flow all the pleasure we can this way convey to a sensible reader. And perhaps there is one reason why a comic writer should of all others be the least excused for deviating from nature, since it may not be always so easy for a serious poet to meet with the great and the admirable; but life everywhere furnishes an accurate observer with the ridiculous.

I have hinted this little concerning burlesque, because I have often heard that name given to performances which have been truly of the comic kind, from the author's having sometimes admitted it in his diction only; which, as it is the dress of poetry, doth, like the dress of men, establish characters (the one of the whole poem, and the other of the whole man), in vulgar opinion, beyond any of their greater excellences: but surely, a certain drollery in stile, where characters and sentiments are perfectly natural, no more constitutes the burlesque, than an empty pomp and dignity of words, where everything else is mean and low, can entitle any performance to the appellation of the true sublime.

And I apprehend my Lord Shaftesbury's opinion of mere

burlesque agrees with mine, when he asserts, There is no such
thing to be found in the writings of the ancients. But perhaps
I have less abhorrence than he professes for it; and that, not
because I have had some little success on the stage this way,
but rather as it contributes more to exquisite mirth and laughter
than any other; and these are probably more wholesome physic
for the mind, and conduce better to purge away spleen, melancholy, and ill affections, than is generally imagined. Nay, I
will appeal to common observation, whether the same companies are not found more full of good-humour and benevolence,
after they have been sweetened for two or three hours with
entertainments of this kind, than when soured by a tragedy or
a grave lecture.

But to illustrate all this by another science, in which, perhaps,
we shall see the distinction more clearly and plainly, let us
examine the works of a comic history painter, with those performances which the Italians call Caricatura, where we shall
find the true excellence of the former to consist in the exactest
copying of nature; insomuch that a judicious eye instantly
rejects anything *outré*, any liberty which the painter hath taken
with the features of that *alma mater*; whereas in the Caricatura
we allow all licence—its aim is to exhibit monsters, not men;
and all distortions and exaggerations whatever are within its
proper province.

Now, what Caricatura is in painting, Burlesque is in writing;
and in the same manner the comic writer and painter correlate
to each other. And here I shall observe, that, as in the former
the painter seems to have the advantage; so it is in the latter
infinitely on the side of the writer; for the Monstrous is much
easier to paint than describe, and the Ridiculous to describe
than paint.

And though perhaps this latter species doth not in either
science so strongly affect and agitate the muscles as the other;
yet it will be owned, I believe, that a more rational and useful
pleasure arises to us from it. He who should call the ingenious
Hogarth a burlesque painter, would, in my opinion, do him very
little honour; for sure it is much easier, much less the subject
of admiration, to paint a man with a nose, or any other feature,
of a preposterous size, or to expose him in some absurd or
monstrous attitude, than to express the affections of men on
canvas. It hath been thought a vast commendation of a painter
to say his figures seem to breathe; but surely it is a much greater
and nobler applause, that they appear to think.

But to return. The Ridiculous only, as I have before said, falls within my province in the present work. Nor will some explanation of this word be thought impertinent by the reader, if he considers how wonderfully it hath been mistaken, even by writers who have professed it: for to what but such a mistake can we attribute the many attempts to ridicule the blackest villanies, and, what is yet worse, the most dreadful calamities? What could exceed the absurdity of an author, who should write the comedy of Nero, with the merry incident of ripping up his mother's belly? or what would give a greater shock to humanity than an attempt to expose the miseries of poverty and distress to ridicule? And yet the reader will not want much learning to suggest such instances to himself.

Besides, it may seem remarkable, that Aristotle, who is so fond and free of definitions, hath not thought proper to define the Ridiculous. Indeed, where he tells us it is proper to comedy, he hath remarked that villany is not its object: but he hath not, as I remember, positively asserted what is. Nor doth the Abbé Bellegarde, who hath written a treatise on this subject, though he shows us many species of it, once trace it to its fountain.

The only source of the true Ridiculous (as it appears to me) is affectation. But though it arises from one spring only, when we consider the infinite streams into which this one branches, we shall presently cease to admire at the copious field it affords to an observer. Now, affectation proceeds from one of these two causes, vanity or hypocrisy: for as vanity puts us on affecting false characters, in order to purchase applause; so hypocrisy sets us on an endeavour to avoid censure, by concealing our vices under an appearance of their opposite virtues. And though these two causes are often confounded (for there is some difficulty in distinguishing them), yet, as they proceed from very different motives, so they are as clearly distinct in their operations: for indeed, the affectation which arises from vanity is nearer to truth than the other, as it hath not that violent repugnancy of nature to struggle with, which that of the hypocrite hath. It may be likewise noted, that affectation doth not imply an absolute negation of those qualities which are affected; and, therefore, though, when it proceeds from hypocrisy, it be nearly allied to deceit; yet when it comes from vanity only, it partakes of the nature of ostentation: for instance, the affectation of liberality in a vain man differs visibly from the same affectation in the avaricious; for though the vain man is not what he would appear, or hath not the virtue he affects,

to the degree he would be thought to have it; yet it sits less
awkwardly on him than on the avaricious man, who is the very
reverse of what he would seem to be.

From the discovery of this affectation arises the Ridiculous,
which always strikes the reader with surprise and pleasure;
and that in a higher and stronger degree when the affectation
arises from hypocrisy, than when from vanity; for to discover
any one to be the exact reverse of what he affects, is more
surprising, and consequently more ridiculous, than to find him
a little deficient in the quality he desires the reputation of.
I might observe that our Ben Jonson, who of all men understood the Ridiculous the best, hath chiefly used the hypocritical
affectation.

Now, from affectation only, the misfortunes and calamities
of life, or the imperfections of nature, may become the objects
of ridicule. Surely he hath a very ill-framed mind who can
look on ugliness, infirmity, or poverty, as ridiculous in themselves: nor do I believe any man living, who meets a dirty
fellow riding through the streets in a cart, is struck with an
idea of the Ridiculous from it; but if he should see the same
figure descend from his coach and six, or bolt from his chair
with his hat under his arm, he would then begin to laugh, and
with justice. In the same manner, were we to enter a poor
house and behold a wretched family shivering with cold and
languishing with hunger, it would not incline us to laughter
(at least we must have very diabolical natures if it would);
but should we discover there a grate, instead of coals, adorned
with flowers, empty plate or china dishes on the sideboard,
or any other affectation of riches and finery, either on their
persons or in their furniture, we might then indeed be excused
for ridiculing so fantastical an appearance. Much less are
natural imperfections the object of derision; but when ugliness
aims at the applause of beauty, or lameness endeavours to display agility, it is then that these unfortunate circumstances,
which at first moved our compassion, tend only to raise our
mirth.

The poet carries this very far:

> None are for being what they are in fault,
> But for not being what they would be thought.

Where if the metre would suffer the word Ridiculous to close
the first line, the thought would be rather more proper. Great
vices are the proper objects of our detestation, smaller faults,

of our pity; but affectation appears to me the only true source of the Ridiculous.

But perhaps it may be objected to me, that I have against my own rules introduced vices, and of a very black kind, into this work. To which I shall answer: first, that it is very difficult to pursue a series of human actions, and keep clear from them. Secondly, that the vices to be found here are rather the accidental consequences of some human frailty or foible, than causes habitually existing in the mind. Thirdly, that they are never set forth as the objects of ridicule, but detestation. Fourthly, that they are never the principal figure at that time on the scene: and, lastly, they never produce the intended evil.

Having thus distinguished Joseph Andrews from the productions of romance writers on the one hand and burlesque writers on the other, and given some few very short hints (for I intended no more) of this species of writing, which I have affirmed to be hitherto unattempted in our language; I shall leave to my good-natured reader to apply my piece to my observations, and will detain him no longer than with a word concerning the characters in this work.

And here I solemnly protest I have no intention to vilify or asperse any one; for though everything is copied from the book of nature, and scarce a character or action produced which I have not taken from my own observations and experience; yet I have used the utmost care to obscure the persons by such different circumstances, degrees, and colours, that it will be impossible to guess at them with any degree of certainty; and if it ever happens otherwise, it is only where the failure characterised is so minute, that it is a foible only which the party himself may laugh at as well as any other.

As to the character of Adams, as it is the most glaring in the whole, so I conceive it is not to be found in any book now extant. It is designed a character of perfect simplicity; and as the goodness of his heart will recommend him to the good-natured, so I hope it will excuse me to the gentlemen of his cloth; for whom, while they are worthy of their sacred order, no man can possibly have a greater respect. They will therefore excuse me, notwithstanding the low adventures in which he is engaged, that I have made him a clergyman; since no other office could have given him so many opportunities of displaying his worthy inclinations.

CONTENTS

	PAGE
BIOGRAPHICAL NOTE	v
INTRODUCTION by A. R. Humphreys	vi
PREFACE by the Author	xvii

BOOK I

CHAP.

I.	Of writing lives in general, and particularly of Pamela	1
II.	Of Mr. Joseph Andrews, his birth, parentage, education, and great endowments	2
III.	Of Mr. Abraham Adams the curate, Mrs. Slipslop the chambermaid and others	5
IV.	What happened after their journey to London	8
V.	The death of Sir Thomas Booby	10
VI.	How Joseph Andrews writ a letter to his sister Pamela	12
VII.	A dialogue between the lady and her maid	15
VIII.	The interview between the lady and Joseph	18
IX.	What passed between the lady and Mrs. Slipslop	22
X.	Joseph writes another letter	25
XI.	Of several new matters not expected	27
XII.	Containing many surprising adventures	29
XIII.	What happened to Joseph during his sickness at the inn	35
XIV.	Being very full of adventures which succeeded each other at the inn	38
XV.	Showing how Mrs. Tow-wouse was a little mollified	42
XVI.	The escape of the thief. Mr. Adams's disappointment.	45
XVII.	A pleasant discourse between the two parsons and the bookseller	53
XVIII.	The history of Betty the chambermaid, and an account of what occasioned the violent scene in the preceding chapter	57

BOOK II

I.	Of divisions in Authors	60
II.	A surprising instance of Mr. Adams's short memory	62
III.	The opinion of two lawyers concerning the same gentleman	66
IV.	The history of Leonora, or the unfortunate jilt	71
V.	A dreadful quarrel which happened at the inn	84
VI.	Conclusion of the unfortunate jilt	91
VII.	A very short chapter, in which parson Adams went a great way	95
VIII.	A notable dissertation by Mr. Abraham Adams	97
XI.	In which the gentleman discants on bravery	99
X.	Giving an account of the strange catastrophe preceding	104
XI.	What happened to them while before the justice	108
XII.	A very delightful adventure	113
XIII.	A dissertation concerning high people and low people.	117
XIV.	An interview between parson Adams and parson Trulliber	122

CHAP.   PAGE

XV. An adventure, the consequence of a new instance which parson Adams gave of his forgetfulness   .   .   . 127

XVI. In which Mr. Adams gave a much greater instance of the honest simplicity of his heart, than of his experience in the ways of this world   130

XVII. A dialogue between Mr. Abraham Adams and his host   . 136

BOOK III

I. Matter prefatory in praise of biography   142

II. A night scene, wherein several wonderful adventures befel Adams and his fellow-travellers   .   .   . 146

III. In which the gentleman relates the history of his life   . 154

IV. A description of Mr. Wilson's way of living. The tragical adventure of the dog, and other grave matters   .   . 174

V. A disputation on schools held on the road   . 178

VI. Moral reflections by Joseph Andrews   181

VII. A scene of roasting, very nicely adapted to the present taste and times   189

VIII. Which some readers will think too short and others too long . 196

IX. Containing as surprising and bloody adventures as can be found in this or perhaps any other authentic history   . 200

X. A discourse between the poet and the player   .   . 203

XI. The exhortations of parson Adams to his friend in affliction 207

XII. More adventures, which we hope will please the reader   . 210

XIII. A dialogue between Mr. Abraham Adams and Mr. Peter Pounce 215

BOOK IV

I. The arrival of Lady Booby and the rest at Booby-hall   . 219

II. A dialogue between Mr. Abraham Adams and the Lady Booby   223

III. What passed between the lady and lawyer Scout   .   . 225

IV. The arrival of Mr. Booby and his lady   .   .   . 228

V. Containing justice business   229

VI. Of which you are desired to read no more than you like   . 234

VII. Philosophical reflections   239

VIII. A discourse between Mr. Adams, Mrs. Adams, Joseph, and Fanny   245

IX. A visit which the polite Lady Booby and her polite friend paid to the parson   250

X. The history of two friends   253

XI. In which the history is continued   258

XII. Where the good-natured reader will see something which will give him no great pleasure   261

XIII. The history returns to the Lady Booby   .   .   . 263

XIV. Containing several curious night-adventures   .   . 267

XV. The arrival of Gaffar and Gammar Andrews   .   . 272

XVI. Being the last, in which this true history is brought to a happy conclusion   276

BOOK I

CHAPTER I

IT is a trite but true observation, that examples work more
forcibly on the mind than precepts: and if this be just in what
is odious and blameable, it is more strongly so in what is amiable
and praiseworthy. Here emulation most effectually operates
upon us, and inspires our imitation in an irresistible manner.
A good man therefore is a standing lesson to all his acquaintance,
and of far greater use in that narrow circle than a good book.

But as it often happens that the best men are but little
known, and consequently cannot extend the usefulness of their
examples a great way; the writer may be called in aid to spread
their history farther, and to present the amiable pictures to
those who have not the happiness of knowing the originals;
and so, by communicating such valuable patterns to the world,
he may perhaps do a more extensive service to mankind than
the person whose life originally afforded the pattern.

In this light I have always regarded those biographers who
have recorded the actions of great and worthy persons of both
sexes. Not to mention those antient writers which of late days
are little read, being written in obsolete, and as they are generally
thought, unintelligible languages, such as Plutarch, Nepos, and
others which I heard of in my youth; our own language affords
many of excellent use and instruction, finely calculated to sow
the seeds of virtue in youth, and very easy to be comprehended
by persons of moderate capacity. Such as the history of John
the Great, who, by his brave and heroic actions against men of
large and athletic bodies, obtained the glorious appellation of
the Giant-killer; that of an Earl of Warwick, whose Christian
name was Guy; the lives of Argalus and Parthenia; and above
all, the history of those seven worthy personages, the Champions
of Christendom. In all these delight is mixed with instruction,
and the reader is almost as much improved as entertained.

But I pass by these and many others to mention two books

lately published, which represent an admirable pattern of the amiable in either sex. The former of these, which deals in male virtue, was written by the great person himself, who lived the life he hath recorded, and is by many thought to have lived such a life only in order to write it. The other is communicated to us by an historian who borrows his lights, as the common method is, from authentic papers and records. The reader, I believe, already conjectures, I mean the lives of Mr. Colley Cibber and of Mrs. Pamela Andrews. How artfully doth the former, by insinuating that he escaped being promoted to the highest stations in Church and State, teach us a contempt of worldly grandeur! how strongly doth he inculcate an absolute submission to our superiors! Lastly, how completely doth he arm us against so uneasy, so wretched a passion as the fear of shame! how clearly doth he expose the emptiness and vanity of that phantom, reputation!

What the female readers are taught by the memoirs of Mrs. Andrews is so well set forth in the excellent essays or letters prefixed to the second and subsequent editions of that work, that it would be here a needless repetition. The authentic history with which I now present the public is an instance of the great good that book is likely to do, and of the prevalence of example which I have just observed: since it will appear that it was by keeping the excellent pattern of his sister's virtues before his eyes, that Mr. Joseph Andrews was chiefly enabled to preserve his purity in the midst of such great temptations. I shall only add that this character of male chastity, though doubtless as desirable and becoming in one part of the human species as in the other, is almost the only virtue which the great apologist hath not given himself for the sake of giving the example to his readers.

CHAPTER II

OF MR. JOSEPH ANDREWS, HIS BIRTH, PARENTAGE, EDUCATION, AND GREAT ENDOWMENTS; WITH A WORD OR TWO CONCERNING ANCESTORS

MR. JOSEPH ANDREWS, the hero of our ensuing history, was esteemed to be the only son of Gaffar and Gammar Andrews, and brother to the illustrious Pamela, whose virtue is at present so famous. As to his ancestors, we have searched with great diligence, but little success; being unable to trace them farther than his great-grandfather, who, as an elderly person in the parish remembers to have heard his father say, was an excellent cudgel-player. Whether he had any ancestors before this, we must leave to the opinion of our curious reader, finding nothing of sufficient certainty to rely on. However, we cannot omit inserting an epitaph which an ingenious friend of ours hath communicated:

> Stay, traveller, for underneath this pew
> Lies fast asleep that merry man Andrew:
> When the last day's great sun shall gild the skies,
> Then he shall from his tomb get up and rise.
> Be merry while thou canst: for surely thou
> Shalt shortly be as sad as he is now.

The words are almost out of the stone with antiquity. But it is needless to observe that Andrew here is writ without an *s*, and is, besides, a Christian name. My friend, moreover, conjectures this to have been the founder of that sect of laughing philosophers since called Merry-andrews.

To waive, therefore, a circumstance which, though mentioned in conformity to the exact rules of biography, is not greatly material, I proceed to things of more consequence. Indeed, it is sufficiently certain that he had as many ancestors as the best man living, and, perhaps, if we look five or six hundred years backwards, might be related to some persons of very great figure at present, whose ancestors within half the last century are buried in as great obscurity. But suppose, for argument's sake, we should admit that he had no ancestors at all, but had sprung up, according to the modern phrase, out of a dunghill, as the Athenians pretended they themselves did from the earth, would not this autokopros [1] have been justly entitled to all the praise arising from his own virtues? Would it not be hard that a man who hath no ancestors should therefore be rendered incapable of acquiring honour; when we see so many who have no virtues enjoying the honour of their forefathers? At ten years old (by which time his education was advanced to writing and reading) he was bound an apprentice, according to the statute, to Sir Thomas Booby, an uncle of Mr. Booby's by the father's side. Sir Thomas having then an estate in his own hands, the young Andrews was at first employed in what in the country they call keeping birds. His office was to perform the part the ancients assigned to the god Priapus, which deity the moderns call by the name of Jack o' Lent;

---

[1] In English, sprung from a dunghill.

but his voice being so extremely musical, that it rather allured
the birds than terrified them, he was soon transplanted from the
fields into the dog-kennel, where he was placed under the
huntsman, and made what the sportsmen term whipper-in.
For this place likewise the sweetness of his voice disqualified
him; the dogs preferring the melody of his chiding to all the
alluring notes of the huntsman, who soon became so incensed
at it, that he desired Sir Thomas to provide otherwise for him,
and constantly laid every fault the dogs were at to the account
of the poor boy, who was now transplanted to the stable.   Here
he soon gave proofs of strength and agility beyond his years,
and constantly rode the most spirited and vicious horses to
water, with an intrepidity which surprised everyone.   While
he was in this station, he rode several races for Sir Thomas,
and this with such expertness and success, that the neighbouring
gentlemen frequently solicited the knight to permit little Joey
(for so he was called) to ride their matches.   The best gamesters,
before they laid their money, always inquired which horse
little Joey was to ride; and the bets were rather proportioned
by the rider than by the horse himself; especially after he had
scornfully refused a considerable bribe to play booty on such
an occasion.   This extremely raised his character, and so pleased
the Lady Booby, that she desired to have him (being now
seventeen years of age) for her own footboy.

Joey was now preferred from the stable to attend on his lady,
to go on her errands, stand behind her chair, wait at her tea-
table, and carry her prayer-book to church; at which place his
voice gave him an opportunity of distinguishing himself by
singing psalms: he behaved likewise in every other respect so
well at Divine service, that it recommended him to the notice
of Mr. Abraham Adams, the curate, who took an opportunity
one day, as he was drinking a cup of ale in Sir Thomas's kitchen,
to ask the young man several questions concerning religion;
with his answers to which he was wonderfully pleased.

CHAPTER III

MR. ABRAHAM ADAMS was an excellent scholar. He was a perfect master of the Greek and Latin languages; to which he added a great share of knowledge in the Oriental tongues; and could read and translate French, Italian, and Spanish. He had applied many years to the most severe study, and had treasured up a fund of learning rarely to be met with in a university. He was, besides, a man of good sense, good parts, and good nature; but was at the same time as entirely ignorant of the ways of this world as an infant just entered into it could possibly be. As he had never any intention to deceive, so he never suspected such a design in others. He was generous, friendly, and brave to an excess; but simplicity was his char-acteristick: he did, no more than Mr. Colley Cibber, apprehend any such passions as malice and envy to exist in mankind; which was indeed less remarkable in a country parson than in a gentleman who hath passed his life behind the scenes,—a place which hath been seldom thought the school of innocence, and where a very little observation would have convinced the great apologist that those passions have a real existence in the human mind.

His virtue, and his other qualifications, as they rendered him equal to his office, so they made him an agreeable and valuable companion, and had so much endeared and well recommended him to a bishop, that at the age of fifty he was provided with a handsome income of twenty-three pounds a year; which, how-ever, he could not make any great figure with, because he lived in a dear country, and was a little encumbered with a wife and six children.

It was this gentleman, who having, as I have said, observed the singular devotion of young Andrews, had found means to question him concerning several particulars; as, how many books there were in the New Testament? which were they? how many chapters they contained? and such like: to all which, Mr. Adams privately said, he answered much better than Sir Thomas, or two other neighbouring justices of the peace could probably have done.

Mr. Adams was wonderfully solicitous to know at what time,

and by what opportunity, the youth became acquainted with these matters: Joey told him that he had very early learnt to read and write by the goodness of his father, who, though he had not interest enough to get him into a charity school, because a cousin of his father's landlord did not vote on the right side for a churchwarden in a borough town, yet had been himself at the expense of sixpence a week for his learning. He told him likewise, that ever since he was in Sir Thomas's family he had employed all his hours of leisure in reading good books; that he had read the Bible, the Whole Duty of Man, and Thomas à Kempis; and that as often as he could, without being perceived, he had studied a great good book, which lay open in the hall window, where he had read, "as how the devil carried away half a church in sermon-time, without hurting one of the congregation; and as how a field of corn ran away down a hill with all the trees upon it, and covered another man's meadow." This sufficiently assured Mr. Adams that the good book meant could be no other than Baker's Chronicle.

The curate, surprised to find such instances of industry and application in a young man who had never met with the least encouragement, asked him, If he did not extremely regret the want of a liberal education, and the not having been born of parents who might have indulged his talents and desire of knowledge? To which he answered, "He hoped he had profited somewhat better from the books he had read than to lament his condition in this world. That, for his part, he was perfectly content with the state to which he was called; that he should endeavour to improve his talent, which was all required of him; but not repine at his own lot, nor envy those of his betters." "Well said, my lad," replied the curate; "and I wish some who have read many more good books, nay, and some who have written good books themselves, had profited so much by them."

Adams had no nearer access to Sir Thomas or my lady than through the waiting-gentlewoman; for Sir Thomas was too apt to estimate men merely by their dress or fortune; and my lady was a woman of gaiety, who had been blest with a town education, and never spoke of any of her country neighbours by any other appellation than that of the brutes. They both regarded the curate as a kind of domestic only, belonging to the parson of the parish, who was at this time at variance with the knight; for the parson had for many years lived in a constant state of civil war, or, which is perhaps as bad, of civil law, with Sir Thomas himself and the tenants of his manor.

The foundation of this quarrel was a modus, by setting which aside an advantage of several shillings per annum would have accrued to the rector; but he had not yet been able to accomplish his purpose, and had reaped hitherto nothing better from the suits than the pleasure (which he used indeed frequently to say was no small one) of reflecting that he had utterly undone many of the poor tenants, though he had at the same time greatly impoverished himself.

Mrs. Slipslop, the waiting-gentlewoman, being herself the daughter of a curate, preserved some respect for Adams: she professed great regard for his learning, and would frequently dispute with him on points of theology; but always insisted on a deference to be paid to her understanding, as she had been frequently at London, and knew more of the world than a country parson could pretend to.

She had in these disputes a particular advantage over Adams: for she was a mighty affecter of hard words, which she used in such a manner that the parson, who durst not offend her by calling her words in question, was frequently at some loss to guess her meaning, and would have been much less puzzled by an Arabian manuscript.

Adams therefore took an opportunity one day, after a pretty long discourse with her on the essence (or, as she pleased to term it, the incence) of matter, to mention the case of young Andrews; desiring her to recommend him to her lady as a youth very susceptible of learning, and one whose instruction in Latin he would himself undertake; by which means he might be qualified for a higher station than that of a footman; and added, she knew it was in his master's power easily to provide for him in a better manner. He therefore desired that the boy might be left behind under his care.

"La! Mr. Adams," said Mrs. Slipslop, "do you think my lady will suffer any preambles about any such matter? She is going to London very concisely, and I am confidous would not leave Joey behind her on any account; for he is one of the genteelest young fellows you may see in a summer's day; and I am confidous she would as soon think of parting with a pair of her grey mares, for she values herself as much on one as the other." Adams would have interrupted, but she proceeded: "And why is Latin more necessitous for a footman than a gentleman? It is very proper that you clergymen must learn it, because you can't preach without it: but I have heard gentlemen say in London, that it is fit for nobody else. I am confidous my lady would be angry with me for mentioning it; and I shall draw myself into no such delemy." At which words her lady's bell rung, and Mr. Adams was forced to retire; nor could he gain a second opportunity with her before their London journey, which happened a few days afterwards. However, Andrews behaved very thankfully and gratefully to him for his intended kindness, which he told him he never would forget, and at the same time received from the good man many admonitions concerning the regulation of his future conduct, and his perseverance in innocence and industry.

CHAPTER IV

WHAT HAPPENED AFTER THEIR JOURNEY TO LONDON

No sooner was young Andrews arrived at London than he began to scrape an acquaintance with his party-coloured brethren, who endeavoured to make him despise his former course of life. His hair was cut after the newest fashion, and became his chief care; he went abroad with it all the morning in papers, and drest it out in the afternoon. They could not, however, teach him to game, swear, drink, nor any other genteel vice the town abounded with. He applied most of his leisure hours to music, in which he greatly improved himself; and became so perfect a connoisseur in that art, that he led the opinion of all the other footmen at an opera, and they never condemned or applauded a single song contrary to his approbation or dislike. He was a little too forward in riots at the play-houses and assemblies; and when he attended his lady at church (which was but seldom) he behaved with less seeming devotion than formerly: however, if he was outwardly a pretty fellow, his morals remained entirely uncorrupted, though he was at the same time smarter and genteeler than any of the beaus in town, either in or out of livery.

His lady, who had often said of him that Joey was the handsomest and genteelest footman in the kingdom, but that it was pity he wanted spirit, began now to find that fault no longer; on the contrary, she was frequently heard to cry out, "Ay, there is some life in this fellow." She plainly saw the effects which the town air hath on the soberest constitutions. She would now walk out with him into Hyde Park in a morning, and when tired, which happened almost every minute, would lean on his arm, and converse with him in great familiarity. Whenever she stept out of her coach, she would take him by the hand, and sometimes, for fear of stumbling, press it very hard; she admitted him to deliver messages at her bedside in a morning, leered at him at table, and indulged him in all those innocent freedoms which women of figure may permit without the least sully of their virtue.

But though their virtue remains unsullied, yet now and then some small arrows will glance on the shadow of it, their reputation; and so it fell out to Lady Booby, who happened to be walking arm-in-arm with Joey one morning in Hyde Park, when Lady Tittle and Lady Tattle came accidentally by in their coach. "Bless me," says Lady Tittle, "can I believe my eyes? Is that Lady Booby?"—"Surely," says Tattle. "But what makes you surprised?"—"Why, is not that her footman?" replied Tittle. At which Tattle laughed, and cried, "An old business, I assure you: is it possible you should not have heard it? The whole town hath known it this half-year." The consequence of this interview was a whisper through a hundred visits, which were separately performed by the two ladies [1] the same afternoon, and might have had a mischievous effect, had it not been stopt by two fresh reputations which were published the day afterwards, and engrossed the whole talk of the town.

But, whatever opinion or suspicion the scandalous inclination of defamers might entertain of Lady Booby's innocent freedoms, it is certain they made no impression on young Andrews, who never offered to encroach beyond the liberties which his lady allowed him,—a behaviour which she imputed to the violent respect he preserved for her, and which served only to heighten a something she began to conceive, and which the next chapter will open a little farther.

---

[1] It may seem an absurdity that Tattle should visit, as she actually did, to spread a known scandal: but the reader may reconcile this by supposing, with me, that, notwithstanding what she says, this was her first acquaintance with it.

CHAPTER V

THE DEATH OF SIR THOMAS BOOBY, WITH THE AFFECTIONATE
AND MOURNFUL BEHAVIOUR OF HIS WIDOW, AND THE GREAT
PURITY OF JOSEPH ANDREWS

AT this time an accident happened which put a stop to those
agreeable walks, which probably would have soon puffed up
the cheeks of Fame, and caused her to blow her brazen trumpet
through the town; and this was no other than the death of Sir
Thomas Booby, who, departing this life, left his disconsolate
lady confined to her house, as closely as if she herself had been
attacked by some violent disease. During the first six days
the poor lady admitted none but Mrs. Slipslop, and three female
friends, who made a party at cards: but on the seventh she
ordered Joey, whom, for a good reason, we shall hereafter call
JOSEPH, to bring up her tea-kettle. The lady being in bed,
called Joseph to her, bade him sit down, and, having accidentally
laid her hand on his, she asked him if he had ever been in love.
Joseph answered, with some confusion, it was time enough for
one so young as himself to think on such things. "As young
as you are," replied the lady, "I am convinced you are no
stranger to that passion. Come, Joey," says she, "tell me truly,
who is the happy girl whose eyes have made a conquest of
you?" Joseph returned, that all the women he had ever seen
were equally indifferent to him. "Oh then," said the lady,
"you are a general lover. Indeed, you handsome fellows, like
handsome women, are very long and difficult in fixing; but
yet you shall never persuade me that your heart is so insus-
ceptible of affection; I rather impute what you say to your
secrecy, a very commendable quality, and what I am far from
being angry with you for. Nothing can be more unworthy in
a young man, than to betray any intimacies with the ladies."
"Ladies! madam," said Joseph, "I am sure I never had the
impudence to think of any that deserve that name." "Don't
pretend to too much modesty," said she, "for that sometimes
may be impertinent: but pray answer me this question. Suppose a lady should happen to like you; suppose she should
prefer you to all your sex, and admit you to the same familiarities
as you might have hoped for if you had been born her equal,
are you certain that no vanity could tempt you to discover her?
Answer me honestly, Joseph; have you so much more sense
and so much more virtue than you handsome young fellows

generally have, who make no scruple of sacrificing our dear
reputation to your pride, without considering the great obligation we lay on you by our condescension and confidence?
Can you keep a secret, my Joey?" "Madam," says he, "I
hope your ladyship can't tax me with ever betraying the secrets
of the family; and I hope, if you was to turn me away, I might
have that character of you." "I don't intend to turn you away,
Joey," said she, and sighed; "I am afraid it is not in my power."
She then raised herself a little in her bed, and discovered one of
the whitest necks that ever was seen; at which Joseph blushed.
"La!" says she, in an affected surprise, "what am I doing?
I have trusted myself with a man alone, naked in bed; suppose
you should have any wicked intentions upon my honour, how
should I defend myself?" Joseph protested that he never had
the least evil design against her. "No," says she, "perhaps
you may not call your designs wicked; and perhaps they are
not so."—He swore they were not. "You misunderstand me,"
says she; "I mean if they were against my honour, they may not
be wicked; but the world calls them so. But then, say you,
the world will never know anything of the matter; yet would
not that be trusting to your secrecy? Must not my reputation
be then in your power? Would you not then be my master?"
Joseph begged her ladyship to be comforted; for that he would
never imagine the least wicked thing against her, and that he
had rather die a thousand deaths than give her any reason to
suspect him. "Yes," said she, "I must have reason to suspect
you. Are you not a man? and, without vanity, I may pretend
to some charms. But perhaps you may fear I should prosecute
you; indeed I hope you do; and yet Heaven knows I should
never have the confidence to appear before a court of justice;
and you know, Joey, I am of a forgiving temper. Tell me, Joey,
don't you think I should forgive you?"—"Indeed, madam,"
says Joseph, "I will never do anything to disoblige your ladyship."—"How," says she, "do you think it would not disoblige me then? Do you think I would willingly suffer you?"
—"I don't understand you, madam," says Joseph.—"Don't
you?" said she, "then you are either a fool, or pretend to be so;
I find I was mistaken in you. So get you downstairs, and never
let me see your face again; your pretended innocence cannot
impose on me."—"Madam," said Joseph, "I would not have
your ladyship think any evil of me. I have always endeavoured
to be a dutiful servant both to you and my master."—"O thou
villain!" answered my lady; "why didst thou mention the name

of that dear man, unless to torment me, to bring his precious
memory to my mind?" (and then she burst into a fit of tears.)
"Get thee from my sight! I shall never endure thee more."
At which words she turned away from him; and Joseph retreated
from the room in a most disconsolate condition, and writ that
letter which the reader will find in the next chapter.

CHAPTER VI

HOW JOSEPH ANDREWS WRIT A LETTER TO HIS SISTER PAMELA

TO MRS. PAMELA ANDREWS, LIVING WITH SQUIRE BOOBY

DEAR SISTER,

Since I received your letter of your good lady's death, we have
had a misfortune of the same kind in our family. My worthy
master Sir Thomas died about four days ago; and, what is worse,
my poor lady is certainly gone distracted. None of the servants
expected her to take it so to heart, because they quarrelled almost
every day of their lives: but no more of that, because you know,
Pamela, I never loved to tell the secrets of my master's family; but
to be sure you must have known they never loved one another;
and I have heard her ladyship wish his honour dead above a
thousand times; but nobody knows what it is to lose a friend till
they have lost him.

Don't tell anybody what I write, because I should not care to
have folks say I discover what passes in our family; but if it had
not been so great a lady, I should have thought she had had a mind
to me. Dear Pamela, don't tell anybody; but she ordered me to
sit down by her bedside, when she was naked in bed; and she held
my hand, and talked exactly as a lady does to her sweetheart in a
stage-play, which I have seen in Covent Garden, while she wanted
him to be no better than he should be.

If madam be mad, I shall not care for staying long in the family;
so I heartily wish you could get me a place, either at the squire's,
or some other neighbouring gentleman's, unless it be true that you
are going to be married to parson Williams, as folks talk, and then
I should be very willing to be his clerk; for which you know I am
qualified, being able to read and to set a psalm.

I fancy I shall be discharged very soon; and the moment I am,
unless I hear from you, I shall return to my old master's country-
seat, if it be only to see parson Adams, who is the best man in the
world. London is a bad place, and there is so little good fellowship,
that the next-door neighbours don't know one another. Pray
give my service to all friends that inquire for me. So I rest

Your loving brother,

JOSEPH ANDREWS.

As soon as Joseph had sealed and directed this letter he

walked downstairs, where he met Mrs. Slipslop, with whom we shall take this opportunity to bring the reader a little better acquainted. She was a maiden gentlewoman of about forty-five years of age, who, having made a small slip in her youth, had continued a good maid ever since. She was not at this time remarkably handsome; being very short, and rather too corpulent in body, and somewhat red, with the addition of pimples in the face. Her nose was likewise rather too large, and her eyes too little; nor did she resemble a cow so much in her breath as in two brown globes which she carried before her; one of her legs was also a little shorter than the other, which occasioned her to limp as she walked. This fair creature had long cast the eyes of affection on Joseph, in which she had not met with quite so good success as she probably wished, though, besides the allurements of her native charms, she had given him tea, sweetmeats, wine, and many other delicacies, of which, by keeping the keys, she had the absolute command. Joseph, however, had not returned the least gratitude to all these favours, not even so much as a kiss; though I would not insinuate she was so easily to be satisfied; for surely then he would have been highly blameable. The truth is, she was arrived at an age when she thought she might indulge herself in any liberties with a man, without the danger of bringing a third person into the world to betray them. She imagined that by so long a self-denial she had not only made amends for the small slip of her youth above hinted at, but had likewise laid up a quantity of merit to excuse any future failings. In a word, she resolved to give a loose to her amorous inclinations, and to pay off the debt of pleasure which she found she owed herself, as fast as possible.

With these charms of person, and in this disposition of mind, she encountered poor Joseph at the bottom of the stairs, and asked him if he would drink a glass of something good this morning. Joseph, whose spirits were not a little cast down, very readily and thankfully accepted the offer; and together they went into a closet, where, having delivered him a full glass of ratafia, and desired him to sit down, Mrs. Slipslop thus began:

"Sure nothing can be a more simple contract in a woman than to place her affections on a boy. If I had ever thought it would have been my fate, I should have wished to die a thousand deaths rather than live to see that day. If we like a man, the lightest hint sophisticates. Whereas a boy proposes upon us to break through all the regulations of modesty, before we can

make any oppression upon him." Joseph, who did not understand a word she said, answered, "Yes, madam."—"Yes,
madam!" replied Mrs. Slipslop with some warmth, "Do you
intend to result my passion? Is it not enough, ungrateful as
you are, to make no return to all the favours I have done you;
but you must treat me with ironing? Barbarous monster!
how have I deserved that my passion should be resulted and
treated with ironing?" "Madam," answered Joseph, "I don't
understand your hard words; but I am certain you have no
occasion to call me ungrateful, for, so far from intending you
any wrong, I have always loved you as well as if you had been
my own mother." "How, sirrah!" says Mrs. Slipslop in a
rage; "your own mother? Do you assinuate that I am old
enough to be your mother? I don't know what a stripling may
think, but I believe a man would refer me to any green-sickness
silly girl whatsomdever: but I ought to despise you rather than
be angry with you, for referring the conversation of girls to
that of a woman of sense."—"Madam," says Joseph, "I am
sure I have always valued the honour you did me by your
conversation, for I know you are a woman of learning."—"Yes,
but, Joseph," said she, a little softened by the compliment to
her learning, "if you had a value for me, you certainly would
have found some method of showing it me; for I am convicted
you must see the value I have for you. Yes, Joseph, my eyes,
whether I would or no, must have declared a passion I cannot
conquer.—Oh! Joseph!"

As when a hungry tigress, who long has traversed the woods
in fruitless search, sees within the reach of her claws a lamb,
she prepares to leap on her prey; or as a voracious pike, of
immense size, surveys through the liquid element a roach or
gudgeon, which cannot escape her jaws, opens them wide to
swallow the little fish; so did Mrs. Slipslop prepare to lay her
violent amorous hands on the poor Joseph, when luckily her
mistress's bell rung, and delivered the intended martyr from her
clutches. She was obliged to leave him abruptly, and to defer
the execution of her purpose till some other time. We shall
therefore return to the Lady Booby, and give our reader some
account of her behaviour, after she was left by Joseph in a
temper of mind not greatly different from that of the inflamed
Slipslop.

CHAPTER VII

SAYINGS OF WISE MEN.   A DIALOGUE BETWEEN THE LADY AND
    HER MAID; AND A PANEGYRIC, OR RATHER SATIRE, ON THE
    PASSION OF LOVE, IN THE SUBLIME STYLE

IT is the observation of some antient sage, whose name I have
forgot, that passions operate differently on the human mind,
as diseases on the body, in proportion to the strength or weakness, soundness or rottenness, of the one and the other.

We hope, therefore, a judicious reader will give himself some
pains to observe, what we have so greatly laboured to describe,
the different operations of this passion of love in the gentle
and cultivated mind of the Lady Booby, from those which it
effected in the less polished and coarser disposition of Mrs.
Slipslop.

Another philosopher, whose name also at present escapes my
memory, hath somewhere said, that resolutions taken in the
absence of the beloved object are very apt to vanish in its
presence; on both which wise sayings the following chapter
may serve as a comment.

No sooner had Joseph left the room in the manner we have
before related than the lady, enraged at her disappointment,
began to reflect with severity on her conduct. Her love was
now changed to disdain, which pride assisted to torment her.
She despised herself for the meanness of her passion, and Joseph
for its ill success. However, she had now got the better of it
in her own opinion, and determined immediately to dismiss
the object. After much tossing and turning in her bed, and
many soliloquies, which if we had no better matter for our
reader we would give him, she at last rung the bell as above
mentioned, and was presently attended by Mrs. Slipslop, who
was not much better pleased with Joseph than the lady herself.

"Slipslop," said Lady Booby, "when did you see Joseph?"
The poor woman was so surprised at the unexpected sound of
his name at so critical a time, that she had the greatest difficulty to conceal the confusion she was under from her mistress;
whom she answered, nevertheless, with pretty good confidence,
though not entirely void of fear of suspicion, that she had not
seen him that morning. "I am afraid," said Lady Booby,
"he is a wild young fellow."—"That he is," said Slipslop, "and
a wicked one too. To my knowledge he games, drinks, swears,
and fights eternally; besides, he is horribly indicted to wenching."

—"Ay!" said the lady, "I never heard that of him."—"O madam!" answered the other, "he is so lewd a rascal, that if your ladyship keeps him much longer, you will not have one virgin in your house except myself. And yet I can't conceive what the wenches see in him, to be so foolishly fond as they are; in my eyes, he is as ugly a scarecrow as I ever upheld." —"Nay," said the lady, "the boy is well enough."—"La! ma'am," cried Slipslop, "I think him the ragmaticallest fellow in the family."—"Sure, Slipslop," says she, "you are mistaken: but which of the women do you most suspect?"—"Madam," says Slipslop, "there is Betty the chambermaid, I am almost convicted, is with child by him."—"Ay!" says the lady, "then pray pay her her wages instantly. I will keep no such sluts in my family. And as for Joseph, you may discard him too." —"Would your ladyship have him paid off immediately?" cries Slipslop, "for perhaps, when Betty is gone he may mend: and really the boy is a good servant, and a strong healthy luscious boy enough."—"This morning," answered the lady with some vehemence. "I wish, madam," cries Slipslop, "your ladyship would be so good as to try him a little longer."—"I will not have my commands disputed," said the lady; "sure you are not fond of him yourself?"—"I, madam!" cried Slipslop, reddening, if not blushing, "I should be sorry to think your ladyship had any reason to respect me of fondness for a fellow; and if it be your pleasure, I shall fulfil it with as much reluctance as possible."—"As little, I suppose you mean," said the lady; "and so about it instantly." Mrs. Slipslop went out, and the lady had scarce taken two turns before she fell to knocking and ringing with great violence. Slipslop, who did not travel post haste, soon returned, and was countermanded as to Joseph, but ordered to send Betty about her business without delay. She went out a second time with much greater alacrity than before; when the lady began immediately to accuse herself of want of resolution, and to apprehend the return of her affection, with its pernicious consequences; she therefore applied herself again to the bell, and re-summoned Mrs. Slipslop into her presence; who again returned, and was told by her mistress that she had considered better of the matter, and was absolutely resolved to turn away Joseph; which she ordered her to do immediately. Slipslop, who knew the violence of her lady's temper, and would not venture her place for any Adonis or Hercules in the universe, left her a third time; which she had no sooner done, than the little god Cupid, fearing he had not yet done the lady's business, took a fresh arrow with the sharpest point out of his quiver, and shot it directly into her heart; in other and plainer language, the lady's passion got the better of her reason. She called back Slipslop once more, and told her she had resolved to see the boy, and examine him herself; therefore bid her send him up. This wavering in her mistress's temper probably put something into the waiting-gentlewoman's head not necessary to mention to the sagacious reader.

Lady Booby was going to call her back again, but could not prevail with herself. The next consideration therefore was, how she should behave to Joseph when he came in. She resolved to preserve all the dignity of the woman of fashion to her servant, and to indulge herself in this last view of Joseph (for that she was most certainly resolved it should be) at his own expense, by first insulting and then discarding him.

O Love, what monstrous tricks dost thou play with thy votaries of both sexes! How dost thou deceive them, and make them deceive themselves! Their follies are thy delight! Their sighs make thee laugh, and their pangs are thy merriment!

Not the great Rich, who turns men into monkeys, wheel-barrows, and whatever else best humours his fancy, hath so strangely metamorphosed the human shape; nor the great Cibber, who confounds all number, gender, and breaks through every rule of grammar at his will, hath so distorted the English language as thou doth metamorphose and distort the human senses.

Thou puttest out our eyes, stoppest up our ears, and takest away the power of our nostrils; so that we can neither see the largest object, hear the loudest noise, nor smell the most poignant perfume. Again, when thou pleasest, thou canst make a mole-hill appear as a mountain, a Jew's-harp sound like a trumpet, and a daisy smell like a violet. Thou canst make cowardice brave, avarice generous, pride humble, and cruelty tender-hearted. In short, thou turnest the heart of man inside out, as a juggler doth a petticoat, and bringest whatsoever pleaseth thee out from it. If there be any one who doubts all this, let him read the next chapter.

CHAPTER VIII

IN WHICH, AFTER SOME VERY FINE WRITING, THE HISTORY GOES
ON, AND RELATES THE INTERVIEW BETWEEN THE LADY AND
JOSEPH; WHERE THE LATTER HATH SET AN EXAMPLE WHICH
WE DESPAIR OF SEEING FOLLOWED BY HIS SEX IN THIS
VICIOUS AGE

Now the rake Hesperus had called for his breeches, and, having
well rubbed his drowsy eyes, prepared to dress himself for all
night; by whose example his brother rakes on earth likewise
leave those beds in which they had slept away the day. Now
Thetis, the good housewife, began to put on the pot, in order
to regale the good man Phœbus after his daily labours were over.
In vulgar language, it was in the evening when Joseph attended
his lady's orders.

But as it becomes us to preserve the character of this lady,
who is the heroine of our tale; and as we have naturally a
wonderful tenderness for that beautiful part of the human species
called the fair sex; before we discover too much of her frailty
to our reader, it will be proper to give him a lively idea of the
vast temptation, which overcame all the efforts of a modest
and virtuous mind; and then we humbly hope his good nature
will rather pity than condemn the imperfection of human virtue.

Nay, the ladies themselves will, we hope, be induced, by
considering the uncommon variety of charms which united in
this young man's person, to bridle their rampant passion for
chastity, and be at least as mild as their violent modesty and
virtue will permit them, in censuring the conduct of a woman
who, perhaps, was in her own disposition as chaste as those
pure and sanctified virgins who, after a life innocently spent in
the gaieties of the town, begin about fifty to attend twice *per
diem* at the polite churches and chapels, to return thanks for
the grace which preserved them formerly amongst beaus from
temptations perhaps less powerful than what now attacked the
Lady Booby.

Mr. Joseph Andrews was now in the one-and-twentieth year
of his age. He was of the highest degree of middle stature;
his limbs were put together with great elegance, and no less
strength; his legs and thighs were formed in the exactest proportion; his shoulders were broad and brawny, but yet his arms
hung so easily, that he had all the symptoms of strength without the least clumsiness. His hair was of a nut-brown colour,

and was displayed in wanton ringlets down his back; his fore-head was high, his eyes dark, and as full of sweetness as of fire; his nose a little inclined to the Roman; his teeth white and even; his lips full, red, and soft, his beard was only rough on his chin and upper lip; but his cheeks, in which his blood glowed, were overspread with a thick down; his countenance had a tenderness joined with a sensibility inexpressible. Add to this the most perfect neatness in his dress, and an air which, to those who have not seen many noblemen, would give an idea of nobility.

Such was the person who now appeared before the lady. She viewed him some time in silence, and twice or thrice before she spake changed her mind as to the manner in which she should begin. At length she said to him, "Joseph, I am sorry to hear such complaints against you: I am told you behave so rudely to the maids, that they cannot do their business in quiet; I mean those who are not wicked enough to hearken to your solicitations. As to others, they may, perhaps, not call you rude; for there are wicked sluts who make one ashamed of one's own sex, and are as ready to admit any nauseous familiarity as fellows to offer it: nay, there are such in my family, but they shall not stay in it; that impudent trollop who is with child by you is discharged by this time."

As a person who is struck through the heart with a thunder-bolt looks extremely surprised, nay, and perhaps is so too——thus the poor Joseph received the false accusation of his mistress; he blushed and looked confounded, which she misinterpreted to be symptoms of his guilt, and thus went on:

"Come hither, Joseph: another mistress might discard you for these offences; but I have a compassion for your youth, and if I could be certain you would be no more guilty—Consider, child," laying her hand carelessly upon his, "you are a handsome young fellow, and might do better; you might make your fortune." "Madam," said Joseph, "I do assure your ladyship I don't know whether any maid in the house is man or woman." "Oh fie! Joseph," answered the lady, "don't commit another crime in denying the truth. I could pardon the first; but I hate a lyar." "Madam," cries Joseph, "I hope your ladyship will not be offended at my asserting my innocence; for, by all that is sacred, I have never offered more than kissing." "Kissing!" said the lady, with great discomposure of counten-ance, and more redness in her cheeks than anger in her eyes; "do you call that no crime? Kissing, Joseph, is as a prologue

to a play. Can I believe a young fellow of your age and complexion will be content with kissing? No, Joseph, there is no
woman who grants that but will grant more; and I am deceived
greatly in you if you would not put her closely to it. What
would you think, Joseph, if I admitted you to kiss me?"
Joseph replied he would sooner die than have any such thought.
"And yet, Joseph," returned she, "ladies have admitted their
footmen to such familiarities; and footmen, I confess to
you, much less deserving them; fellows without half your
charms — for such might almost excuse the crime. Tell me
therefore, Joseph, if I should admit you to such freedom,
what would you think of me?—tell me freely." "Madam,"
said Joseph, "I should think your ladyship condescended
a great deal below yourself." "Pugh!" said she; "that
I am to answer to myself: but would not you insist on
more? Would you be contented with a kiss? Would not your
inclinations be all on fire rather by such a favour?" "Madam,"
said Joseph, "if they were, I hope I should be able to controul
them, without suffering them to get the better of my virtue."
You have heard, reader, poets talk of the statue of Surprise;
you have heard likewise, or else you have heard very little,
how Surprise made one of the sons of Crœsus speak, though he
was dumb. You have seen the faces, in the eighteen-penny
gallery, when, through the trap-door, to soft or no music, Mr.
Bridgewater, Mr. William Mills, or some other of ghostly
appearance, hath ascended, with a face all pale with powder,
and a shirt all bloody with ribbons;—but from none of these,
nor from Phidias or Praxiteles, if they should return to life—
no, not from the inimitable pencil of my friend Hogarth, could
you receive such an idea of surprise as would have entered in
at your eyes had they beheld the Lady Booby when those last
words issued out from the lips of Joseph. "Your virtue!"
said the lady, recovering after a silence of two minutes; "I
shall never survive it. Your virtue!—intolerable confidence!
Have you the assurance to pretend, that when a lady demeans
herself to throw aside the rules of decency, in order to honour you
with the highest favour in her power, your virtue should resist
her inclination? that, when she had conquered her own virtue,
she should find an obstruction in yours?" "Madam," said
Joseph, "I can't see why her having no virtue should be a
reason against my having any; or why, because I am a man,
or because I am poor, my virtue must be subservient to her
pleasures." "I am out of patience," cries the lady: "did ever

mortal hear of a man's virtue? Did ever the greatest or the gravest men pretend to any of this kind? Will magistrates who punish lewdness, or parsons who preach against it, make any scruple of committing it? And can a boy, a stripling, have the confidence to talk of his virtue?" "Madam," says Joseph, "that boy is the brother of Pamela, and would be ashamed that the chastity of his family, which is preserved in her, should be stained in him. If there are such men as your ladyship mentions, I am sorry for it; and I wish they had an opportunity of reading over those letters which my father hath sent me of my sister Pamela's; nor do I doubt but such an example would amend them." "You impudent villain!" cries the lady in a rage; "do you insult me with the follies of my relation, who hath exposed himself all over the country upon your sister's account? a little vixen, whom I have always wondered my late Lady Booby ever kept in her house. Sirrah! get out of my sight, and prepare to set out this night; for I will order you your wages immediately, and you shall be stripped and turned away." "Madam," says Joseph, "I am sorry I have offended your ladyship, I am sure I never intended it." "Yes, sirrah," cries she, "you have had the vanity to misconstrue the little innocent freedom I took, in order to try whether what I had heard was true. O' my conscience, you have had the assurance to imagine I was fond of you myself." Joseph answered, he had only spoke out of tenderness for his virtue; at which words she flew into a violent passion, and refusing to hear more, ordered him instantly to leave the room.

He was no sooner gone than she burst forth into the following exclamation:—"Whither doth this violent passion hurry us? What meannesses do we submit to from its impulse! Wisely we resist its first and least approaches; for it is then only we can assure ourselves the victory. No woman could ever safely say, so far only will I go. Have I not exposed myself to the refusal of my footman? I cannot bear the reflection." Upon which she applied herself to the bell, and rung it with infinitely more violence than was necessary—the faithful Slipslop attending near at hand: to say the truth, she had conceived a suspicion at her last interview with her mistress, and had waited ever since in the antechamber, having carefully applied her ears to the keyhole during the whole time that the preceding conversation passed between Joseph and the lady.

CHAPTER IX

WHAT PASSED BETWEEN THE LADY AND MRS. SLIPSLOP; IN
WHICH WE PROPHESY THERE ARE SOME STROKES WHICH
EVERY ONE WILL NOT TRULY COMPREHEND AT THE FIRST
READING

"SLIPSLOP," said the lady, "I find too much reason to believe
all thou hast told me of this wicked Joseph; I have determined
to part with him instantly; so go you to the steward, and bid
him pay his wages." Slipslop, who had preserved hitherto a
distance to her lady—rather out of necessity than inclination—
and who thought the knowledge of this secret had thrown down
all distinction between them, answered her mistress very pertly
—"She wished she knew her own mind; and that she was
certain she would call her back again before she was got half-
way downstairs." The lady replied, she had taken a resolution
and was resolved to keep it. "I am sorry for it," cries Slipslop,
"and, if I had known you would have punished the poor lad
so severely, you should never have heard a particle of the
matter. Here's a fuss indeed about nothing!" "Nothing!"
returned my lady; "do you think I will countenance lewdness
in my house?" "If you will turn away every footman," said
Slipslop, "that is a lover of the sport, you must soon open the
coach door yourself, or get a set of mophrodites to wait upon
you; and I am sure I hated the sight of them even singing in
an opera." "Do as I bid you," says my lady, "and don't
shock my ears with your beastly language." "Marry-come-
up," cries Slipslop, "people's ears are sometimes the nicest
part about them."
The lady, who began to admire the new style in which her
waiting-gentlewoman delivered herself, and by the conclusion
of her speech suspected somewhat of the truth, called her back,
and desired to know what she meant by the extraordinary
degree of freedom in which she thought proper to indulge her
tongue. "Freedom!" says Slipslop; "I don't know what you
call freedom, madam; servants have tongues as well as their
mistresses." "Yes, and saucy ones too," answered the lady;
"but I assure you I shall bear no such impertinence." "Impertinence! I don't know that I am impertinent," says Slipslop.
"Yes, indeed you are," cries my lady, "and unless you mend
your manners, this house is no place for you." "Manners!"
cries Slipslop; "I never was thought to want manners nor

modesty neither; and for places, there are more places than one; and I know what I know." "What do you know, mistress?" answered the lady. "I am not obliged to tell that to everybody," says Slipslop, "any more than I am obliged to keep it a secret." "I desire you would provide yourself," answered the lady. "With all my heart," replied the waiting-gentlewoman; and so departed in a passion, and slapped the door after her.

The lady too plainly perceived that her waiting-gentlewoman knew more than she would willingly have had her acquainted with; and this she imputed to Joseph's having discovered to her what passed at the first interview. This, therefore, blew up her rage against him, and confirmed her in a resolution of parting with him.

But the dismissing Mrs. Slipslop was a point not so easily to be resolved upon. She had the utmost tenderness for her reputation, as she knew on that depended many of the most valuable blessings of life; particularly cards, making curtsies in public places, and, above all, the pleasure of demolishing the reputations of others, in which innocent amusement she had an extraordinary delight. She therefore determined to submit to any insult from a servant, rather than run a risque of losing the title to so many great privileges.

She therefore sent for her steward, Mr. Peter Pounce, and ordered him to pay Joseph his wages, to strip off his livery, and to turn him out of the house that evening.

She then called Slipslop up, and, after refreshing her spirits with a small cordial, which she kept in her closet, she began in the following manner:

"Slipslop, why will you, who know my passionate temper, attempt to provoke me by your answers? I am convinced you are an honest servant, and should be very unwilling to part with you. I believe, likewise, you have found me an indulgent mistress on many occasions, and have as little reason on your side to desire a change. I can't help being surprised, therefore, that you will take the surest method to offend me— I mean, repeating my words, which you know I have always detested."

The prudent waiting-gentlewoman had duly weighed the whole matter, and found, on mature deliberation, that a good place in possession was better than one in expectation. As she found her mistress, therefore, inclined to relent, she thought proper also to put on some small condescension, which was as readily accepted; and so the affair was reconciled, all offences forgiven, and a present of a gown and petticoat made her, as an instance of her lady's future favour.

She offered once or twice to speak in favour of Joseph; but found her lady's heart so obdurate, that she prudently dropt all such efforts. She considered there were more footmen in the house, and some as stout fellows, though not quite so handsome, as Joseph; besides, the reader hath already seen her tender advances had not met with the encouragement she might have reasonably expected. She thought she had thrown away a great deal of sack and sweetmeats on an ungrateful rascal; and, being a little inclined to the opinion of that female sect, who hold one lusty young fellow to be nearly as good as another lusty young fellow, she at last gave up Joseph and his cause, and, with a triumph over her passion highly commendable, walked off with her present, and with great tranquillity paid a visit to a stone-bottle, which is of sovereign use to a philosophical temper.

She left not her mistress so easy. The poor lady could not reflect without agony that her dear reputation was in the power of her servants. All her comfort as to Joseph, was that she hoped he did not understand her meaning; at least she could say for herself, she had not plainly expressed anything to him; and as to Mrs. Slipslop, she imagined she could bribe her to secrecy.

But what hurt her most was, that in reality she had not so entirely conquered her passion; the little god lay lurking in her heart, though anger and disdain so hoodwinked her, that she could not see him. She was a thousand times on the very brink of revoking the sentence she had passed against the poor youth. Love became his advocate, and whispered many things in his favour. Honour likewise endeavoured to vindicate his crime, and Pity to mitigate his punishment. On the other side, Pride and Revenge spoke as loudly against him. And thus the poor lady was tortured with perplexity, opposite passions distracting and tearing her mind different ways.

So have I seen, in the hall of Westminster, where Serjeant Bramble hath been retained on the right side, and Serjeant Puzzle on the left, the balance of opinion (so equal were their fees) alternately incline to either scale. Now Bramble throws in an argument, and Puzzle's scale strikes the beam; again Bramble shares the like fate, overpowered by the weight of Puzzle. Here Bramble hits, there Puzzle strikes; here one has you, there t'other has you; till at last all becomes one scene of confusion in the tortured minds of the hearers; equal wagers are laid on the success, and neither judge nor jury can possibly make anything of the matter; all things are so enveloped by the careful serjeants in doubt and obscurity.

Or, as it happens in the conscience, where honour and honesty pull one way, and a bribe and necessity another.——If it was our present business only to make similes, we could produce many more to this purpose; but a simile (as well as a word) to the wise.——We shall therefore see a little after our hero, for whom the reader is doubtless in some pain.

CHAPTER X

JOSEPH WRITES ANOTHER LETTER: HIS TRANSACTIONS WITH MR.
   PETER POUNCE, ETC., WITH HIS DEPARTURE FROM LADY
   BOOBY

THE disconsolate Joseph would not have had an understanding sufficient for the principal subject of such a book as this, if he had any longer misunderstood the drift of his mistress; and indeed, that he did not discern it sooner, the reader will be pleased to impute to an unwillingness in him to discover what he must condemn in her as a fault. Having therefore quitted her presence, he retired into his own garret, and entered himself into an ejaculation on the numberless calamities which attended beauty, and the misfortune it was to be handsomer than one's neighbours.

He then sat down, and addressed himself to his sister Pamela in the following words:

DEAR SISTER PAMELA,

Hoping you are well, what news have I to tell you! O Pamela! my mistress is fallen in love with me—that is, what great folks call falling in love—she has a mind to ruin me; but I hope I shall have more resolution and more grace than to part with my virtue to any lady upon earth.

Mr. Adams hath often told me, that chastity is as great a virtue in a man as in a woman. He says he never knew any more than his wife, and I shall endeavour to follow his example. Indeed, it is owing entirely to his excellent sermons and advice, together with your letters, that I have been able to resist a temptation, which, he says, no man complies with, but he repents in this world, or is damned for it in the next; and why should I trust to repentance on my deathbed, since I may die in my sleep? What fine things are good advice and good example! But I am glad she turned me out of the chamber as she did: for I had once almost forgotten every word parson Adams had ever said to me.

I don't doubt, dear sister, but you will have grace to preserve your virtue against all trials; and I beg you earnestly to pray I may be enabled to preserve mine; for truly it is very severely attacked by more than one; but I hope I shall copy your example, and that of Joseph my namesake, and maintain my virtue against all temptations.

Joseph had not finished his letter, when he was summoned downstairs by Mr. Peter Pounce, to receive his wages; for, besides that out of eight pounds a year he allowed his father and mother four, he had been obliged, in order to furnish himself with musical instruments, to apply to the generosity of the aforesaid Peter, who, on urgent occasions, used to advance the servants their wages: not before they were due, but before they were payable; that is, perhaps, half a year after they were due; and this at the moderate premium of fifty per cent. or a little more: by which charitable methods, together with lending money to other people, and even to his own master and mistress, the honest man had, from nothing, in a few years amassed a small sum of twenty thousand pounds or thereabouts.

Joseph having received his little remainder of wages, and having stript off his livery, was forced to borrow a frock and breeches of one of the servants (for he was so beloved in the family, that they would all have lent him anything): and, being told by Peter that he must not stay a moment longer in the house than was necessary to pack up his linen, which he easily did in a very narrow compass, he took a melancholy leave of his fellow-servants, and set out at seven in the evening.

He had proceeded the length of two or three streets, before he absolutely determined with himself whether he should leave the town that night, or, procuring a lodging, wait till the morning. At last, the moon shining very bright helped him to come to a resolution of beginning his journey immediately, to which likewise he had some other inducements; which the reader, without being a conjurer, cannot possibly guess, till we have given him those hints which it may be now proper to open.

CHAPTER XI

OF SEVERAL NEW MATTERS NOT EXPECTED

IT is an observation sometimes made, that to indicate our idea of a simple fellow, we say, he is easily to be seen through: nor do I believe it a more improper denotation of a simple book. Instead of applying this to any particular performance, we chuse rather to remark the contrary in this history, where the scene opens itself by small degrees; and he is a sagacious reader who can see two chapters before him.

For this reason, we have not hitherto hinted a matter which now seems necessary to be explained; since it may be wondered at, first, that Joseph made such extraordinary haste out of town, which hath been already shown; and secondly, which will be now shown, that, instead of proceeding to the habitation of his father and mother, or to his beloved sister Pamela, he chose rather to set out full speed to the Lady Booby's country-seat, which he had left on his journey to London.

Be it known, then, that in the same parish where this seat stood there lived a young girl whom Joseph (though the best of sons and brothers) longed more impatiently to see than his parents or his sister. She was a poor girl, who had formerly been bred up in Sir John's family; whence, a little before the journey to London, she had been discarded by Mrs. Slipslop, on account of her extraordinary beauty: for I never could find any other reason.

This young creature (who now lived with a farmer in the parish) had been always beloved by Joseph, and returned his affection. She was two years only younger than our hero. They had been acquainted from their infancy, and had conceived a very early liking for each other; which had grown to such a degree of affection, that Mr. Adams had with much ado prevented them from marrying, and persuaded them to wait till a few years' service and thrift had a little improved their experience, and enabled them to live comfortably together.

They followed this good man's advice, as indeed his word was little less than a law in his parish; for as he had shown his parishioners, by an uniform behaviour of thirty-five years' duration, that he had their good entirely at heart, so they consulted him on every occasion, and very seldom acted contrary to his opinion.

Nothing can be imagined more tender than was the parting

between these two lovers. A thousand sighs heaved the bosom of Joseph, a thousand tears distilled from the lovely eyes of Fanny (for that was her name). Though her modesty would only suffer her to admit his eager kisses, her violent love made her more than passive in his embraces; and she often pulled him to her breast with a soft pressure, which though perhaps it would not have squeezed an insect to death, caused more emotion in the heart of Joseph than the closest Cornish hug could have done.

The reader may perhaps wonder that so fond a pair should, during a twelvemonth's absence, never converse with one another: indeed, there was but one reason which did or could have prevented them; and this was, that poor Fanny could neither write nor read: nor could she be prevailed upon to transmit the delicacies of her tender and chaste passion by the hands of an amanuensis.

They contented themselves therefore with frequent inquiries after each other's health, with a mutual confidence in each other's fidelity, and the prospect of their future happiness.

Having explained these matters to our reader, and, as far as possible, satisfied all his doubts, we return to honest Joseph, whom we left just set out on his travels by the light of the moon.

Those who have read any romance or poetry, antient or modern, must have been informed that love hath wings: by which they are not to understand, as some young ladies by mistake have done, that a lover can fly; the writers, by this ingenious allegory, intending to insinuate no more than that lovers do not march like horse-guards; in short, that they put the best leg foremost; which our lusty youth, who could walk with any man, did so heartily on this occasion, that within four hours he reached a famous house of hospitality well known to the western traveller   It presents you a lion on the sign-post: and the master, who was christened Timotheus, is commonly called plain Tim. Some have conceived that he hath particularly chosen the lion for his sign, as he doth in countenance greatly resemble that magnanimous beast, though his disposition savours more of the sweetness of the lamb. He is a person well received among all sorts of men, being qualified to render himself agreeable to any; as he is well versed in history and politics, hath a smattering in law and divinity, cracks a good jest, and plays wonderfully well on the French horn.

A violent storm of hail forced Joseph to take shelter in this inn, where he remembered Sir Thomas had dined in his way to town. Joseph had no sooner seated himself by the kitchen fire than Timotheus, observing his livery, began to condole the loss of his late master; who was, he said, his very particular and intimate acquaintance, with whom he had cracked many a merry bottle, ay many a dozen, in his time. He then remarked, that all these things were over now, all passed, and just as if they had never been; and concluded with an excellent observation on the certainty of death, which his wife said was indeed very true. A fellow now arrived at the same inn with two horses, one of which he was leading farther down into the country to meet his master; these he put into the stable, and came and took his place by Joseph's side, who immediately knew him to be the servant of a neighbouring gentleman, who used to visit at their house.

This fellow was likewise forced in by the storm; for he had orders to go twenty miles farther that evening, and luckily on the same road which Joseph himself intended to take. He, therefore, embraced this opportunity of complimenting his friend with his master's horse (notwithstanding he had received express commands to the contrary), which was readily accepted; and so, after they had drank a loving pot, and the storm was over, they set out together.

CHAPTER XII

CONTAINING MANY SURPRISING ADVENTURES WHICH JOSEPH
ANDREWS MET WITH ON THE ROAD, SCARCE CREDIBLE TO
THOSE WHO HAVE NEVER TRAVELLED IN A STAGE-COACH

NOTHING remarkable happened on the road till their arrival at the inn to which the horses were ordered; whither they came about two in the morning. The moon then shone very bright; and Joseph, making his friend a present of a pint of wine, and thanking him for the favour of his horse, notwithstanding all entreaties to the contrary, proceeded on his journey on foot.

He had not gone above two miles, charmed with the hope of shortly seeing his beloved Fanny, when he was met by two fellows in a narrow lane, and ordered to stand and deliver. He readily gave them all the money he had, which was somewhat less than two pounds; and told them he hoped they would be so generous as to return him a few shillings, to defray his charges on his way home.

One of the ruffians answered with an oath, "Yes, we'll give you something presently: but first strip and be d—n'd to you." —"Strip," cried the other, "or I'll blow your brains to the devil." Joseph, remembering that he had borrowed his coat and breeches of a friend, and that he should be ashamed of making any excuse for not returning them, replied, he hoped they would not insist on his clothes, which were not worth much, but consider the coldness of the night. "You are cold, are you, you rascal?" said one of the robbers: "I'll warm you with a vengeance"; and, damning his eyes, snapped a pistol at his head; which he had no sooner done than the other levelled a blow at him with his stick, which Joseph, who was expert at cudgel-playing, caught with his, and returned the favour so successfully on his adversary, that he laid him sprawling at his feet, and at the same instant received a blow from behind, with the butt end of a pistol, from the other villain, which felled him to the ground, and totally deprived him of his senses.

The thief who had been knocked down had now recovered himself; and both together fell to belabouring poor Joseph with their sticks, till they were convinced they had put an end to his miserable being: they then stripped him entirely naked, threw him into a ditch, and departed with their booty.

The poor wretch, who lay motionless a long time, just began to recover his senses as a stage-coach came by. The postillion, hearing a man's groans, stopt his horses, and told the coachman, he was certain there was a dead man lying in the ditch, for he heard him groan. "Go on, sirrah," says the coachman; "we are confounded late, and have no time to look after dead men." A lady, who heard what the postillion said, and likewise heard the groan, called eagerly to the coachman to stop and see what was the matter. Upon which he bid the postillion alight, and look into the ditch. He did so, and returned, "that there was a man sitting upright, as naked as ever he was born."—"O J—sus!" cried the lady; "a naked man! Dear coachman, drive on and leave him." Upon this the gentlemen got out of the coach; and Joseph begged them to have mercy upon him: for that he had been robbed and almost beaten to death. "Robbed!" cries an old gentleman: "let us make all the haste imaginable, or we shall be robbed too." A young man who belonged to the law answered, "He wished they had passed by without taking any notice; but that now they might be proved to have been last in his company; if he should die they might be called to some account for his murder. He therefore thought it advisable to save the poor creature's life, for their own sakes, if possible; at least, if he died, to prevent the jury's finding that they fled for it. He was therefore of opinion to take the man into the coach, and carry him to the next inn." The lady insisted, "That he should not come into the coach. That if they lifted him in, she would herself alight: for she had rather stay in that place to all eternity than ride with a naked man." The coachman objected, "That he could not suffer him to be taken in unless somebody would pay a shilling for his carriage the four miles." Which the two gentlemen refused to do. But the lawyer, who was afraid of some mischief happening to himself, if the wretch was left behind in that condition, saying no man could be too cautious in these matters, and that he remembered very extraordinary cases in the books, threatened the coachman, and bid him deny taking him up at his peril; for that, if he died, he should be indicted for his murder; and if he lived, and brought an action against him, he would willingly take a brief in it. These words had a sensible effect on the coachman, who was well acquainted with the person who spoke them; and the old gentleman above mentioned, thinking the naked man would afford him frequent opportunities of showing his wit to the lady, offered to join with the company in giving a mug of beer for his fare; till, partly alarmed by the threats of the one, and partly by the promises of the other, and being perhaps a little moved with compassion at the poor creature's condition, who stood bleeding and shivering with the cold, he at length agreed; and Joseph was now advancing to the coach, where, seeing the lady, who held the sticks of her fan before her eyes, he absolutely refused, miserable as he was, to enter, unless he was furnished with sufficient covering to prevent giving the least offence to decency—so perfectly modest was this young man; such mighty effects had the spotless example of the amiable Pamela, and the excellent sermons of Mr. Adams, wrought upon him.

Though there were several greatcoats about the coach, it was not easy to get over this difficulty which Joseph had started. The two gentlemen complained they were cold, and could not spare a rag; the man of wit saying, with a laugh, that charity began at home; and the coachman, who had two greatcoats spread under him, refused to lend either, lest they should be made bloody: the lady's footman desired to be excused for the same reason, which the lady herself, notwithstanding her abhorrence of a naked man, approved: and it is more than probable poor Joseph, who obstinately adhered to his modest resolution, must have perished, unless the postillion (a lad who hath been since transported for robbing a hen-roost) had voluntarily stript off a greatcoat, his only garment, at the same time swearing a great oath (for which he was rebuked by the passengers), "that he would rather ride in his shirt all his life than suffer a fellow-creature to lie in so miserable a condition."

Joseph, having put on the greatcoat, was lifted into the coach, which now proceeded on its journey. He declared himself almost dead with the cold, which gave the man of wit an occasion to ask the lady if she could not accommodate him with a dram. She answered, with some resentment, "She wondered at his asking her such a question; but assured him she never tasted any such thing."

The lawyer was inquiring into the circumstances of the robbery, when the coach stopt, and one of the ruffians, putting a pistol in, demanded their money of the passengers, who readily gave it them; and the lady, in her fright, delivered up a little silver bottle, of about a half-pint size, which the rogue, clapping it to his mouth, and drinking her health, declared, held some of the best Nantes he had ever tasted: this the lady afterwards assured the company was the mistake of her maid, for that she had ordered her to fill the bottle with Hungary-water.

As soon as the fellows were departed, the lawyer, who nad, it seems, a case of pistols in the seat of the coach, informed the company, that if it had been daylight, and he could have come at his pistols, he would not have submitted to the robbery: he likewise set forth that he had often met highwaymen when he travelled on horseback, but none ever durst attack him; concluding that, if he had not been more afraid for the lady than for himself, he should not have now parted with his money so easily.

As wit is generally observed to love to reside in empty pockets, so the gentleman whose ingenuity we have above remarked, as soon as he had parted with his money, began to grow wonderfully facetious. He made frequent allusions to Adam and Eve, and said many excellent things on figs and fig-leaves; which perhaps gave more offence to Joseph than to any other in the company.

The lawyer likewise made several very pretty jests without departing from his profession. He said, "If Joseph and the lady were alone, he would be more capable of making a conveyance to her, as his affairs were not fettered with any incumbrance; he'd warrant he soon suffered a recovery by a writ of entry, which was the proper way to create heirs in tail; that, for his own part, he would engage to make so firm a settlement in a coach, that there should be no danger of an ejectment," with an inundation of the like gibberish, which he continued to vent till the coach arrived at an inn, where one servant-maid only was up, in readiness to attend the coachman, and furnish him with cold meat and a dram. Joseph desired to alight, and that he might have a bed prepared for him, which the maid readily promised to perform; and, being a good-natured wench, and not so squeamish as the lady had been, she clapt a large fagot on the fire, and, furnishing Joseph with a greatcoat belonging to one of the hostlers, desired him to sit down and warm himself whilst she made his bed. The coachman, in the meantime, took an opportunity to call up a surgeon, who lived within a few doors; after which, he reminded his passengers how late they were, and, after they had taken leave of Joseph, hurried them off as fast as he could.

The wench soon got Joseph to bed, and promised to use her interest to borrow him a shirt; but imagining, as she afterwards said, by his being so bloody, that he must be a dead man, she ran with all speed to hasten the surgeon, who was more than half drest, apprehending that the coach had been overturned, and some gentleman or lady hurt. As soon as the wench had informed him at his window that it was a poor foot-passenger who had been stripped of all he had, and almost murdered, he chid her for disturbing him so early, slipped off his clothes again, and very quietly returned to bed and to sleep.

Aurora now began to show her blooming cheeks over the hills, whilst ten millions of feathered songsters, in jocund chorus, repeated odes a thousand times sweeter than those of our laureat, and sung both the day and the song; when the master of the inn, Mr. Tow-wouse, arose, and learning from his maid an account of the robbery, and the situation of his poor naked guest, he shook his head, and cried, "good-lack-a-day!" and then ordered the girl to carry him one of his own shirts.

Mrs. Tow-wouse was just awake, and had stretched out her arms in vain to fold her departed husband, when the maid entered the room. "Who's there? Betty?"—"Yes, madam." —"Where's your master?"—"He's without, madam; he hath sent me for a shirt to lend a poor naked man, who hath been robbed and murdered."—"Touch one if you dare, you slut," said Mrs. Tow-wouse: "your master is a pretty sort of a man, to take in naked vagabonds, and clothe them with his own clothes. I shall have no such doings. If you offer to touch anything, I'll throw the chamber-pot at your head. Go, send your master to me."—"Yes, madam," answered Betty. As soon as he came in, she thus began: "What the devil do you mean by this, Mr. Tow-wouse? Am I to buy shirts to lend to a set of scabby rascals?"—"My dear," said Mr. Tow-wouse, "this is a poor wretch."—"Yes," says she, "I know it is a poor wretch; but what the devil have we to do with poor wretches? The law makes us provide for too many already. We shall have thirty or forty poor wretches in red coats shortly."— "My dear," cries Tow-wouse, "this man hath been robbed of all he hath."—"Well then," said she, "where's his money to pay his reckoning? Why doth not such a fellow go to an alehouse? I shall send him packing as soon as I am up, I assure you."—"My dear," said he, "common charity won't suffer you to do that."—"Common charity, a f—t!" says she, "common charity teaches us to provide for ourselves and our families; and I and mine won't be ruined by your charity, I assure you." —"Well," says he, "my dear, do as you will, when you are up; you know I never contradict you."—"No," says she; "if the devil was to contradict me, I would make the house too hot to hold him."

With such like discourses they consumed near half-an-hour, whilst Betty provided a shirt from the hostler, who was one of her sweethearts, and put it on poor Joseph. The surgeon had likewise at last visited him, and washed and drest his wounds, and was now come to acquaint Mr. Tow-wouse that his guest was in such extreme danger of his life, that he scarce saw any hopes of his recovery. "Here's a pretty kettle of fish," cries Mrs. Tow-wouse, "you have brought upon us! We are like to have a funeral at our own expense." Tow-wouse (who, notwithstanding his charity, would have given his vote as freely as ever he did at an election, that any other house in the king-dom should have quiet possession of his guest) answered, "My dear, I am not to blame; he was brought hither by the stage-coach, and Betty had put him to bed before I was stirring." —"I'll Betty her," says she.—At which, with half her garments on, the other half under her arm, she sallied out in quest of the unfortunate Betty, whilst Tow-wouse and the surgeon went to pay a visit to poor Joseph, and inquire into the circumstances of this melancholy affair.

CHAPTER XIII

WHAT HAPPENED TO JOSEPH DURING HIS SICKNESS AT THE INN,
WITH THE CURIOUS DISCOURSE BETWEEN HIM AND MR.
BARNABAS, THE PARSON OF THE PARISH

As soon as Joseph had communicated a particular history of
the robbery, together with a short account of himself, and his
intended journey, he asked the surgeon if he apprehended him
to be in any danger: to which the surgeon very honestly answered,
"He feared he was; for that his pulse was very exalted and
feverish, and, if his fever should prove more than symptomatic,
it would be impossible to save him." Joseph, fetching a deep
sigh, cried, "Poor Fanny, I would I could have lived to see
thee! but God's will be done."

The surgeon then advised him, if he had any worldly affairs
to settle, that he would do it as soon as possible; for, though he
hoped he might recover, yet he thought himself obliged to
acquaint him he was in great danger; and if the malign con-
coction of his humours should cause a suscitation of his fever,
he might soon grow delirious and incapable to make his will.
Joseph answered, "That it was impossible for any creature in
the universe to be in a poorer condition than himself; for since
the robbery he had not one thing of any kind whatever which
he could call his own." "I had," said he, "a poor little piece
of gold, which they took away, that would have been a comfort
to me in all my afflictions; but surely, Fanny, I want nothing
to remind me of thee. I have thy dear image in my heart, and
no villain can ever tear it thence."

Joseph desired paper and pens, to write a letter, but they
were refused him; and he was advised to use all his endeavours
to compose himself. They then left him; and Mr. Tow-wouse
sent to a clergyman to come and administer his good offices to
the soul of poor Joseph, since the surgeon despaired of making
any successful applications to his body.

Mr. Barnabas (for that was the clergyman's name) came as
soon as sent for; and, having first drank a dish of tea with the
landlady, and afterwards a bowl of punch with the landlord,
he walked up to the room where Joseph lay; but, finding him
asleep, returned to take the other sneaker; which when he had
finished, he again crept softly up to the chamber-door, and,
having opened it, heard the sick man talking to himself in the
following manner:

"O most adorable Pamela! most virtuous sister! whose example could alone enable me to withstand all the temptations of riches and beauty, and to preserve my virtue pure and chaste for the arms of my dear Fanny, if it had pleased Heaven that I should ever have come unto them. What riches, or honours, or pleasures, can make us amends for the loss of innocence? Doth not that alone afford us more consolation than all worldly acquisitions? What but innocence and virtue could give any comfort to such a miserable wretch as I am? Yet these can make me prefer this sick and painful bed to all the pleasures I should have found in my lady's. These can make me face death without fear; and though I love my Fanny more than ever man loved a woman, these can teach me to resign myself to the Divine will without repining. O thou delightful charming creature! if Heaven had indulged thee to my arms, the poorest, humblest state would have been a paradise; I could have lived with thee in the lowest cottage without envying the palaces, the dainties, or the riches of any man breathing. But I must leave thee, leave thee for ever, my dearest angel! I must think of another world; and I heartily pray thou may'st meet comfort in this."—Barnabas thought he had heard enough, so down-stairs he went, and told Tow-wouse he could do his guest no service; for that he was very light-headed, and had uttered nothing but a rhapsody of nonsense all the time he stayed in the room.

The surgeon returned in the afternoon, and found his patient in a higher fever, as he said, than when he left him, though not delirious; for, notwithstanding Mr. Barnabas's opinion, he had not been once out of his senses since his arrival at the inn.

Mr. Barnabas was again sent for, and with much difficulty prevailed on to make another visit. As soon as he entered the room he told Joseph "He was come to pray by him, and to prepare him for another world: in the first place, therefore, he hoped he had repented of all his sins." Joseph answered, "He hoped he had; but there was one thing which he knew not whether he should call a sin; if it was, he feared he should die in the commission of it; and that was, the regret of parting with a young woman whom he loved as tenderly as he did his heart-strings." Barnabas bade him be assured "that any repining at the Divine will was one of the greatest sins he could commit; that he ought to forget all carnal affections, and think of better things." Joseph said, "That neither in this world nor the next could he forget his Fanny; and that the thought, however grievous, of parting from her for ever, was not half so tormenting as the fear of what she would suffer when she knew his misfortune." Barnabas said, "That such fears argued a diffidence and despondence very criminal; that he must divest himself of all human passions, and fix his heart above." Joseph answered, "That was what he desired to do, and should be obliged to him if he would enable him to accomplish it." Barnabas repiied, "That must be done by grace." Joseph besought him to discover how he might attain it. Barnabas answered, "By prayer and faith." He then questioned him concerning his forgiveness of the thieves. Joseph answered, "He feared that was more than he could do; for nothing would give him more pleasure than to hear they were taken."—"That," cries Barnabas, "is for the sake of justice."—"Yes," said Joseph, "but if I was to meet them again, I am afraid I should attack them, and kill them too, if I could."—"Doubtless," answered Barnabas, "it is lawful to kill a thief; but can you say you forgive them as a Christian ought?" Joseph desired to know what that forgiveness was. "That is," answered Barnabas, "to forgive them as—as—it is to forgive them as —in short, it is to forgive them as a Christian."—Joseph replied, "He forgave them as much as he could."—"Well, well," said Barnabas, "that will do." He then demanded of him, "If he remembered any more sins unrepented of; and if he did, he desired him to make haste and repent of them as fast as he could, that they might repeat over a few prayers together." Joseph answered, "He could not recollect any great crimes he had been guilty of, and that those he had committed he was sincerely sorry for." Barnabas said that was enough, and then proceeded to prayer with all the expedition he was master of, some company then waiting for him below in the parlour, where the ingredients for punch were all in readiness; but no one would squeeze the oranges till he came.

Joseph complained he was dry, and desired a little tea; which Barnabas reported to Mrs. Tow-wouse, who answered, "She had just done drinking it, and could not be slopping all day"; but ordered Betty to carry him up some small beer.

Betty obeyed her mistress's commands; but Joseph, as soon as he had tasted it, said, he feared it would increase his fever, and that he longed very much for tea; to which the good-natured Betty answered, he should have tea, if there was any in the land; she accordingly went and bought him some herself, and attended him with it; where we will leave her and Joseph together for some time, to entertain the reader with other matters.

CHAPTER XIV

BEING VERY FULL OF ADVENTURES WHICH SUCCEEDED EACH OTHER AT THE INN

IT was now the dusk of the evening, when a grave person rode into the inn, and, committing his horse to the hostler, went directly into the kitchen, and, having called for a pipe of tobacco, took his place by the fireside, where several other persons were likewise assembled.

The discourse ran altogether on the robbery which was committed the night before, and on the poor wretch who lay above in the dreadful condition in which we have already seen him. Mrs. Tow-wouse said, "She wondered what the devil Tom Whipwell meant by bringing such guests to her house, when there were so many alehouses on the road proper for their reception. But she assured him, if he died, the parish should be at the expense of the funeral." She added, "Nothing would serve the fellow's turn but tea, she would assure him." Betty, who was just returned from her charitable office, answered, she believed he was a gentleman, for she never saw a finer skin in her life. "Pox on his skin!" replied Mrs. Tow-wouse, "I suppose that is all we are like to have for the reckoning. I desire no such gentlemen should ever call at the Dragon" (which it seems was the sign of the inn).

The gentleman lately arrived discovered a great deal of emotion at the distress of this poor creature, whom he observed to be fallen not into the most compassionate hands. And indeed, if Mrs. Tow-wouse had given no utterance to the sweetness of her temper, nature had taken such pains in her countenance, that Hogarth himself never gave more expression to a picture.

Her person was short, thin, and crooked. Her forehead projected in the middle, and thence descended in a declivity to the top of her nose, which was sharp and red, and would have hung over her lips, had not nature turned up the end of it. Her lips were two bits of skin, which, whenever she spoke, she drew together in a purse. Her chin was peaked; and at the upper end of that skin which composed her cheeks, stood two bones, that almost hid a pair of small red eyes. Add to this a voice most wonderfully adapted to the sentiments it was to convey, being both loud and hoarse.

It is not easy to say whether the gentleman had conceived a greater dislike for his landlady or compassion for her unhappy guest. He inquired very earnestly of the surgeon, who was now come into the kitchen, whether he had any hopes of his recovery? He begged him to use all possible means towards it, telling him, "it was the duty of men of all professions to apply their skill gratis for the relief of the poor and necessitous." The surgeon answered, "He should take proper care; but he defied all the surgeons in London to do him any good."—"Pray, sir," said the gentleman, "what are his wounds?"—"Why, do you know anything of wounds?" says the surgeon (winking upon Mrs. Tow-wouse).—"Sir, I have a small smattering in surgery," answered the gentleman.—"A smattering—ho, ho, ho!" said the surgeon; "I believe it is a smattering indeed."

The company were all attentive, expecting to hear the doctor, who was what they call a dry fellow, expose the gentleman.

He began therefore with an air of triumph: "I suppose, sir, you have travelled?"—"No, really, sir," said the gentleman. —"Ho! then you have practised in the hospitals perhaps?"— "No, sir."—"Hum! not that neither? Whence, sir, then, if I may be so bold to inquire, have you got your knowledge in surgery?"—"Sir," answered the gentleman, "I do not pretend to much; but the little I know I have from books."—"Books!" cries the doctor. "What, I suppose you have read Galen and Hippocrates!"—"No, sir," said the gentleman.—"How! you understand surgery," answers the doctor, "and not read Galen and Hippocrates?"—"Sir," cries the other, "I believe there are many surgeons who have never read these authors."— "I believe so too," says the doctor, "more shame for them; but, thanks to my education, I have them by heart, and very seldom go without them both in my pocket."—"They are pretty large books," said the gentleman.—"Aye," said the doctor, "I believe I know how large they are better than you." (At which he fell a winking, and the whole company burst into a laugh.)

The doctor pursuing his triumph, asked the gentleman, "If he did not understand physic as well as surgery."—"Rather better," answered the gentleman.—"Aye, like enough," cries the doctor, with a wink. "Why, I know a little of physic too." —"I wish I knew half so much," said Tow-wouse, "I'd never wear an apron again."—"Why, I believe, landlord," cries the doctor, "there are few men, though I say it, within twelve miles of the place, that handle a fever better. *Veniente accurrite morbo:* that is my method. I suppose, brother, you understand *Latin?*"—"A little," says the gentleman.—"Aye, and Greek now, I'll warrant you: *Ton dapomibominos poluflosboio Thalasses.* But I have almost forgot these things: I could have repeated Homer by heart once."——"Ifags! the gentleman has caught a traytor," says Mrs. Tow-wouse; at which they all fell a laughing.

The gentleman, who had not the least affection for joking, very contentedly suffered the doctor to enjoy his victory, which he did with no small satisfaction; and, having sufficiently sounded his depth, told him, "He was thoroughly convinced of his great learning and abilities; and that he would be obliged to him if he would let him know his opinion of his patient's case above-stairs."—"Sir," says the doctor, "his case is that of a dead man—the contusion on his head has perforated the internal membrane of the occiput, and divelicated that radical small minute invisible nerve which coheres to the pericranium; and this was attended with a fever at first symptomatic, then pneumatic; and he is at length grown deliriuus, or delirious, as the vulgar express it."

He was proceeding in this learned manner, when a mighty noise interrupted him. Some young fellows in the neighbourhood had taken one of the thieves, and were bringing him into the inn. Betty ran upstairs with this news to Joseph, who begged they might search for a little piece of broken gold, which had a ribband tied to it, and which he could swear to amongst all the hoards of the richest men in the universe.

Notwithstanding the fellow's persisting in his innocence, the mob were very busy in searching him, and presently, among other things, pulled out the piece of gold just mentioned; which Betty no sooner saw than she laid violent hands on it, and conveyed it up to Joseph, who received it with raptures of joy, and, hugging it in his bosom, declared he could now die contented.

Within a few minutes afterwards came in some other fellows with a bundle which they had found in a ditch, and which was indeed the cloaths which had been stripped off from Joseph, and the other things they had taken from him.

The gentleman no sooner saw the coat than he declared he knew the livery; and, if it had been taken from the poor creature above-stairs, desired he might see him; for that he was very well acquainted with the family to whom that livery belonged.

He was accordingly conducted up by Betty; but what, reader,

was the surprise on both sides, when he saw Joseph was the person in bed, and when Joseph discovered the face of his good friend Mr. Abraham Adams!

It would be impertinent to insert a discourse which chiefly turned on the relation of matters already well known to the reader; for, as soon as the curate had satisfied Joseph concerning the perfect health of his Fanny, he was on his side very inquisitive into all the particulars which had produced this unfortunate accident.

To return therefore to the kitchen, where a great variety of company were now assembled from all the rooms of the house, as well as the neighbourhood: so much delight do men take in contemplating the countenance of a thief.

Mr. Tow-wouse began to rub his hands with pleasure at seeing so large an assembly; who would, he hoped, shortly adjourn into several apartments, in order to discourse over the robbery, and drink a health to all honest men. But Mrs. Tow-wouse, whose misfortune it was commonly to see things a little perversely, began to rail at those who brought the fellow into her house; telling her husband, "They were very likely to thrive who kept a house of entertainment for beggars and thieves."

The mob had now finished their search, and could find nothing about the captive likely to prove any evidence; for as to the cloaths, though the mob were very well satisfied with that proof, yet, as the surgeon observed, they could not convict him, because they were not found in his custody; to which Barnabas agreed, and added that these were *bona waviata*, and belonged to the lord of the manor.

"How," says the surgeon, "do you say these goods belong to the lord of the manor?"—"I do," cried Barnabas.—"Then I deny it," says the surgeon: "what can the lord of the manor have to do in the case? Will any one attempt to persuade me that what a man finds is not his own?"—"I have heard," says an old fellow in the corner, "justice Wise-one say, that, if every man had his right, whatever is found belongs to the king of London."—"That may be true," says Barnabas, "in some sense; for the law makes a difference between things stolen and things found; for a thing may be stolen that never is found, and a thing may be found that never was stolen: Now, goods that are both stolen and found are *waviata*; and they belong to the lord of the manor."—"So the lord of the manor is the receiver of stolen goods," says the doctor; at which there was an universal laugh, being first begun by himself.

While the prisoner, by persisting in his innocence, had almost (as there was no evidence against him) brought over Barnabas, the surgeon, Tow-wouse, and several others to his side, Betty informed them that they had overlooked a little piece of gold, which she had carried up to the man in bed, and which he offered to swear to amongst a million, aye, amongst ten thousand. This immediately turned the scale against the prisoner, and every one now concluded him guilty. It was resolved, therefore, to keep him secured that night, and early in the morning to carry him before a justice.

CHAPTER XV

SHOWING HOW MRS. TOW-WOUSE WAS A LITTLE MOLLIFIED; AND HOW OFFICIOUS MR. BARNABAS AND THE SURGEON WERE TO PROSECUTE THE THIEF: WITH A DISSERTATION ACCOUNTING FOR THEIR ZEAL, AND THAT OF MANY OTHER PERSONS NOT MENTIONED IN THIS HISTORY

BETTY told her mistress she believed the man in bed was a greater man than they took him for; for, besides the extreme whiteness of his skin, and the softness of his hands, she observed a very great familiarity between the gentleman and him; and added, she was certain they were intimate acquaintance, if not relations.

This somewhat abated the severity of Mrs. Tow-wouse's countenance. She said, "God forbid she should not discharge the duty of a Christian, since the poor gentleman was brought to her house. She had a natural antipathy to vagabonds; but could pity the misfortunes of a Christian as soon as another." Tow-wouse said, "If the traveller be a gentleman, though he hath no money about him now, we shall most likely be paid hereafter; so you may begin to score whenever you will." Mrs. Tow-wouse answered, "Hold your simple tongue, and don't instruct me in my business. I am sure I am sorry for the gentleman's misfortune with all my heart; and I hope the villain who hath used him so barbarously will be hanged. Betty, go see what he wants. God forbid he should want anything in my house."

Barnabas and the surgeon went up to Joseph to satisfy themselves concerning the piece of gold; Joseph was with

difficulty prevailed upon to show it them, but would by no
entreaties be brought to deliver it out of his own possession.
He however attested this to be the same which had been taken
from him, and Betty was ready to swear to the finding it on
the thief.

The only difficulty that remained was, how to produce this gold
before the justice; for as to carrying Joseph himself, it seemed
impossible; nor was there any great likelihood of obtaining it
from him, for he had fastened it with a ribband to his arm, and
solemnly vowed that nothing but irresistible force should ever
separate them; in which resolution, Mr. Adams, clenching a
fist rather less than the knuckle of an ox, declared he would
support him.

A dispute arose on this occasion concerning evidence not
very necessary to be related here; after which the surgeon
dressed Mr. Joseph's head, still persisting in the imminent
danger in which his patient lay, but concluding, with a very
important look, "That he began to have some hopes; that he
should send him a sanative soporiferous draught, and would
see him in the morning." After which Barnabas and he departed
and left Mr. Joseph and Mr. Adams together.

Adams informed Joseph of the occasion of this journey which
he was making to London, namely, to publish three volumes of
sermons; being encouraged, as he said, by an advertisement
lately set forth by the society of booksellers, who proposed to
purchase any copies offered to them, at a price to be settled by
two persons; but though he imagined he should get a considerable sum of money on this occasion, which his family were
in urgent need of, he protested he would not leave Joseph in
his present condition: finally, he told him, "He had nine
shillings and threepence halfpenny in his pocket, which he was
welcome to use as he pleased."

This goodness of parson Adams brought tears into Joseph's
eyes; he declared, "He had now a second reason to desire life,
that he might show his gratitude to such a friend." Adams
bade him "be cheerful; for that he plainly saw the surgeon,
besides his ignorance, desired to make a merit of curing him,
though the wounds in his head, he perceived, were by no means
dangerous; that he was convinced he had no fever, and doubted
not but he would be able to travel in a day or two."

These words infused a spirit into Joseph; he said, "He found
himself very sore from the bruises, but had no reason to think
any of his bones injured, or that he had received any harm in his

inside, unless that he felt something very odd in his stomach; but he knew not whether that might not arise from not having eaten one morsel for above twenty-four hours." Being then asked if he had any inclination to eat, he answered in the affirmative. Then parson Adams desired him to "name what he had the greatest fancy for; whether a poached egg, or chicken-broth." He answered, "He could eat both very well; but that he seemed to have the greatest appetite for a piece of boiled beef and cabbage."

Adams was pleased with so perfect a confirmation that he had not the least fever, but advised him to a lighter diet for that evening. He accordingly ate either a rabbit or a fowl, I never could with any tolerable certainty discover which; after this he was, by Mrs. Tow-wouse's order, conveyed into a better bed and equipped with one of her husband's shirts.

In the morning early, Barnabas and the surgeon came to the inn, in order to see the thief conveyed before the justice. They had consumed the whole night in debating what measures they should take to produce the piece of gold in evidence against him; for they were both extremely zealous in the business, though neither of them were in the least interested in the prosecution; neither of them had ever received any private injury from the fellow, nor had either of them ever been suspected of loving the public well enough to give them a sermon or a dose of physic for nothing.

To help our reader, therefore, as much as possible to account for this zeal, we must inform him that, as this parish was so unfortunate as to have no lawyer in it, there had been a constant contention between the two doctors, spiritual and physical, concerning their abilities in a science, in which, as neither of them professed it, they had equal pretensions to dispute each other's opinions. These disputes were carried on with great contempt on both sides, and had almost divided the parish; Mr. Tow-wouse and one half of the neighbours inclining to the surgeon, and Mrs. Tow-wouse with the other half to the parson. The surgeon drew his knowledge from those inestimable fountains, called The Attorney's Pocket Companion, and Mr. Jacob's Law-Tables; Barnabas trusted entirely to Wood's Institutes. It happened on this occasion, as was pretty frequently the case, that these two learned men differed about the sufficiency of evidence; the doctor being of opinion that the maid's oath would convict the prisoner without producing the gold; the parson, *è contra, totis viribus*. To display their parts, therefore, before the justice and the parish, was the sole motive which we can discover to this zeal which both of them pretended to have for public justice.

O Vanity! how little is thy force acknowledged, or thy operations discerned! How wantonly dost thou deceive mankind under different disguises! Sometimes thou dost wear the face of pity, sometimes of generosity: nay, thou hast the assurance even to put on those glorious ornaments which belong only to heroic virtue. Thou odious, deformed monster! whom priests have railed at, philosophers despised, and poets ridiculed; is there a wretch so abandoned as to own thee for an acquaintance in public?—yet, how few will refuse to enjoy thee in private? nay, thou art the pursuit of most men through their lives. The greatest villainies are daily practised to please thee; nor is the meanest thief below, or the greatest hero above, thy notice. Thy embraces are often the sole aim and sole reward of the private robbery and the plundered province. It is to pamper up thee, thou harlot, that we attempt to withdraw from others what we do not want, or to withhold from them what they do. All our passions are thy slaves. Avarice itself is often no more than thy handmaid, and even Lust thy pimp. The bully Fear, like a coward, flies before thee, and Joy and Grief hide their heads in thy presence.

I know thou wilt think that whilst I abuse thee I court thee, and that thy love hath inspired me to write this sarcastical panegyric on thee; but thou art deceived: I value thee not of a farthing; nor will it give me any pain if thou shouldst prevail on the reader to censure this digression as arrant nonsense; for know, to thy confusion, that I have introduced thee for no other purpose than to lengthen out a short chapter, and so I return to my history.

CHAPTER XVI

THE ESCAPE OF THE THIEF. MR. ADAMS'S DISAPPOINTMENT. THE ARRIVAL OF TWO VERY EXTRAORDINARY PERSONAGES, AND THE INTRODUCTION OF PARSON ADAMS TO PARSON BARNABAS

BARNABAS and the surgeon, being returned, as we have said, to the inn, in order to convey the thief before the justice, were greatly concerned to find that a small accident had happened, which somewhat disconcerted them; and this was no other than the thief's escape, who had modestly withdrawn himself by night, declining all ostentation, and not chusing, in imitation of some great men, to distinguish himself at the expense of being pointed at.

When the company had retired the evening before, the thief was detained in a room where the constable, and one of the young fellows who took him, were planted as his guard. About the second watch a general complaint of drought was made, both by the prisoner and his keepers. Among whom it was at last agreed that the constable should remain on duty, and the young fellow call up the tapster; in which disposition the latter apprehended not the least danger, as the constable was well armed, and could besides easily summon him back to his assistance, if the prisoner made the least attempt to gain his liberty.

The young fellow had not long left the room before it came into the constable's head that the prisoner might leap on him by surprise, and, thereby preventing him of the use of his weapons, especially the long staff in which he chiefly confided, might reduce the success of a struggle to an equal chance. He wisely, therefore, to prevent this inconvenience, slipt out of the room himself, and locked the door, waiting without with his staff in his hand, ready lifted to fell the unhappy prisoner, if by ill fortune he should attempt to break out.

But human life, as hath been discovered by some great man or other (for I would by no means be understood to affect the honour of making any such discovery), very much resembles a game at chess; for as in the latter, while a gamester is too attentive to secure himself very strongly on one side the board, he is apt to leave an unguarded opening on the other; so doth it often happen in life, and so did it happen on this occasion; for whilst the cautious constable with such wonderful sagacity had possessed himself of the door, he most unhappily forgot the window.

The thief, who played on the other side, no sooner perceived this opening than he began to move that way; and, finding the passage easy, he took with him the young fellow's hat, and without any ceremony stepped into the street and made the best of his way.

The young fellow, returning with a double mug of strong beer, was a little surprised to find the constable at the door; but much more so when, the door being opened, he perceived the prisoner had made his escape, and which way. He threw down the beer, and, without uttering anything to the constable except a hearty curse or two, he nimbly leapt out of the window, and went again in pursuit of his prey, being very unwilling to lose the reward which he had assured himself of.

The constable hath not been discharged of suspicion on this account; it hath been said that, not being concerned in the taking of the thief, he could not have been entitled to any part of the reward if he had been convicted; that the thief had several guineas in his pocket; that it was very unlikely he should have been guilty of such an oversight; that his pretence for leaving the room was absurd; that it was his constant maxim, that a wise man never refused money on any conditions; that at every election he always had sold his vote to both parties, &c.

But, notwithstanding these and many other such allegations, I am sufficiently convinced of his innocence; having been positively assured of it by those who received their information from his own mouth; which, in the opinion of some moderns, is the best and indeed only evidence.

All the family were now up, and with many others assembled in the kitchen, where Mr. Tow-wouse was in some tribulation; the surgeon having declared that by law he was liable to be indicted for the thief's escape, as it was out of his house; he was a little comforted, however, by Mr. Barnabas's opinion, that as the escape was by night the indictment would not lie.

Mrs. Tow-wouse delivered herself in the following words: "Sure never was such a fool as my husband; would any other person living have left a man in the custody of such a drunken drowsy blockhead as Tom Suckbribe?" (which was the constable's name); "and if he could be indicted without any harm to his wife and children, I should be glad of it." (Then the bell rung in Joseph's room.) "Why Betty, John, Chamberlain, where the devil are you all? Have you no ears, or no conscience, not to tend the sick better? See what the gentleman wants. Why don't you go yourself, Mr. Tow-wouse? But any one may die for you; you have no more feeling than a deal board. If a man lived a fortnight in your house without spending a penny, you would never put him in mind of it. See whether he drinks tea or coffee for breakfast." "Yes, my dear," cried Tow-wouse. She then asked the doctor and Mr. Barnabas what morning's draught they chose, who answered, they had a pot of cyder-and at the fire; which we will leave them merry over, and return to Joseph.

He had rose pretty early this morning; but, though his wounds were far from threatening any danger, he was so sore with the bruises, that it was impossible for him to think of undertaking a journey yet; Mr. Adams, therefore, whose stock was visibly decreased with the expenses of supper and breakfast, and which could not survive that day's scoring, began to consider how it was possible to recruit it. At last he cried, "He had luckily hit on a sure method, and, though it would oblige him to return himself home together with Joseph, it mattered not much." He then sent for Tow-wouse, and, taking him into another room, told him "he wanted to borrow three guineas, for which he would put ample security into his hands." Tow-wouse, who expected a watch, or ring, or something of double the value, answered, "He believed he could furnish him." Upon which Adams, pointing to his saddle-bag, told him, with a face and voice full of solemnity, "that there were in that bag no less than nine volumes of manuscript sermons, as well worth a hundred pounds as a shilling was worth twelve pence, and that he would deposit one of the volumes in his hands by way of pledge; not doubting but that he would have the honesty to return it on his repayment of the money; for otherwise he must be a very great loser, seeing that every volume would at least bring him ten pounds, as he had been informed by a neighbouring clergyman in the country; for," said he, "as to my own part, having never yet dealt in printing, I do not pretend to ascertain the exact value of such things."

Tow-wouse, who was a little surprised at the pawn, said (and not without some truth), "That he was no judge of the price of such kind of goods; and as for money he really was very short." Adams answered, "Certainly he would not scruple to lend him three guineas on what was undoubtedly worth at least ten." The landlord replied, "He did not believe he had so much money in the house, and besides, he was to make up a sum. He was very confident that the books were of much higher value, and heartily sorry it did not suit him." He then cried out, "Coming, sir!" though nobody called; and ran downstairs without any fear of breaking his neck.

Poor Adams was extremely dejected at this disappointment, nor knew he what further stratagem to try. He immediately applied to his pipe, his constant friend and comfort in his afflictions; and, leaning over the rails, he devoted himself to meditation, assisted by the inspiring fumes of tobacco.

He had on a nightcap drawn over his wig, and a short great-coat, which half covered his cassock—a dress which, added to something comical enough in his countenance, composed a figure likely to attract the eyes of those who were not over given to observation.

Whilst he was smoking his pipe in this posture, a coach and six, with a numerous attendance, drove into the inn. There alighted from the coach a young fellow and a brace of pointers, after which another young fellow leapt from the box, and shook the former by the hand; and both, together with the dogs, were instantly conducted by Mr. Tow-wouse into an apartment; whither, as they passed, they entertained themselves with the following short facetious dialogue:

"You are a pretty fellow for a coachman, Jack!" says he from the coach; "you had almost overturned us just now."—"Pox take you!" says the coachman; "if I had only broke your neck, it would have been saving somebody else the trouble; but I should have been sorry for the pointers."—"Why, you son of a b—," answered the other, "if nobody could shoot better than you, the pointers would be of no use."—"D—n me," says the coachman, "I will shoot with you five guineas a shot."—"You be hanged," says the other; "for five guineas you shall shoot at my a—."—"Done," says the coachman; "I'll pepper you better than ever you was peppered by Jenny Bouncer."—"Pepper your grandmother," says the other; "Here's Tow-wouse will let you shoot at him for a shilling a time."—"I know his honour better," cries Tow-wouse; "I never saw a surer shot at a partridge. Every man misses now and then; but if I could shoot half as well as his honour, I would desire no better livelihood than I could get by my gun."—"Pox on you," says the coachman, "you demolish more game now than your head's worth. There's a bitch, Tow-wouse: by G— she never blinked [1] a bird in her life."—"I have a puppy, not a year old, shall hunt with her for a hundred," cries the other gentleman.—"Done," says the coachman: "but you will be pox'd before you make the bet." — "If you have a mind for a bet," cries the coachman, "I will match my spotted dog with your white bitch for a hundred, play or pay."—"Done," says the other: "and I'll run Baldface against Slouch with you for another."—"No," cries he from the box; "but I'll venture Miss Jenny against Baldface, or Hannibal either."—"Go to the devil," cries he from the coach: "I will make every bet your own way, to be sure! I will match Hannibal with Slouch for a thousand, if you dare; and I say done first."

They were now arrived; and the reader will be very contented to leave them, and repair to the kitchen; where Barnabas, the surgeon, and an exciseman were smoking their pipes over some

---

[1] To blink is a term used to signify the dog's passing by a bird without pointing at it.

cyder-and; and where the servants who attended the two noble gentlemen we have just seen alight, were now arrived.

"Tom," cries one of the footmen, "there's parson Adams smoking his pipe in the gallery."—"Yes," says Tom; "I pulled off my hat to him, and the parson spoke to me."

"Is the gentleman a clergyman, then?" says Barnabas (for his cassock had been tied up when he arrived). "Yes, sir," answered the footman; "and one there be but few like."—"Aye," said Barnabas; "if I had known it sooner, I should have desired his company; I would always show a proper respect for the cloth: but what say you, doctor, shall we adjourn into a room, and invite him to take part of a bowl of punch?"

This proposal was immediately agreed to and executed; and parson Adams accepting the invitation, much civility passed between the two clergymen, who both declared the great honour they had for the cloth. They had not been long together before they entered into a discourse on small tithes, which continued a full hour, without the doctor or the exciseman's having one opportunity to offer a word.

It was then proposed to begin a general conversation, and the exciseman opened on foreign affairs; but a word unluckily dropping from one of them introduced a dissertation on the hardships suffered by the inferior clergy; which, after a long duration, concluded with bringing the nine volumes of sermons on the carpet.

Barnabas greatly discouraged poor Adams; he said, "The age was so wicked, that nobody read sermons: would you think it, Mr. Adams?" said he, "I once intended to print a volume of sermons myself, and they had the approbation of two or three bishops; but what do you think a bookseller offered me?" "Twelve guineas perhaps," cried Adams.—"Not twelve pence, I assure you," answered Barnabas: "nay, the dog refused me a Concordance in exchange. At last I offered to give him the printing them, for the sake of dedicating them to that very gentleman who just now drove his own coach into the inn; and, I assure you, he had the impudence to refuse my offer; by which means I lost a good living, that was afterwards given away in exchange for a pointer, to one who—but I will not say anything against the cloth. So you may guess, Mr. Adams, what you are to expect; for if sermons would have gone down, I believe—I will not be vain; but to be concise with you, three bishops said they were the best that ever were writ: but indeed there are a pretty moderate number printed already, and not all sold yet."—

"Pray, sir," said Adams, "to what do you think the numbers may amount?"—"Sir," answered Barnabas, "a bookseller told me, he believed five thousand volumes at least."—"Five thousand?" quoth the surgeon: "What can they be writ upon? I remember when I was a boy, I used to read one Tillotson's sermons; and, I am sure, if a man practised half so much as is in one of those sermons, he will go to heaven."—"Doctor," cries Barnabas, "you have a profane way of talking, for which I must reprove you. A man can never have his duty too freely inculcated into him. And as for Tillotson, to be sure he was a good writer, and said things very well; but comparisons are odious; another man may write as well as he——I believe there are some of my sermons,"—— and then he applied the candle to his pipe.—"And I believe there are some of my discourses," cries Adams, "which the bishops would not think totally unworthy of being printed; and I have been informed I might procure a very large sum (indeed an immense one) on them."—"I doubt that," answered Barnabas: "however, if you desire to make some money of them, perhaps you may sell them by advertising the manuscript sermons of a clergyman lately deceased, all warranted originals, and never printed. And now I think of it, I should be obliged to you, if there be ever a funeral one among them, to lend it to me; for I am this very day to preach a funeral sermon, for which I have not penned a line, though I am to have a double price."—Adams answered, "He had but one, which he feared would not serve his purpose, being sacred to the memory of a magistrate, who had exerted himself very singularly in the preservation of the morality of his neighbours, insomuch that he had neither alehouse nor lewd woman in the parish where he lived."—"No," replied Barnabas, "that will not do quite so well, for the deceased upon whose virtues I am to harangue, was a little too much addicted to liquor, and publicly kept a mistress.——I believe I must take a common sermon, and trust to my memory to introduce something handsome on him."—"To your invention rather," said the doctor: "your memory will be apter to put you out; for no man living remembers anything good of him."

With such kind of spiritual discourse, they emptied the bowl of punch, paid their reckoning, and separated: Adams and the doctor went up to Joseph, parson Barnabas departed to celebrate the aforesaid deceased, and the exciseman descended into the cellar to gauge the vessels.

Joseph was now ready to sit down to a loin of mutton, and waited for Mr. Adams, when he and the doctor came in. The doctor, having felt his pulse and examined his wounds, declared him much better, which he imputed to that sanative soporiferous draught, a medicine "whose virtues," he said, "were never to be sufficiently extolled." And great indeed they must be, if Joseph was so much indebted to them as the doctor imagined; since nothing more than those effluvia which escaped the cork could have contributed to his recovery; for the medicine had stood untouched in the window ever since its arrival.

Joseph passed that day, and the three following, with his friend Adams, in which nothing so remarkable happened as the swift progress of his recovery. As he had an excellent habit of body, his wounds were now almost healed; and his bruises gave him so little uneasiness, that he pressed Mr. Adams to let him depart; told him that he should never be able to return sufficient thanks for all his favours, but begged that he might no longer delay his journey to London.

Adams, notwithstanding the ignorance, as he conceived it, of Mr. Tow-wouse, and the envy (for such he thought it) of Mr. Barnabas, had great expectations from his sermons: seeing therefore Joseph in so good a way, he told him he would agree to his setting out the next morning in the stage-coach, that he believed he should have sufficient, after the reckoning paid, to procure him one day's conveyance in it, and afterwards he would be able to get on on foot, or might be favoured with a lift in some neighbour's waggon, especially as there was then to be a fair in the town whither the coach would carry him, to which numbers from his parish resorted—And as to himself, he agreed to proceed to the great city.

They were now walking in the inn-yard, when a fat, fair, short person rode in, and, alighting from his horse, went directly up to Barnabas, who was smoking his pipe on a bench. The parson and the stranger shook one another very lovingly by the hand, and went into a room together.

The evening now coming on, Joseph retired to his chamber, whither the good Adams accompanied him, and took this opportunity to expatiate on the great mercies God had lately shown him, of which he ought not only to have the deepest inward sense, but likewise to express outward thankfulness for them. They therefore fell both on their knees, and spent a considerable time in prayer and thanksgiving.

They had just finished when Betty came in and told Mr. Adams Mr. Barnabas desired to speak to him on some business of consequence below-stairs. Joseph desired, if it was likely to

detain him long, he would let him know it, that he might go to
bed, which Adams promised, and in that case they wished one
another good-night.

CHAPTER XVII

A PLEASANT DISCOURSE BETWEEN THE TWO PARSONS AND THE
BOOKSELLER, WHICH WAS BROKE OFF BY AN UNLUCKY
ACCIDENT HAPPENING IN THE INN, WHICH PRODUCED A DIA-
LOGUE BETWEEN MRS. TOW-WOUSE AND HER MAID OF NO
GENTLE KIND

As soon as Adams came into the room Mr. Barnabas introduced
him to the stranger, who was, he told him, a bookseller, and
would be as likely to deal with him for his sermons as any man
whatever. Adams, saluting the stranger, answered Barnabas
that he was very much obliged to him; that nothing could be
more convenient, for he had no other business to the great city,
and was heartily desirous of returning with the young man, who
was just recovered of his misfortune. He then snapt his
fingers (as was usual with him), and took two or three turns
about the room in an ecstasy. And to induce the bookseller to
be as expeditious as possible, as likewise to offer him a better
price for his commodity, he assured them their meeting was
extremely lucky for himself; for that he had the most pressing
occasion for money at that time, his own being almost spent, and
having a friend then in the same inn, who was just recovered
from some wounds he had received from robbers, and was in a
most indigent condition. "So that nothing," says he, "could
be so opportune for the supplying both our necessities as my
making an immediate bargain with you."

As soon as he had seated himself, the stranger began in these
words: "Sir, I do not care absolutely to deny engaging in what
my friend Mr. Barnabas recommends; but sermons are mere
drugs. The trade is so vastly stocked with them, that really,
unless they come out with the name of Whitefield or Wesley, or
some other such great man, as a bishop, or those sort of people, I
don't care to touch; unless now it was a sermon preached on the
30th of January; or we could say in the title-page, published at
the earnest request of the congregation, or the inhabitants; but,
truly, for a dry piece of sermons, I had rather be excused;
especially as my hands are so full at present. However, sir, as
Mr. Barnabas mentioned them to me, I will, if you please, take

the manuscript with me to town, and send you my opinion of it in a very short time."

"Oh!" said Adams, "if you desire it, I will read two or three discourses as a specimen." This Barnabas, who loved sermons no better than a grocer doth figs, immediately objected to, and advised Adams to let the bookseller have his sermons: telling him, "If he gave him a direction, he might be certain of a speedy answer"; adding, he need not scruple trusting them in his possession. "No," said the bookseller, "if it was a play that had been acted twenty nights together, I believe it would be safe."

Adams did not at all relish the last expression; he said "he was sorry to hear sermons compared to plays."—"Not by me, I assure you," cried the bookseller, "though I don't know whether the licensing act may not shortly bring them to the same footing; but I have formerly known a hundred guineas given for a play."—"More shame for those who gave it," cried Barnabas.—"Why so?" said the bookseller, "for they got hundreds by it."—"But is there no difference between conveying good or ill instructions to mankind?" said Adams: "Would not an honest mind rather lose money by the one than gain it by the other?"—"If you can find any such, I will not be their hindrance," answered the bookseller; "but I think those persons who get by preaching sermons are the properest to lose by printing them: for my part, the copy that sells best will be always the best copy in my opinion; I am no enemy to sermons, but because they don't sell: for I would as soon print one of Whitefield's as any farce whatever."

"Whoever prints such heterodox stuff ought to be hanged," says Barnabas. "Sir," said he, turning to Adams, "this fellow's writings (I know not whether you have seen them) are levelled at the clergy. He would reduce us to the example of the primitive ages, forsooth! and would insinuate to the people that a clergyman ought to be always preaching and praying. He pretends to understand the Scripture literally; and would make mankind believe that the poverty and low estate which was recommended to the Church in its infancy, and was only temporary doctrine adapted to her under persecution, was to be preserved in her flourishing and established state. Sir, the principles of Toland, Woolston, and all the freethinkers, are not calculated to do half the mischief, as those professed by this fellow and his followers."

"Sir," answered Adams, "if Mr. Whitefield had carried his doctrine no farther than you mention, I should have remained, as I once was, his well-wisher. I am, myself, as great an enemy to the luxury and splendour of the clergy as he can be. I do not, more than he, by the flourishing estate of the Church, understand the palaces, equipages, dress, furniture, rich dainties, and vast fortunes of her ministers. Surely those things, which savour so strongly of this world, become not the servants of one who professed His kingdom was not of it. But when he began to call nonsense and enthusiasm to his aid, and set up the detestable doctrine of faith against good works, I was his friend no longer; for surely that doctrine was coined in hell; and one would think none but the devil himself could have the confidence to preach it. For can anything be more derogatory to the honour of God than for men to imagine that the all-wise Being will here-after say to the good and virtuous, 'Notwithstanding the purity of thy life, notwithstanding that constant rule of virtue and good-ness in which you walked upon earth, still, as thou didst not believe everything in the true orthodox manner, thy want of faith shall condemn thee'? Or, on the other side, can any doctrine have a more pernicious influence on society, than a persuasion that it will be a good plea for the villain at the last day —'Lord, it is true I never obeyed one of thy commandments, yet punish me not, for I believe them all'?"—"I suppose, sir," said the bookseller, "your sermons are of a different kind."—"Aye, sir," said Adams; "the contrary, I thank Heaven, is inculcated in almost every page, or I should belie my own opinion, which hath always been, that a virtuous and good Turk, or heathen, are more acceptable in the sight of their Creator than a vicious and wicked Christian, though his faith was as perfectly orthodox as St. Paul's himself."—"I wish you success," says the bookseller, "but must beg to be excused, as my hands are so very full at present; and indeed, I am afraid you will find a backwardness in the trade to engage in a book which the clergy would be certain to cry down." —"God forbid," says Adams, "any books should be propagated which the clergy would cry down; but if you mean by the clergy, some few designing factious men, who have it at heart to establish some favourite schemes at the price of the liberty of mankind, and the very essence of religion, it is not in the power of such persons to decry any book they please; witness that excellent book called, 'A Plain Account of the Nature and End of the Sacra-ment'; a book written (if I may venture on the expression) with the pen of an angel, and calculated to restore the true use of Christianity, and of that sacred institution; for what could tend more to the noble purposes of religion than frequent cheerful meetings among the members of a society, in which they should, in the presence of one another, and in the service of the Supreme Being, make promises of being good, friendly, and benevolent to each other? Now, this excellent book was attacked by a party, but unsuccessfully." At these words Barnabas fell a-ringing with all the violence imaginable; upon which a servant attending, he bid him "bring a bill immediately; for that he was in company, for aught he knew, with the devil himself; and he expected to hear the Alcoran, the Leviathan, or Woolston commended, if he staid a few minutes longer." Adams desired, "as he was so much moved at his mentioning a book which he did without apprehending any possibility of offence, that he would be so kind to propose any objections he had to it, which he would endeavour to answer."—"I propose objections!" said Barnabas, "I never read a syllable in any such wicked book; I never saw it in my life, I assure you."—Adams was going to answer, when a most hideous uproar began in the inn, Mrs. Tow-wouse, Mr. Tow-wouse, and Betty, all lifting up their voices together; but Mrs. Tow-wouse's voice, like a bass viol in a concert, was clearly and distinctly distinguished among the rest, and was heard to articulate the following sounds:—"O you damn'd villain! is this the return to all the care I have taken of your family? This the reward of my virtue? Is this the manner in which you behave to one who brought you a fortune, and preferred you to so many matches, all your betters? To abuse my bed, my own bed, with my own servant! but I'll maul the slut, I'll tear her nasty eyes out! Was ever such a pitiful dog, to take up with such a mean trollop? If she had been a gentlewoman, like myself, it had been some excuse; but a beggarly, saucy, dirty servant-maid. Get you out of my house, you whore." To which she added another name, which we do not care to stain our paper with. It was a monosyllable beginning with a b—, and indeed was the same as if she had pronounced the words, she-dog. Which term we shall, to avoid offence, use on this occasion, though indeed both the mistress and the maid uttered the above-mentioned b—, a word extremely disgustful to females of the lower sort. Betty had borne all hitherto with patience, and had uttered only lamentations; but the last appellation stung her to the quick. "I am a woman as well as yourself," she roared out, "and no she-dog; and if I have been a little naughty, I am not the first; if I have been no better than I should be," cries she, sobbing, "that's no reason why you should call me out of my name; my be-betters are wo-rse than me."— "Huzzy, huzzy," says Mrs. Tow-wouse, "have you the impudence to answer me? Did I not catch you, you saucy"—and then again repeated the terrible word so odious to female ears. "I can't bear that name," answered Betty: "if I have been wicked, I am to answer for it myself in the other world; but I have done nothing that's unnatural; and I will go out of your house this moment, for I will never be called she-dog by any mistress in England." Mrs. Tow-wouse then armed herself with the spit, but was prevented from executing any dreadful purpose by Mr. Adams, who confined her arms with the strength of a wrist which Hercules would not have been ashamed of. Mr. Tow-wouse, being caught, as our lawyers express it, with the manner, and having no defence to make, very prudently withdrew himself; and Betty committed herself to the protection of the hostler, who, though she could not conceive him pleased with what had happened, was, in her opinion, rather a gentler beast than her mistress.

Mrs. Tow-wouse, at the intercession of Mr. Adams, and finding the enemy vanished, began to compose herself, and at length recovered the usual serenity of her temper, in which we will leave her, to open to the reader the steps which led to a catastrophe, common enough, and comical enough too perhaps, in modern history, yet often fatal to the repose and well-being of families, and the subject of many tragedies, both in life and on the stage.

CHAPTER XVIII

THE HISTORY OF BETTY THE CHAMBERMAID, AND AN ACCOUNT OF WHAT OCCASIONED THE VIOLENT SCENE IN THE PRECEDING CHAPTER

BETTY, who was the occasion of all this hurry, had some good qualities. She had good-nature, generosity, and compassion, but unfortunately, her constitution was composed of those warm ingredients which, though the purity of courts or nunneries might have happily controuled them, were by no means able to endure the ticklish situation of a chambermaid at an inn; who is daily liable to the solicitations of lovers of all complexions; to the dangerous addresses of fine gentlemen of the army, who sometimes are obliged to reside with them a whole year together; and, above all, are exposed to the caresses of footmen, stage-coachmen, and drawers; all of whom employ the whole artillery of kissing, flattering, bribing, and every other weapon which is to be found in the whole armoury of love, against them.

Betty, who was but one-and-twenty, had now lived three years in this dangerous situation, during which she had escaped pretty well. An ensign of foot was the first person who made an impression on her heart; he did indeed raise a flame in her which required the care of a surgeon to cool.

While she burnt for him, several others burnt for her. Officers of the army, young gentlemen travelling the western circuit, inoffensive squires, and some of graver character, were set a-fire by her charms!

At length, having perfectly recovered the effects of her first unhappy passion, she seemed to have vowed a state of perpetual chastity. She was long deaf to all the sufferings of her lovers, till one day at a neighbouring fair, the rhetoric of John the hostler, with a new straw hat and a pint of wine, made a second conquest over her.

She did not, however, feel any of those flames on this occasion which had been the consequence of her former amour; nor, indeed, those other ill effects which prudent young women very justly apprehend from too absolute an indulgence to the pressing endearments of their lovers. This latter, perhaps, was a little owing to her not being entirely constant to John, with whom she permitted Tom Whipwell the stage-coachman, and now and then a handsome young traveller, to share her favours.

Mr. Tow-wouse had for some time cast the languishing eyes of affection on this young maiden. He had laid hold on every opportunity of saying tender things to her, squeezing her by the hand, and sometimes kissing her lips; for, as the violence of his passion had considerably abated to Mrs. Tow-wouse, so, like water, which is stopt from its usual current in one place, it naturally sought a vent in another. Mrs. Tow-wouse is thought to have perceived this abatement, and, probably, it added very little to the natural sweetness of her temper; for though she was as true to her husband as the dial to the sun, she was rather more desirous of being shone on, as being more capable of feeling his warmth.

Ever since Joseph's arrival, Betty had conceived an extraordinary liking to him, which discovered itself more and more as he grew better and better; till that fatal evening, when, as she was warming his bed, her passion grew to such a height, and so perfectly mastered both her modesty and her reason, that, after many fruitless hints and sly insinuations, she at last threw down the warming-pan, and, embracing him with great eagerness, swore he was the handsomest creature she had ever seen.

Joseph, in great confusion, leapt from her, and told her he was sorry to see a young woman cast off all regard to modesty; but she had gone too far to recede, and grew so very indecent, that Joseph was obliged, contrary to his inclination, to use some violence to her; and, taking her in his arms, he shut her out of the room, and locked the door.

How ought man to rejoice that his chastity is always in his own power; that, if he hath sufficient strength of mind, he hath always a competent strength of body to defend himself, and cannot, like a poor weak woman, be ravished against his will!

Betty was in the most violent agitation at this disappointment. Rage and lust pulled her heart, as with two strings, two different ways; one moment she thought of stabbing Joseph; the next, of taking him in her arms, and devouring him with kisses; but the latter passion was far more prevalent. Then she thought of revenging his refusal on herself; but, whilst she was engaged in this meditation, happily death presented himself to her in so many shapes, of drowning, hanging, poisoning, &c., that her distracted mind could resolve on none. In this perturbation of spirit, it accidentally occurred to her memory that her master's bed was not made; she therefore went directly to his room, where he happened at that time to be engaged at his bureau. As soon as she saw him, she attempted to retire; but he called her back, and, taking her by the hand, squeezed her so tenderly, at the same time whispering so many soft things into her ears, and then pressed her so closely with his kisses, that the vanquished fair one, whose passions were already raised, and which were not so whimsically capricious that one man only could lay them, though, perhaps, she would have rather preferred that one— the vanquished fair one quietly submitted, I say, to her master's will, who had just attained the accomplishment of his bliss when Mrs. Tow-wouse unexpectedly entered the room, and caused all that confusion which we have before seen, and which it is not necessary, at present, to take any farther notice of; since, without the assistance of a single hint from us, every reader of any speculation or experience, though not married himself, may easily conjecture that it concluded with the discharge of Betty, the submission of Mr. Tow-wouse, with some things to be performed on his side by way of gratitude for his wife's goodness in being reconciled to him, with many hearty promises never to offend any more in the like manner; and, lastly, his quietly and contentedly bearing to be reminded of his transgressions, as a kind of penance, once or twice a day during the residue of his life.

BOOK II

CHAPTER I

OF DIVISIONS IN AUTHORS

THERE are certain mysteries or secrets in all trades, from the highest to the lowest, from that of prime-ministering to this of authoring, which are seldom discovered unless to members of the same calling. Among those used by us gentlemen of the latter occupation, I take this of dividing our works into books and chapters to be none of the least considerable. Now, for want of being truly acquainted with this secret, common readers imagine, that by this art of dividing we mean only to swell our works to a much larger bulk than they would otherwise be extended to. These several places therefore in our paper, which are filled with our books and chapters, are understood as so much buckram, stays, and stay-tape in a taylor's bill, serving only to make up the sum total, commonly found at the bottom of our first page and of his last.

But in reality the case is otherwise, and in this as well as all other instances we consult the advantage of our reader, not our own; and indeed, many notable uses arise to him from this method; for, first, those little spaces between our chapters may be looked upon as an inn or resting-place where he may stop and take a glass or any other refreshment as it pleases him. Nay, our fine readers will, perhaps, be scarce able to travel farther than through one of them in a day. As to those vacant pages which are placed between our books, they are to be regarded as those stages where in long journeys the traveller stays some time to repose himself, and consider of what he hath seen in the parts he hath already passed through; a consideration which I take the liberty to recommend a little to the reader; for, however swift his capacity may be, I would not advise him to travel through these pages too fast; for if he doth, he may probably miss the seeing some curious productions of nature, which will be observed by the slower and more accurate reader. A volume without any such places of rest resembles the opening of wilds or seas, which tires the eye and fatigues the spirit when entered upon.

Secondly, what are the contents prefixed to every chapter but so many inscriptions over the gates of inns (to continue the same metaphor), informing the reader what entertainment he is to expect, which if he likes not, he may travel on to the next; for, in biography, as we are not tied down to an exact concatenation equally with other historians, so a chapter or two (for instance, this I am now writing) may be often passed over without any injury to the whole. And in these inscriptions I have been as faithful as possible, not imitating the celebrated Montaigne, who promises you one thing and gives you another; nor some title-page authors, who promise a great deal and produce nothing at all.

There are, besides these more obvious benefits, several others which our readers enjoy from this art of dividing; though perhaps most of them too mysterious to be presently understood by any who are not initiated into the science of authoring. To mention, therefore, but one which is most obvious, it prevents spoiling the beauty of a book by turning down its leaves, a method otherwise necessary to those readers who (though they read with great improvement and advantage) are apt, when they return to their study after half-an-hour's absence, to forget where they left off.

These divisions have the sanction of great antiquity. Homer not only divided his great work into twenty-four books (in compliment perhaps to the twenty-four letters to which he had very particular obligations), but, according to the opinion of some very sagacious critics, hawked them all separately, delivering only one book at a time (probably by subscription). He was the first inventor of the art which hath so long lain dormant, of publishing by numbers; an art now brought to such perfection, that even dictionaries are divided and exhibited piecemeal to the public; nay, one bookseller hath (to encourage learning and ease the public) contrived to give them a dictionary in this divided manner for only fifteen shillings more than it would have cost entire.

Virgil hath given us his poem in twelve books, an argument of his modesty; for by that, doubtless, he would insinuate that he pretends to no more than half the merit of the Greek; for the same reason, our Milton went originally no farther than ten; till, being puffed up by the praise of his friends, he put himself on the same footing with the Roman poet.

I shall not, however, enter so deep into this matter as some very learned critics have done; who have with infinite labour and acute discernment discovered what books are proper for embellishment, and what require simplicity only, particularly with regard to similes, which I think are now generally agreed to become any book but the first.

I will dismiss this chapter with the following observation: that it becomes an author generally to divide a book, as it does a butcher to joint his meat, for such assistance is of great help to both the reader and the carver. And now, having indulged myself a little, I will endeavour to indulge the curiosity of my reader, who is no doubt impatient to know what he will find in the subsequent chapters of this book.

CHAPTER II

A SURPRISING INSTANCE OF MR. ADAMS'S SHORT MEMORY, WITH THE UNFORTUNATE CONSEQUENCES WHICH IT BROUGHT ON JOSEPH

MR. ADAMS and Joseph were now ready to depart different ways, when an accident determined the former to return with his friend, which Tow-wouse, Barnabas, and the bookseller had not been able to do. This accident was, that those sermons, which the parson was travelling to London to publish, were, O my good reader! left behind; what he had mistaken for them in the saddlebags being no other than three shirts, a pair of shoes, and some other necessaries, which Mrs. Adams, who thought her husband would want shirts more than sermons on his journey, had carefully provided him.

This discovery was now luckily owing to the presence of Joseph at the opening the saddlebags; who, having heard his friend say he carried with him nine volumes of sermons, and not being of that sect of philosophers who can reduce all the matter of the world into a nutshell, seeing there was no room for them in the bags, where the parson had said they were deposited, had the curiosity to cry out, "Bless me, sir, where are your sermons?" The parson answered, "There, there, child; there they are, under my shirts." Now it happened that he had taken forth his last shirt, and the vehicle remained visibly empty. "Sure, sir," says Joseph, "there is nothing in the bags." Upon which Adams, starting, and testifying some surprise, cried, "Hey! fie, fie upon it! they are not here sure enough. Ay, they are certainly left behind."

Joseph was greatly concerned at the uneasiness which he apprehended his friend must feel from this disappointment; he begged him to pursue his journey, and promised he would himself return with the books to him with the utmost expedition.

"No, thank you, child," answered Adams; "it shall not be so. What would it avail me, to tarry in the great city, unless I had my discourses with me, which are *ut ita dicam*, the sole cause, the *aitia monotate* of my peregrination? No, child, as this accident hath happened, I am resolved to return back to my cure, together with you; which indeed my inclination sufficiently leads me to. This disappointment may perhaps be intended for my good." He concluded with a verse out of Theocritus, which signifies no more than that sometimes it rains, and sometimes the sun shines.

Joseph bowed with obedience and thankfulness for the inclination which the parson expressed of returning with him; and now the bill was called for, which, on examination, amounted within a shilling to the sum Mr. Adams had in his pocket. Perhaps the reader may wonder how he was able to produce a sufficient sum for so many days: that he may not be surprised, therefore, it cannot be unnecessary to acquaint him that he had borrowed a guinea of a servant belonging to the coach and six, who had been formerly one of his parishioners, and whose master, the owner of the coach, then lived within three miles of him; for so good was the credit of Mr. Adams, that even Mr. Peter, the Lady Booby's steward, would have lent him a guinea with very little security.

Mr. Adams discharged the bill, and they were both setting out, having agreed to ride and tie; a method of travelling much used by persons who have but one horse between them, and is thus performed. The two travellers set out together, one on horseback, the other on foot: now, as it generally happens that he on horseback outgoes him on foot, the custom is, that, when he arrives at the distance agreed on, he is to dismount, tie the horse to some gate, tree, post, or other thing, and then proceed on foot; when the other comes up to the horse he unties him, mounts, and gallops on, till, having passed by his fellow-traveller, he likewise arrives at the place of tying. And this is that method of travelling so much in use among our prudent ancestors, who knew that horses had mouths as well as legs, and that they could not use the latter without being at the expense of suffering the beasts themselves to use the former. This was the method in use in those days when, instead of a coach and six, a member of parliament's lady used to mount a pillion behind her husband; and a grave serjeant at law condescended to amble into Westminster on an easy pad, with his clerk kicking his heels behind him.

Adams was now gone some minutes, having insisted on Joseph's beginning the journey on horseback, and Joseph had his foot in the stirrup, when the hostler presented him a bill for the horse's board during his residence at the inn. Joseph said Mr. Adams had paid all; but this matter, being referred to Mr. Tow-wouse, was by him decided in favour of the hostler, and indeed with truth and justice; for this was a fresh instance of the shortness of memory which did not arise from want of parts, but that continual hurry in which parson Adams was always involved.

Joseph was now reduced to a dilemma which extremely puzzled him. The sum due for horse-meat was twelve shillings (for Adams, who had borrowed the beast of his clerk, had ordered him to be fed as well as they could feed him), and the cash in his pocket amounted to sixpence (for Adams had divided the last shilling with him). Now, though there have been some ingenious persons who have contrived to pay twelve shillings with sixpence, Joseph was not one of them. He had never contracted a debt in his life, and was consequently the less ready at an expedient to extricate himself. Tow-wouse was willing to give him credit till next time, to which Mrs. Tow-wouse would have probably consented (for such was Joseph's beauty, that it had made some impression even on that piece of flint which that good woman wore in her bosom by way of heart). Joseph would have found, therefore, very likely the passage free, had he not, when he honestly discovered the nakedness of his pockets, pulled out that little piece of gold which we have mentioned before. This caused Mrs. Tow-wouse's eyes to water; she told Joseph she did not conceive a man could want money whilst he had gold in his pocket. Joseph answered that he had such a value for that little piece of gold, that he would not part with it for a hundred times the riches which the greatest esquire in the county was worth. "A pretty way, indeed," said Mrs. Tow-wouse, "to run in debt, and then refuse to part with your money because you have a value for it! I never knew any piece of gold of more value than as many shillings as it would change for."—"Not to preserve my life from starving, nor to redeem it from a robber, would I part with this dear piece!" answered Joseph. "What," says Mrs. Tow-wouse, "I suppose it was given you by some vile trollop, some miss or other; if it had been the present of a virtuous woman, you would not have had such a value for it. My husband is a fool if he parts with the horse without being paid for him."— "No, no, I can't part with the horse, indeed, till I have the money," cried Tow-wouse. A resolution highly commended by a lawyer then in the yard, who declared Mr. Tow-wouse might justify the detainer.

As we cannot therefore at present get Mr. Joseph out of the inn, we shall leave him in it, and carry our reader on after parson Adams, who, his mind being perfectly at ease, fell into a contemplation on a passage in Æschylus, which entertained him for three miles together, without suffering him once to reflect on his fellow-traveller.

At length, having spun out his thread, and being now at the summit of a hill, he cast his eyes backwards, and wondered that he could not see any sign of Joseph. As he left him ready to mount the horse, he could not apprehend any mischief had happened, neither could he suspect that he missed his way, it being so broad and plain; the only reason which presented itself to him was, that he had met with an acquaintance who had prevailed with him to delay some time in discourse.

He therefore resolved to proceed slowly forwards, not doubting but that he should be shortly overtaken; and soon came to a large water, which, filling the whole road, he saw no method of passing unless by wading through, which he accordingly did up to his middle; but was no sooner got to the other side than he perceived, if he had looked over the hedge, he would have found a footpath capable of conducting him without wetting his shoes.

His surprise at Joseph's not coming up grew now very troublesome: he began to fear he knew not what; and as he determined to move no farther, and, if he did not shortly overtake him, to return back, he wished to find a house of public entertainment where he might dry his clothes and refresh himself with a pint; but, seeing no such (for no other reason than because he did not cast his eyes a hundred yards forwards), he sat himself down on a stile, and pulled out his Æschylus.

A fellow passing presently by, Adams asked him if he could direct him to an alehouse. The fellow, who had just left it, and perceived the house and sign to be within sight, thinking he had jeered him, and being of a morose temper, bade him follow his nose and be d—n'd. Adams told him he was a saucy jackanapes; upon which the fellow turned about angrily; but, perceiving Adams clench his fist, he thought proper to go on without taking any farther notice.

A horseman, following immediately after, and being asked the same question, answered, "Friend, there is one within a stone's throw; I believe you may see it before you." Adams, lifting up his eyes, cried, "I protest, and so there is"; and, thanking his informer, proceeded directly to it.

CHAPTER III

THE OPINION OF TWO LAWYERS CONCERNING THE SAME GENTLE-
MAN, WITH MR. ADAMS'S INQUIRY INTO THE RELIGION OF
HIS HOST

HE had just entered the house, and called for his pint, and seated
himself, when two horsemen came to the door, and, fastening
their horses to the rails, alighted. They said there was a violent
shower of rain coming on, which they intended to weather there,
and went into a little room by themselves, not perceiving Mr.
Adams.

One of these immediately asked the other, "If he had seen a
more comical adventure a great while?" Upon which the other
said, "He doubted whether, by law, the landlord could justify
detaining the horse for his corn and hay." But the former
answered, "Undoubtedly he can; it is an adjudged case, and I
have known it tried."

Adams, who, though he was, as the reader may suspect, a little
inclined to forgetfulness, never wanted more than a hint to
remind him, overhearing their discourse, immediately suggested
to himself that this was his own horse, and that he had forgot to
pay for him, which, upon inquiry, he was certified of by the
gentlemen; who added, that the horse was likely to have more
rest than food, unless he was paid for.

The poor parson resolved to return presently to the inn, though
he knew no more than Joseph how to procure his horse his
liberty; he was, however, prevailed on to stay under covert,
till the shower, which was now very violent, was over.

The three travellers then sat down together over a mug of good
beer; when Adams, who had observed a gentleman's house as he
passed along the road, inquired to whom it belonged; one of the
horsemen had no sooner mentioned the owner's name, than the
other began to revile him in the most opprobrious terms. The
English language scarce affords a single reproachful word, which
he did not vent on this occasion. He charged him likewise with
many particular facts. He said, "He no more regarded a field
of wheat when he was hunting, than he did the highway; that he
had injured several poor farmers by trampling their corn under
his horse's heels; and if any of them begged him with the utmost
submission to refrain, his horsewhip was always ready to do them
justice." He said, "That he was the greatest tyrant to the
neighbours in every other instance, and would not suffer a farmer

to keep a gun, though he might justify it by law; and in his own family so cruel a master, that he never kept a servant a twelve-month. In his capacity as a justice," continued he, "he behaves so partially, that he commits or acquits just as he is in the humour, without any regard to truth or evidence; the devil may carry any one before him for me; I would rather be tried before some judges, than be a prosecutor before him: if I had an estate in the neighbourhood, I would sell it for half the value rather than live near him."

Adams shook his head, and said, "He was sorry such men were suffered to proceed with impunity, and that riches could set any man above the law." The reviler, a little after, retiring into the yard, the gentleman who had first mentioned his name to Adams began to assure him "that his companion was a prejudiced person. It is true," says he, "perhaps, that he may have sometimes pursued his game over a field of corn, but he hath always made the party ample satisfaction: that so far from tyrannising over his neighbours, or taking away their guns, he himself knew several farmers not qualified, who not only kept guns, but killed game with them; that he was the best of masters to his servants, and several of them had grown old in his service; that he was the best justice of peace in the kingdom, and, to his certain knowledge, had decided many difficult points, which were referred to him, with the greatest equity and the highest wisdom; and he verily believed, several persons would give a year's purchase for an estate near him, than under the wings of any other great man." He had just finished his encomium when his companion returned and acquainted him the storm was over. Upon which they presently mounted their horses and departed.

Adams, who was in the utmost anxiety at those different characters of the same person, asked his host if he knew the gentleman: for he began to imagine they had by mistake been speaking of two several gentlemen. "No, no, master," answered the host (a shrewd cunning fellow); "I know the gentleman very well of whom they have been speaking, as I do the gentlemen who spoke of him. As for riding over other men's corn, to my knowledge he hath not been on horseback these two years. I never heard he did any injury of that kind; and as to making reparation, he is not so free of his money as that comes to neither. Nor did I ever hear of his taking away any man's gun; nay, I know several who have guns in their houses; but as for killing game with them, no man is stricter; and I believe he would ruin any who did. You heard one of the gentlemen say he was the worst master in the world, and the other that he is the best; but for my own part, I know all his servants, and never heard from any of them that he was either one or the other."—"Aye! aye!" says Adams; "and how doth he behave as a justice, pray?"—"Faith, friend," answered the host, "I question whether he is in the commission; the only cause I have heard he hath decided a great while, was one between those very two persons who just went out of this house; and I am sure he determined that justly, for I heard the whole matter."—"Which did he decide in favour of?" quoth Adams.—"I think I need not answer that question," cried the host, "after the different characters you have heard of him. It is not my business to contradict gentlemen while they are drinking in my house; but I knew neither of them spoke a syllable of truth."—"God forbid!" said Adams, "that men should arrive at such a pitch of wickedness to belye the character of their neighbour from a little private affection, or, what is infinitely worse, a private spite. I rather believe we have mistaken them, and they mean two other persons; for there are many houses on the road."—"Why, prithee, friend," cries the host, "dost thou pretend never to have told a lye in thy life?"—"Never a malicious one, I am certain," answered Adams, "nor with a design to injure the reputation of any man living."—"Pugh! malicious; no, no," replied the host; "not malicious with a design to hang a man, or bring him into trouble; but surely, out of love to oneself, one must speak better of a friend than an enemy."—"Out of love to yourself, you should confine yourself to truth," says Adams, "for by doing otherwise you injure the noblest part of yourself, your immortal soul. I can hardly believe any man such an idiot to risque the loss of that by any trifling gain, and the greatest gain in this world is but dirt in comparison of what shall be revealed hereafter." Upon which the host, taking up the cup, with a smile, drank a health to hereafter; adding, "He was for something present."—"Why," says Adams very gravely, "do not you believe another world?" To which the host answered, "Yes; he was no atheist."—"And you believe you have an immortal soul?" cries Adams. He answered, "God forbid he should not."—"And heaven and hell?" said the parson. The host then bid him "not to profane; for those were things not to be mentioned nor thought of but in church." Adams asked him, "Why he went to church, if what he learned there had no influence on his conduct in life?" "I go to church," answered the host, "to say my prayers and behave godly."—"And dost

not thou," cried Adams, "believe what thou hearest at church?"
—"Most part of it, master," returned the host. "And dost
not thou then tremble," cries Adams, "at the thought of eternal
punishment?"—"As for that, master," said he, "I never once
thought about it; but what signifies talking about matters so
far off? The mug is out, shall I draw another?"

Whilst he was going for that purpose, a stage-coach drove up
to the door. The coachman coming into the house was asked
by the mistress what passengers he had in his coach? "A
parcel of squinny-gut b—s," says he; "I have a good mind to
overturn them; you won't prevail upon them to drink anything,
I assure you." Adams asked him, "If he had not seen a young
man on horseback on the road" (describing Joseph). "Aye,"
said the coachman, "a gentlewoman in my coach that is his
acquaintance redeemed him and his horse; he would have been
here before this time, had not the storm driven him to shelter."
"God bless her!" said Adams, in a rapture; nor could he delay
walking out to satisfy himself who this charitable woman was;
but what was his surprise when he saw his old acquaintance,
Madam Slipslop? Hers indeed was not so great, because she
had been informed by Joseph that he was on the road. Very
civil were the salutations on both sides; and Mrs. Slipslop rebuked
the hostess for denying the gentleman to be there when she asked
for him; but indeed the poor woman had not erred designedly;
for Mrs. Slipslop asked for a clergyman, and she had unhappily mistaken Adams for a person travelling to a neighbouring
fair with the thimble and button, or some other such operation; for he marched in a swinging great but short white coat
with black buttons, a short wig, and a hat which, so far from
having a black hatband, had nothing black about it.

Joseph was now come up, and Mrs. Slipslop would have had
him quit his horse to the parson, and come himself into the coach;
but he absolutely refused, saying, he thanked Heaven he was
well enough recovered to be very able to ride; and added, he
hoped he knew his duty better than to ride in a coach while
Mr. Adams was on horseback.

Mrs. Slipslop would have persisted longer, had not a lady in
the coach put a short end to the dispute, by refusing to suffer a
fellow in a livery to ride in the same coach with herself; so it was
at length agreed that Adams should fill the vacant place in the
coach, and Joseph should proceed on horseback.

They had not proceeded far before Mrs. Slipslop, addressing
herself to the parson, spoke thus:—"There hath been a strange

alteration in our family, Mr. Adams, since Sir Thomas's death."
"A strange alteration indeed," says Adams, "as I gather from
some hints which have dropped from Joseph."—"Aye," says
she, "I could never have believed it; but the longer one lives
in the world, the more one sees. So Joseph hath given you
hints." "But of what nature will always remain a perfect
secret with me," cries the parson: "he forced me to promise
before he would communicate anything. I am indeed concerned
to find her ladyship behave in so unbecoming a manner. I
always thought her in the main a good lady, and should never
have suspected her of thoughts so unworthy a Christian, and
with a young lad her own servant." "These things are no
secrets to me, I assure you," cries Slipslop, "and I believe they
will be none anywhere shortly; for ever since the boy's departure,
she hath behaved more like a mad woman than anything else."
"Truly, I am heartily concerned," says Adams, "for she was a
good sort of a lady. Indeed, I have often wished she had attended a little more constantly at the service, but she hath done
a great deal of good in the parish." "O Mr. Adams," says
Slipslop, "people that don't see all, often know nothing. Many
things have been given away in our family, I do assure you,
without her knowledge. I have heard you say in the pulpit we
ought not to brag; but indeed I can't avoid saying, if she had
kept the keys herself, the poor would have wanted many a cordial which I have let them have. As for my late master, he
was as worthy a man as ever lived, and would have done infinite
good if he had not been controlled; but he loved a quiet life,
Heaven rest his soul! I am confident he is there, and enjoys a
quiet life, which some folks would not allow him here."—
Adams answered, "He had never heard this before, and was
mistaken if she herself (for he remembered she used to commend
her mistress and blame her master) had not formerly been of
another opinion." "I don't know," replied she, "what I might
once think; but now I am confidous matters are as I tell you;
the world will shortly see who hath been deceived; for my part,
I say nothing, but that it is wondersome how some people can
carry all things with a grave face."

Thus Mr. Adams and she discoursed, till they came opposite
to a great house which stood at some distance from the road:
a lady in the coach spying it, cried, "Yonder lives the unfortunate Leonora, if one can justly call a woman unfortunate
whom we must own at the same time guilty and the author of
her own calamity." This was abundantly sufficient to awaken

the curiosity of Mr. Adams, as indeed it did that of the whole company, who jointly solicited the lady to acquaint them with Leonora's history, since it seemed, by what she had said, to contain something remarkable.

The lady, who was perfectly well-bred, did not require many entreaties, and having only wished their entertainment might make amends for the company's attention, she began in the following manner.

CHAPTER IV

THE HISTORY OF LEONORA, OR THE UNFORTUNATE JILT

LEONORA was the daughter of a gentleman of fortune; she was tall and well-shaped, with a sprightliness in her countenance which often attracts beyond more regular features joined with an insipid air: nor is this kind of beauty less apt to deceive than allure; the good humour which it indicates being often mistaken for good nature, and the vivacity for true understanding.

Leonora, who was now at the age of eighteen, lived with an aunt of hers in a town in the north of England. She was an extreme lover of gaiety, and very rarely missed a ball or any other public assembly; where she had frequent opportunities of satisfying a greedy appetite of vanity, with the preference which was given her by the men to almost every other woman present.

Among many young fellows who were particular in their gallantries towards her, Horatio soon distinguished himself in her eyes beyond all his competitors; she danced with more than ordinary gaiety when he happened to be her partner; neither the fairness of the evening, nor the musick of the nightingale, could lengthen her walk like his company. She affected no longer to understand the civilities of others; whilst she inclined so attentive an ear to every compliment of Horatio, that she often smiled even when it was too delicate for her comprehension.

"Pray, madam," says Adams, "who was this squire Horatio?"

Horatio, says the lady, was a young gentleman of good family, bred to the law, and had been some few years called to the degree of a barrister. His face and person were such as the generality allowed handsome; but he had a dignity in his air very rarely to be seen. His temper was of the saturnine complexion, and without the least taint of moroseness. He had wit and humour, with an inclination to satire, which he indulged rather too much.

This gentleman, who had contracted the most violent passion for Leonora, was the last person who perceived the probability of its success. The whole town had made the match for him before he himself had drawn a confidence from her actions sufficient to mention his passion to her; for it was his opinion (and perhaps he was there in the right) that it is highly impolitick to talk seriously of love to a woman before you have made such a progress in her affections, that she herself expects and desires to hear it.

But whatever diffidence the fears of a lover may create, which are apt to magnify every favour conferred on a rival, and to see the little advances towards themselves through the other end of the perspective, it was impossible that Horatio's passion should so blind his discernment as to prevent his conceiving hopes from the behaviour of Leonora, whose fondness for him was now as visible to an indifferent person in their company as his for her.

"I never knew any of these forward sluts come to good" (says the lady who refused Joseph's entrance into the coach), "nor shall I wonder at anything she doth in the sequel."

The lady proceeded in her story thus: It was in the midst of a gay conversation in the walks one evening, when Horatio whispered to Leonora, that he was desirous to take a turn or two with her in private, for that he had something to communicate to her of great consequence. "Are you sure it is of consequence?" said she, smiling. "I hope," answered he, "you will think so too, since the whole future happiness of my life must depend on the event."

Leonora, who very much suspected what was coming, would have deferred it till another time; but Horatio, who had more than half conquered the difficulty of speaking by the first motion, was so very importunate, that she at last yielded, and, leaving the rest of the company, they turned aside into an unfrequented walk.

They had retired far out of the sight of the company, both maintaining a strict silence. At last Horatio made a full stop, and taking Leonora, who stood pale and trembling, gently by the hand, he fetched a deep sigh, and then, looking on her eyes with all the tenderness imaginable, he cried out in a faltering accent, "O Leonora! is it necessary for me to declare to you on what the future happiness of my life must be founded? Must I say there is something belonging to you which is a bar to my happiness, and which unless you will part with, I must be miserable!"—"What can that be?" replied Leonora. "No wonder," said he, "you are surprised that I should make an objection to anything which is yours: yet sure you may guess, since it is the only one which the riches of the world, if they were mine, should purchase for me. Oh, it is that which you must part with to bestow all the rest! Can Leonora, or rather will she, doubt longer? Let me then whisper it in her ears—It is your name, madam. It is by parting with that, by your condescension to be for ever mine, which must at once prevent me from being the most miserable, and will render me the happiest of mankind."

Leonora, covered with blushes, and with as angry a look as she could possibly put on, told him, "That had she suspected what his declaration would have been, he should not have decoyed her from her company, that he had so surprised and frighted her, that she begged him to convey her back as quick as possible"; which he, trembling very near as much as herself, did.

"More fool he," cried Slipslop; "it is a sign he knew very little of our sect."—"Truly, madam," said Adams, "I think you are in the right: I should have insisted to know a piece of her mind, when I had carried matters so far." But Mrs. Grave-airs desired the lady to omit all such fulsome stuff in her story, for that it made her sick.

Well, then, madam, to be as concise as possible, said the lady, many weeks had not passed after this interview before Horatio and Leonora were what they call on a good footing together. All ceremonies except the last were now over; the writings were now drawn, and everything was in the utmost forwardness preparative to the putting Horatio in possession of all his wishes. I will, if you please, repeat you a letter from each of them, which I have got by heart, and which will give you no small idea of their passion on both sides.

Mrs. Grave-airs objected to hearing these letters; but being put to the vote, it was carried against her by all the rest in the coach; parson Adams contending for it with the utmost vehemence.

HORATIO TO LEONORA

"How vain, most adorable creature, is the pursuit of pleasure, in the absence of an object to which the mind is entirely devoted, unless it have some relation to that object! I was last night condemned to the society of men of wit and learning, which, however agreeable it might have formerly been to me, now only gave me a suspicion that they imputed my absence in conversation to the true cause. For which reason, when your engagements forbid me the ecstatic happiness of seeing you, I am always desirous to be alone; since my sentiments for Leonora are so delicate, that I cannot bear the apprehension of another's prying into those delightful endearments with which the warm imagination of a lover will sometimes indulge him, and which I suspect my eyes then betray. To fear this discovery of our thoughts may perhaps appear too ridiculous a nicety to minds not susceptible of all the tendernesses of this delicate passion. And surely we shall suspect there are few such, when we consider that it requires every human virtue to exert itself in its full extent; since the beloved, whose happiness it ultimately respects, may give us charming opportunities of being brave in her defence, generous to her wants, compassionate to her afflictions, grateful to her kindness; and in the same manner, of exercising every other virtue, which he who would not do to any degree, and that with the utmost rapture, can never deserve the name of a lover. It is, therefore, with a view to the delicate modesty of your mind that I cultivate it so purely in my own; and it is that which will sufficiently suggest to you the uneasiness I bear from those liberties, which men to whom the world allow politeness will sometimes give themselves on these occasions.

"Can I tell you with what eagerness I expect the arrival of that blest day, when I shall experience the falsehood of a common assertion, that the greatest human happiness consists in hope? A doctrine which no person had ever stronger reason to believe than myself at present, since none ever tasted such bliss as fires my bosom with the thoughts of spending my future days with such a companion, and that every action of my life will have the glorious satisfaction of conducing to your happiness."

LEONORA TO HORATIO [1]

"The refinement of your mind has been so evidently proved by every word and action ever since I had the first pleasure of knowing you, that I thought it impossible my good opinion of Horatio could have been heightened to any additional proof of merit. This very thought was my amusement when I received your last letter, which, when I opened, I confess I was surprised to find the delicate sentiments expressed there so far exceeding what I thought could come even from you (although I know all the

[1] This letter was written by a young lady on reading the former.

generous principles human nature is capable of are centred in your breast), that words cannot paint what I feel of the reflection that my happiness shall be the ultimate end of all your actions.

"Oh, Horatio! what a life must that be, where the meanest domestic cares are sweetened by the pleasing consideration that the man on earth who best deserves, and to whom you are most inclined to give your affections, is to reap either profit or pleasure from all you do! In such a case toils must be turned into diversions, and nothing but the unavoidable inconveniences of life can make us remember that we are mortal.

"If the solitary turn of your thoughts, and the desire of keeping them undiscovered, makes even the conversation of men of wit and learning tedious to you, what anxious hours must I spend, who am condemned by custom to the conversation of women, whose natural curiosity leads them to pry into all my thoughts, and whose envy can never suffer Horatio's heart to be possessed by any one, without forcing them into malicious designs against the person who is so happy as to possess it! But, indeed, if ever envy can possibly have any excuse, or even alleviation, it is in this case, where the good is so great, and it must be equally natural to all to wish it for themselves; nor am I ashamed to own it: and to your merit, Horatio, I am obliged, that prevents my being in that most uneasy of all the situations I can figure in my imagination, of being led by inclination to love the person whom my own judgment forces me to condemn."

Matters were in so great forwardness between this fond couple, that the day was fixed for their marriage, and was now within a fortnight, when the sessions chanced to be held for that county in a town about twenty miles' distance from that which is the scene of our story. It seems, it is usual for the young gentlemen of the bar to repair to these sessions, not so much for the sake of profit as to show their parts and learn the law of the justices of peace; for which purpose one of the wisest and gravest of all the justices is appointed speaker, or chairman, as they modestly call it, and he reads them a lecture, and instructs them in the true knowledge of the law.

"You are here guilty of a little mistake," says Adams, "which, if you please, I will correct: I have attended at one of these quarter-sessions, where I observed the counsel taught the justices, instead of learning anything of them."

It is not very material, said the lady. Hither repaired Horatio, who, as he hoped by his profession to advance his fortune, which was not at present very large, for the sake of his dear Leonora, he resolved to spare no pains, nor lose any opportunity of improving or advancing himself in it.

The same afternoon in which he left the town, as Leonora stood at her window, a coach and six passed by, which she declared to be the completest, genteelest, prettiest equipage she ever saw; adding these remarkable words, "Oh, I am in love with that equipage!" which, though her friend Florella at that time did not greatly regard, she hath since remembered.

In the evening an assembly was held, which Leonora honoured with her company; but intended to pay her dear Horatio the compliment of refusing to dance in his absence.

Oh, why have not women as good resolution to maintain their vows as they have often good inclinations in making them?

The gentleman who owned the coach and six came to the assembly. His clothes were as remarkably fine as his equipage could be. He soon attracted the eyes of the company; all the smarts, all the silk waistcoats with silver and gold edgings, were eclipsed in an instant.

"Madam," said Adams, "if it be not impertinent, I should be glad to know how this gentleman was drest."

Sir, answered the lady, I have been told he had on a cut velvet coat of a cinnamon colour, lined with a pink satten, embroidered all over with gold; his waistcoat, which was cloth of silver, was embroidered with gold likewise. I cannot be particular as to the rest of his dress; but it was all in the French fashion, for Bellarmine (that was his name) was just arrived from Paris.

This fine figure did not more entirely engage the eyes of every lady in the assembly than Leonora did his. He had scarce beheld her, but he stood motionless and fixed as a statue, or at least would have done so if good breeding had permitted him. However, he carried it so far before he had power to correct himself, that every person in the room easily discovered where his admiration was settled. The other ladies began to single out their former partners, all perceiving who would be Bellarmine's choice; which they however endeavoured, by all possible means, to prevent: many of them saying to Leonora, "O madam! I suppose we shan't have the pleasure of seeing you dance to-night"; and then crying out, in Bellarmine's hearing, "Oh! Leonora will not dance, I assure you: her partner is not here." One maliciously attempted to prevent her, by sending a disagreeable fellow to ask her, that so she might be obliged either to dance with him, or sit down; but this scheme proved abortive.

Leonora saw herself admired by the fine stranger, and envied by every woman present. Her little heart began to flutter within her, and her head was agitated with a convulsive motion: she seemed as if she would speak to several of her acquaintance, but had nothing to say; for, as she would not mention her present triumph, so she could not disengage her thoughts one moment from the contemplation of it. She had never tasted anything like this happiness. She had before known what it was to torment a single woman; but to be hated and secretly cursed by a whole assembly was a joy reserved for this blessed moment. As this vast profusion of ecstasy had confounded her under-standing, so there was nothing so foolish as her behaviour: she played a thousand childish tricks, distorted her person into several shapes, and her face into several laughs, without any reason. In a word, her carriage was as absurd as her desires, which were to affect an insensibility of the stranger's admiration, and at the same time a triumph, from that admiration, over every woman in the room.

In this temper of mind, Bellarmine, having inquired who she was, advanced to her, and with a low bow begged the honour of dancing with her, which she, with as low a curtsy, imme-diately granted. She danced with him all night, and enjoyed, perhaps, the highest pleasure that she was capable of feeling.

At these words, Adams fetched a deep groan, which frighted the ladies, who told him, "They hoped he was not ill." He answered, "He groaned only for the folly of Leonora."

Leonora retired (continued the lady) about six in the morning, but not to rest. She tumbled and tossed in her bed, with very short intervals of sleep, and those entirely filled with dreams of the equipage and fine clothes she had seen, and the balls, operas, and ridottos, which had been the subject of their conversation.

In the afternoon, Bellarmine, in the dear coach and six, came to wait on her. He was indeed charmed with her person, and was, on inquiry, so well pleased with the circumstances of her father (for he himself, notwithstanding all his finery, was not quite so rich as a Crœsus or an Attâlus).—"Attâlus," says Mr. Adams: "but pray how came you acquainted with these names?" The lady smiled at the question, and proceeded. He was so pleased, I say, that he resolved to make his addresses to her directly. He did so accordingly, and that with so much warmth and briskness, that he quickly baffled her weak repulses, and obliged the lady to refer him to her father, who, she knew, would quickly declare in favour of a coach and six.

Thus what Horatio had by sighs and tears, love and tenderness, been so long obtaining, the French-English Bellarmine with gaiety and gallantry possessed himself of in an instant. In other words, what modesty had employed a full year in raising, impudence demolished in twenty-four hours.

Here Adams groaned a second time; but the ladies, who began to smoke him, took no notice.

From the opening of the assembly to the end of Bellarmine's visit, Leonora had scarce one thought of Horatio; but he now began, though an unwelcome guest, to enter into her mind. She wished she had seen the charming Bellarmine and his charming equipage before matters had gone so far. "Yet why," says she, "should I wish to have seen him before; or what signifies it that I have seen him now? Is not Horatio my lover, almost my husband? Is he not as handsome, nay handsomer than Bellarmine? Aye, but Bellarmine is the genteeler, and the finer man; yes, that he must be allowed. Yes, yes, he is that certainly. But did not I, no longer ago than yesterday, love Horatio more than all the world? Aye, but yesterday I had not seen Bellarmine. But doth not Horatio doat on me, and may he not in despair break his heart if I abandon him? Well, and hath not Bellarmine a heart to break too? Yes, but I promised Horatio first, but that was poor Bellarmine's misfortune; if I had seen him first, I should certainly have preferred him. Did not the dear creature prefer me to every woman in the assembly, when every she was laying out for him? When was it in Horatio's power to give me such an instance of affection? Can he give me an equipage, or any of those things which Bellarmine will make me mistress of? How vast is the difference between being the wife of a poor counsellor and the wife of one of Bellarmine's fortune! If I marry Horatio, I shall triumph over no more than one rival; but by marrying Bellarmine, I shall be the envy of all my acquaintance. What happiness! But can I suffer Horatio to die? for he hath sworn he cannot survive my loss: but perhaps he may not die: if he should, can I prevent it? Must I sacrifice myself to him? besides, Bellarmine may be as miserable for me too." She was thus arguing with herself, when some young ladies called her to the walks, and a little relieved her anxiety for the present.

The next morning Bellarmine breakfasted with her in presence of her aunt, whom he sufficiently informed of his passion for Leonora. He was no sooner withdrawn than the old lady began to advise her niece on this occasion. "You see, child," says she, "what fortune hath thrown in your way; and I hope you will not withstand your own preferment." Leonora, sighing, begged her not to mention any such thing, when she knew her engagements to Horatio. "Engagements to a fig!" cried the aunt; "you should thank Heaven on your knees that you have it yet in your power to break them. Will any woman hesitate a moment whether she shall ride in a coach or walk on foot all the days of her life? But Bellarmine drives six, and Horatio not even a pair."—"Yes, but, madam, what will the world say?" answered Leonora: "will not they condemn me?"—"The world is always on the side of prudence," cries the aunt, "and would surely condemn you if you sacrificed your interest to any motive whatever. Oh! I know the world very well; and you show your ignorance, my dear, by your objection. O' my conscience! the world is wiser. I have lived longer in it than you; and I assure you there is not anything worth our regard besides money; nor did I ever know one person who married from other considerations, who did not afterwards heartily repent it. Besides, if we examine the two men, can you prefer a sneaking fellow, who hath been bred at the university, to a fine gentleman just come from his travels? All the world must allow Bellarmine to be a fine gentleman, positively a fine gentleman, and a handsome man."—"Perhaps, madam, I should not doubt, if I knew how to be handsomely off with the other."—"Oh! leave that to me," says the aunt. "You know your father hath not been acquainted with the affair. Indeed, for my part I thought it might do well enough, not dreaming of such an offer; but I'll disengage you: leave me to give the fellow an answer. I warrant you shall have no further trouble."

Leonora was at length satisfied with her aunt's reasoning; and Bellarmine supping with her that evening, it was agreed he should the next morning go to her father and propose the match, which she consented should be consummated at his return.

The aunt retired soon after supper; and, the lovers being left together, Bellarmine began in the following manner: "Yes, madam; this coat, I assure you, was made at Paris, and I defy the best English taylor even to imitate it. There is not one of them can cut, madam; they can't cut. If you observe how this skirt is turned, and this sleeve: a clumsy English rascal can do nothing like it. Pray, how do you like my liveries?" Leonora answered, "She thought them very pretty."—"All French," says he, "I assure you, except the greatcoats; I never trust anything more than a greatcoat to an Englishman. You know one must encourage our own people what one can, especially as, before I had a place, I was in the country interest, he, he, he! But for myself, I would see the dirty island at the bottom of the sea, rather than wear a single rag of English work about me: and I am sure, after you have made one tour to Paris, you will be of the same opinion with regard to your own clothes. You can't conceive what an addition a French dress would be to your beauty; I positively assure you, at the first opera I saw since I came over, I mistook the English ladies for chambermaids, he, he, he!"

With such sort of polite discourse did the gay Bellarmine entertain his beloved Leonora, when the door opened on a sudden, and Horatio entered the room. Here 'tis impossible to express the surprise of Leonora.

"Poor woman!" says Mrs. Slipslop, "what a terrible quandary she must be in!"—"Not at all," says Mrs. Grave-airs; "such sluts can never be confounded."—"She must have then more than Corinthian assurance," said Adams; "aye, more than Lais herself."

A long silence, continued the lady, prevailed in the whole company. If the familiar entrance of Horatio struck the greatest astonishment into Bellarmine, the unexpected presence of Bellarmine no less surprised Horatio. At length Leonora, collecting all the spirit she was mistress of, addressed herself to the latter, and pretended to wonder at the reason of so late a visit. "I should indeed," answered he, "have made some apology for disturbing you at this hour, had not my finding you in company assured me I do not break in upon your repose." Bellarmine rose from his chair, traversed the room in a minuet step, and hummed an opera tune, while Horatio, advancing to Leonora, asked her in a whisper if that gentleman was not a relation of hers; to which she answered with a smile, or rather sneer, "No, he is no relation of mine yet"; adding, "she could not guess the meaning of his question." Horatio told her softly, "It did not arise from jealousy."—"Jealousy! I assure you, it would be very strange in a common acquaintance to give himself any of those airs." These words a little surprised Horatio; but, before he had time to answer, Bellarmine danced up to the lady and told her, "He feared he interrupted some business between her and the gentleman."—"I can have no business," said she, "with the gentleman, nor any other, which need be any secret to you."

"You'll pardon me," said Horatio, "if I desire to know who

this gentleman is who is to be entrusted with all our secrets."—
"You'll know soon enough," cries Leonora; "but I can't guess
what secrets can ever pass between us of such mighty consequence."—"No, madam!" cries Horatio; "I am sure you would
not have me understand you in earnest."—"'Tis indifferent
to me," says she, "how you understand me; but I think so un-
seasonable a visit is difficult to be understood at all, at least
when people find one engaged: though one's servants do not
deny one, one may expect a well-bred person should soon take the
hint."—"Madam," said Horatio, "I did not imagine any engagement with a stranger, as it seems this gentleman is, would have
made my visit impertinent, or that any such ceremonies were
to be preserved between persons in our situation."—"Sure you
are in a dream," says she, "or would persuade me that I am in
one. I know no pretensions a common acquaintance can have
to lay aside the ceremonies of good breeding."—"Sure," said
he, "I am in a dream; for it is impossible I should be really
esteemed a common acquaintance by Leonora, after what has
passed between us?"—"Passed between us! Do you intend
to affront me before this gentleman?"—"D—n me, affront the
lady," says Bellarmine, cocking his hat, and strutting up to
Horatio: "does any man dare affront this lady before me, d—n
me?"—"Hark'ee, sir," says Horatio, "I would advise you to
lay aside that fierce air; for I am mightily deceived if this lady
has not a violent desire to get your worship a good drubbing."—
"Sir," said Bellarmine, "I have the honour to be her protector;
and, d—n me, if I understand your meaning."—"Sir," answered
Horatio, "she is rather your protectress; but give yourself no
more airs, for you see I am prepared for you" (shaking his whip
at him). "Oh! *serviteur très humble*," says Bellarmine: "*Je
vous entend parfaitment bien.*" At which time the aunt, who
had heard of Horatio's visit, entered the room, and soon satisfied
all his doubts. She convinced him that he was never more
awake in his life, and that nothing more extraordinary had
happened in his three days' absence than a small alteration
in the affections of Leonora; who now burst into tears, and
wondered what reason she had given him to use her in so barbarous a manner. Horatio desired Bellarmine to withdraw
with him; but the ladies prevented it by laying violent hands
on the latter; upon which the former took his leave without any
great ceremony, and departed, leaving the lady with his rival
to consult for his safety, which Leonora feared her indiscretion
might have endangered; but the aunt comforted her with

assurances that Horatio would not venture his person against so accomplished a cavalier as Bellarmine, and that, being a lawyer, he would seek revenge in his own way, and the most they had to apprehend from him was an action.

They at length, therefore, agreed to permit Bellarmine to retire to his lodgings, having first settled all matters relating to the journey which he was to undertake in the morning, and their preparations for the nuptials at his return.

But, alas! as wise men have observed, the seat of valour is not the countenance; and many a grave and plain man will, on a just provocation, betake himself to that mischievous metal, cold iron; while men of a fiercer brow, and sometimes with that emblem of courage, a cockade, will more prudently decline it.

Leonora was waked in the morning, from a visionary coach and six, with the dismal account that Bellarmine was run through the body by Horatio; that he lay languishing at an inn, and the surgeons had declared the wound mortal. She immediately leaped out of the bed, danced about the room in a frantic manner, tore her hair and beat her breast in all the agonies of despair; in which sad condition her aunt, who likewise arose at the news, found her. The good old lady applied her utmost art to comfort her niece. She told her, "While there was life there was hope; but that if he should die her affliction would be of no service to Bellarmine, and would only expose herself, which might, probably, keep her some time without any future offer; that, as matters had happened, her wisest way would be to think no more of Bellarmine, but to endeavour to regain the affections of Horatio."—"Speak not to me," cried the disconsolate Leonora; "is it not owing to me that poor Bellarmine has lost his life? Have not these cursed charms (at which words she looked steadfastly in the glass) been the ruin of the most charming man of this age? Can I ever bear to contemplate my own face again (with her eyes still fixed on the glass)? Am I not the murderess of the finest gentleman? No other woman in the town could have made any impression on him."—"Never think of things past," cries the aunt: "think of regaining the affections of Horatio."— "What reason," said the niece, "have I to hope he would forgive me? No, I have lost him as well as the other, and it was your wicked advice which was the occasion of all; you seduced me, contrary to my inclinations, to abandon poor Horatio (at which words she burst into tears); you prevailed upon me, whether I would or no, to give up my affections for him; had it not been for you, Bellarmine never would have entered into my thoughts;

had not his addresses been backed by your persuasions, they
never would have made any impression on me; I should have
defied all the fortune and equipage in the world; but it was you,
it was you, who got the better of my youth and simplicity, and
forced me to lose my dear Horatio for ever."

The aunt was almost borne down with this torrent of words;
she, however, rallied all the strength she could, and, drawing
her mouth up in a purse, began: "I am not surprised, niece, at
this ingratitude. Those who advise young women for their
interest, must always expect such a return: I am convinced my
brother will thank me for breaking off your match with Horatio,
at any rate."—"That may not be in your power yet," answered
Leonora, "though it is very ungrateful in you to desire or
attempt it, after the presents you have received from him."
(For indeed true it is, that many presents, and some pretty
valuable ones, had passed from Horatio to the old lady; but
as true it is, that Bellarmine, when he breakfasted with her and
her niece, had complimented her with a brilliant from his finger,
of much greater value than all she had touched of the other.)

The aunt's gall was on float to reply, when a servant brought
a letter into the room, which Leonora, hearing it came from
Bellarmine, with great eagerness opened, and read as follows:

Most Divine Creature,
  The wound which I fear you have heard I received from my rival
is not like to be so fatal as those shot into my heart which have
been fired from your eyes, *tout brillant*. Those are the only cannons
by which I am to fall; for my surgeon gives me hopes of being soon
able to attend your *ruelle*; till when, unless you would do me an
honour which I have scarce the *hardiesse* to think of, your absence
will be the greatest anguish which can be felt by,
                              Madam,
              Avec toute le respecte in the world,
                  Your most obedient, most absolute
                          Dévoté,
                              BELLARMINE.

As soon as Leonora perceived such hopes of Bellarmine's
recovery, and that the gossip Fame had, according to custom,
so enlarged his danger, she presently abandoned all further
thoughts of Horatio, and was soon reconciled to her aunt, who
received her again into favour, with a more Christian forgiveness
than we generally meet with. Indeed, it is possible she might
be a little alarmed at the hints which her niece had given her
concerning the presents. She might apprehend such rumours,
should they get abroad, might injure a reputation which, by

frequenting church twice a day, and preserving the utmost rigour and strictness in her countenance and behaviour for many years, she had established.

Leonora's passion returned now for Bellarmine with greater force, after its small relaxation, than ever. She proposed to her aunt to make him a visit in his confinement, which the old lady, with great and commendable prudence, advised her to decline: "For," says she, "should any accident intervene to prevent your intended match, too forward a behaviour with this lover may injure you in the eyes of others. Every woman, till she is married, ought to consider of, and provide against, the possibility of the affair's breaking off." Leonora said, "She should be indifferent to whatever might happen in such a case; for she had now so absolutely placed her affections on this dear man (so she called him), that, if it was her misfortune to lose him, she should for ever abandon all thoughts of mankind." She, therefore, resolved to visit him, notwithstanding all the prudent advice of her aunt to the contrary, and that very afternoon executed her resolution.

The lady was proceeding in her story, when the coach drove into the inn where the company were to dine, sorely to the dissatisfaction of Mr. Adams, whose ears were the most hungry part about him; he being, as the reader may perhaps guess, of an insatiable curiosity, and heartily desirous of hearing the end of this amour, though he professed he could scarce wish success to a lady of so inconstant a disposition.

CHAPTER V

A DREADFUL QUARREL WHICH HAPPENED AT THE INN WHERE THE COMPANY DINED, WITH ITS BLOODY CONSEQUENCES TO MR. ADAMS

As soon as the passengers had alighted from the coach, Mr. Adams, as was his custom, made directly to the kitchen, where he found Joseph sitting by the fire, and the hostess anointing his leg; for the horse which Mr. Adams had borrowed of his clerk had so violent a propensity to kneeling, that one would have thought it had been his trade, as well as his master's; nor would he always give any notice of such his intention; he was often found on his knees when the rider least expected it. This foible, however, was of no great inconvenience to the parson, who was accustomed to it; and, as his legs almost touched the ground when he bestrode the beast, had but little way to fall, and threw himself forward on such occasions with so much dexterity that he never received any mischief; the horse and he frequently rolling many paces' distance, and afterwards both getting up and meeting as good friends as ever.

Poor Joseph, who had not been used to such kind of cattle, though an excellent horseman, did not so happily disengage himself; but, falling with his leg under the beast, received a violent contusion, to which the good woman was, as we have said, applying a warm hand, with some camphorated spirits, just at the time when the parson entered the kitchen.

He had scarce expressed his concern for Joseph's misfortune, before the host likewise entered. He was by no means of Mr. Tow-wouse's gentle disposition; and was, indeed, perfect master of his house, and everything in it but his guests.

This surly fellow, who always proportioned his respect to the appearance of a traveller, from "God bless your honour," down to plain "Coming presently," observing his wife on her knees to a footman, cried out, without considering his circumstances, "What a pox is the woman about? why don't you mind the company in the coach? Go and ask them what they will have for dinner."—"My dear," says she, "you know they can have nothing but what is at the fire, which will be ready presently, and really the poor young man's leg is very much bruised." At which words she fell to chafing more violently than before: the bell then happening to ring, he damn'd his wife, and bid her go into the company, and not stand there rubbing all day, for he did not believe the young fellow's leg was so bad as he pretended; and if it was, within twenty miles he would find a surgeon to cut it off. Upon these words, Adams fetched two strides across the room; and snapping his fingers over his head, muttered aloud, He would excommunicate such a wretch for a farthing, for he believed the devil had more humanity. These words occasioned a dialogue between Adams and the host, in which there were two or three sharp replies, till Joseph bade the latter know how to behave himself to his betters. At which the host (having first strictly surveyed Adams) scornfully repeating the word "betters," flew into a rage, and, telling Joseph he was as able to walk out of his house as he had been to walk into it, offered to lay violent hands on him; which perceiving, Adams dealt him so sound a compliment over his face with his fist, that the blood immediately gushed out of his nose in a stream. The host, being unwilling to be outdone in courtesy, especially by a person of Adams's figure, returned the favour with so much gratitude, that the parson's nostrils began to look a little redder than usual. Upon which he again assailed his antagonist, and with another stroke laid him sprawling on the floor.

The hostess, who was a better wife than so surly a husband deserved, seeing her husband all bloody and stretched along, hastened presently to his assistance, or rather to revenge the blow, which, to all appearance, was the last he would ever receive; when, lo! a pan full of hog's blood, which unluckily stood on the dresser, presented itself first to her hands. She seized it in her fury, and without any reflection, discharged it into the parson's face; and with so good an aim, that much the greater part first saluted his countenance, and trickled thence in so large a current down to his beard, and over his garments, that a more horrible spectacle was hardly to be seen, or even imagined. All which was perceived by Mrs. Slipslop, who entered the kitchen at that instant. This good gentlewoman, not being of a temper so extremely cool and patient as perhaps was required to ask many questions on this occasion, flew with great impetuosity at the hostess's cap, which, together with some of her hair, she plucked from her head in a moment, giving her, at the same time, several hearty cuffs in the face; which by frequent practice on the inferior servants, she had learned an excellent knack of delivering with a good grace. Poor Joseph could hardly rise from his chair; the parson was employed in wiping the blood from his eyes, which had entirely blinded him; and the landlord was but just beginning to stir; whilst Mrs. Slipslop, holding down the landlady's face with her left hand, made so dexterous an use of her right, that the poor woman began to roar, in a key which alarmed all the company in the inn.

There happened to be in the inn, at this time, besides the ladies who arrived in the stage-coach, the two gentlemen who were present at Mr. Tow-wouse's when Joseph was detained for his horse's meat, and whom we have before mentioned to have stopt at the alehouse with Adams. There was likewise a gentleman just returned from his travels to Italy; all whom the horrid outcry of murder presently brought into the kitchen, where the several combatants were found in the postures already described.

It was now no difficulty to put an end to the fray, the conquerors being satisfied with the vengeance they had taken, and the conquered having no appetite to renew the fight. The principal figure, and which engaged the eyes of all, was Adams, who was all over covered with blood, which the whole company concluded to be his own, and consequently imagined him no longer for this world. But the host, who had now recovered from his blow, and was risen from the ground, soon delivered them from this apprehension, by damning his wife for wasting the hog's puddings, and telling her all would have been very well if she had not intermeddled, like a b—— as she was; adding, he was very glad the gentlewoman had paid her, though not half what she deserved. The poor woman had indeed fared much the worst; having, besides the unmerciful cuffs received, lost a quantity of hair, which Mrs. Slipslop in triumph held in her left hand.

The traveller, addressing himself to Mrs. Grave-airs, desired her not to be frightened; for here had been only a little boxing, which he said, to their *disgracia*, the English were *accustomata* to: adding, it must be, however, a sight somewhat strange to him, who was just come from Italy; the Italians not being addicted to the *cuffardo*, but *bastonza*, says he. He then went up to Adams, and telling him he looked like the ghost of Othello, bid him not shake his gory locks at him, for he could not say he did it. Adams very innocently answered, "Sir, I am far from accusing you." He then returned to the lady, and cried, "I find the bloody gentleman is *uno insipido del nullo senso*. *Dammato di me*, if I have seen such a *spectaculo* in my way from Viterbo."

One of the gentlemen having learnt from the host the occasion of this bustle, and being assured by him that Adams had struck the first blow, whispered in his ear, "He'd warrant he would recover."—"Recover! master," said the host, smiling: "yes, yes, I am not afraid of dying with a blow or two neither: I am not such a chicken as that."——"Pugh!" said the gentleman, "I mean you will recover damages in that action which, undoubtedly, you intend to bring, as soon as a writ can be returned from London; for you look like a man of too much spirit and courage to suffer any one to beat you without bringing your action against him: he must be a scandalous fellow indeed who would put up with a drubbing whilst the law is open to revenge it; besides, he hath drawn blood from you, and spoiled your coat; and the jury will give damages for that too. An excellent new coat upon my word; and now not worth a shilling! I don't care," continued he, "to intermeddle in these cases; but you have a right to my evidence; and if I am sworn, I must speak the truth. I saw you sprawling on the floor, and blood gushing from your nostrils. You may take your own opinion; but was I in your circumstances, every drop of my blood should convey an ounce of gold into my pocket: remember I don't advise you to go to law; but if your jury were Christians, they must give swinging damages. That's all."—"Master," cried the host, scratching his head, "I have no stomach to law, I thank you. I have seen enough of that in the parish, where two of my neighbours have been at law about a house, till they have both lawed themselves into a gaol." At which words he turned about, and began to inquire again after his hog's puddings; nor would it probably have been a sufficient excuse for his wife, that she spilt them in his defence, had not some awe of the company, especially of the Italian traveller, who was a person of great dignity, withheld his rage.

Whilst one of the above-mentioned gentlemen was employed, as we have seen him, on the behalf of the landlord, the other was no less hearty on the side of Mr. Adams, whom he advised to bring his action immediately. He said the assault of the wife was in law the assault of the husband, for they were but one person; and he was liable to pay damages, which he said must be considerable, where so bloody a disposition appeared. Adams answered, If it was true that they were but one person, he had assaulted the wife; for he was sorry to own he had struck the husband the first blow. "I am sorry you own it too," cries the gentleman; "for it could not possibly appear to the court; for here was no evidence present but the lame man in the chair, whom I suppose to be your friend, and would consequently say nothing but what made for you."—"How, sir," says Adams, "do you take me for a villain, who would prosecute revenge in cold blood, and use unjustifiable means to obtain it? If you knew me, and my order, I should think you affronted both." At the word order, the gentleman stared (for he was too bloody to be of any modern order of knights); and, turning hastily about, said, "Every man knew his own business."

Matters being now composed, the company retired to their several apartments; the two gentlemen congratulating each other on the success of their good offices in procuring a perfect reconciliation between the contending parties; and the traveller went to his repast, crying, "As the Italian poet says:

> *Je voi* very well *que tutta e pace,*
> So send up dinner, good Boniface."

The coachman began now to grow importunate with his passengers, whose entrance into the coach was retarded by Mrs. Grave-airs insisting, against the remonstrance of all the rest, that she would not admit a footman into the coach; for poor

Joseph was too lame to mount a horse. A young lady, who was, as it seems, an earl's grand-daughter, begged it with almost tears in her eyes. Mr. Adams prayed, and Mrs. Slipslop scolded; but all to no purpose. She said, "She would not demean herself to ride with a footman: that there were waggons on the road: that if the master of the coach desired it, she would pay for two places; but would suffer no such fellow to come in."—"Madam," says Slipslop, "I am sure no one can refuse another coming into a stage-coach."—"I don't know, madam," says the lady; "I am not much used to stage-coaches; I seldom travel in them."—"That may be, madam," replied Slipslop; "very good people do; and some people's betters, for aught I know." Mrs. Grave-airs said, "Some folks might sometimes give their tongues a liberty, to some people that were their betters, which did not become them; for her part, she was not used to converse with servants." Slipslop returned, "Some people kept no servants to converse with; for her part, she thanked Heaven she lived in a family where there were a great many, and had more under her own command than any paultry little gentlewoman in the kingdom." Mrs. Grave-airs cried, "She believed her mistress would not encourage such sauciness to her betters."—"My betters," says Slipslop, "who is my betters, pray?"—"I am your betters," answered Mrs. Grave-airs, "and I'll acquaint your mistress."—At which Mrs. Slipslop laughed aloud, and told her, "Her lady was one of the great gentry; and such little paultry gentlewomen as some folks, who travelled in stage-coaches, would not easily come at her."

This smart dialogue between some people and some folks was going on at the coach door when a solemn person, riding into the inn, and seeing Mrs. Grave-airs, immediately accosted her with "Dear child, how do you?" She presently answered, "O papa, I am glad you have overtaken me."—"So am I," answered he; "for one of our coaches is just at hand; and, there being room for you in it, you shall go no farther in the stage unless you desire it."—"How can you imagine I should desire it?" says she; so, bidding Slipslop ride with her fellow, if she pleased, she took her father by the hand, who was just alighted, and walked with him into a room.

Adams instantly asked the coachman in a whisper, "If he knew who the gentleman was?" The coachman answered, "He was now a gentleman, and kept his horse and man; but times are altered, master," said he; "I remember when he was no better born than myself."—"Ay! ay!" says Adams. "My father drove the squire's coach," answered he, "when that very man rode postillion; but he is now his steward; and a great gentleman." Adams then snapped his fingers, and cried, "He thought she was some such trollop."

Adams made haste to acquaint Mrs. Slipslop with this good news, as he imagined it; but found a reception different from what he expected. The prudent gentlewoman, who despised the anger of Mrs. Grave-airs whilst she conceived her the daughter of a gentleman of small fortune, now she heard her alliance with the upper servants of a great family in her neighbourhood, began to fear her interest with the mistress. She wished she had not carried the dispute so far, and began to think of endeavouring to reconcile herself to the young lady before she left the inn; when, luckily, the scene at London, which the reader can scarce have forgotten, presented itself to her mind, and comforted her with such assurance, that she no longer apprehended any enemy with her mistress.

Everything being now adjusted, the company entered the coach, which was just on its departure, when one lady recollected she had left her fan, a second her gloves, a third a snuff-box, and a fourth a smelling-bottle behind her; to find all which occasioned some delay and much swearing to the coachman.

As soon as the coach had left the inn, the women all together fell to the character of Mrs. Grave-airs; whom one of them declared she had suspected to be some low creature, from the beginning of their journey, and another affirmed she had not even the looks of a gentlewoman: a third warranted she was no better than she should be; and, turning to the lady who had related the story in the coach, said, "Did you ever hear, madam, anything so prudish as her remarks? Well, deliver me from the censoriousness of such a prude." The fourth added, "O madam! all these creatures are censorious; but for my part, I wonder where the wretch was bred; indeed, I must own I have seldom conversed with these mean kind of people, so that it may appear stranger to me; but to refuse the general desire of a whole company had something in it so astonishing, that, for my part, I own I should hardly believe it if my own ears had not been witnesses to it."—"Yes, and so handsome a young fellow," cries Slipslop; "the woman must have no compulsion in her: I believe she is more of a Turk than a Christian; I am certain, if she had any Christian woman's blood in her veins, the sight of such a young fellow must have warmed it. Indeed, there are some wretched, miserable old objects, that turn one's stomach; I should not wonder if she had refused such a one; I am as nice as herself, and should have cared no more than herself for the company of stinking old fellows; but, hold up thy head, Joseph, thou art none of those; and she who hath not compulsion for thee is a Myhummetman, and I will maintain it." This conversation made Joseph uneasy as well as the ladies; who, perceiving the spirits which Mrs. Slipslop was in (for indeed she was not a cup too low), began to fear the consequence; one of them therefore desired the lady to conclude the story. "Aye, madam," said Slipslop, "I beg your ladyship to give us that story you commensated in the morning"; which request that well-bred woman immediately complied with.

CHAPTER VI

CONCLUSION OF THE UNFORTUNATE JILT

LEONORA, having once broke through the bounds which custom and modesty impose on her sex, soon gave an unbridled indulgence to her passion. Her visits to Bellarmine were more constant, as well as longer, than his surgeon's: in a word, she became absolutely his nurse; made his water-gruel, administered him his medicines; and, notwithstanding the prudent advice of her aunt to the contrary, almost intirely resided in her wounded lover's apartment.

The ladies of the town began to take her conduct under consideration: it was the chief topic of discourse at their tea-tables, and was very severely censured by the most part; especially by Lindamira, a lady whose discreet and starch carriage, together with a constant attendance at church three times a day, had utterly defeated many malicious attacks on her own reputation; for such was the envy that Lindamira's virtue had attracted, that, notwithstanding her own strict behaviour and strict enquiry into the lives of others, she had not been able to escape being the mark of some arrows herself, which, however, did her no injury; a blessing, perhaps, owed by her to the clergy, who were her chief male companions, and with two or three of whom she had been barbarously and unjustly calumniated.

"Not so unjustly neither, perhaps," says Slipslop; "for the clergy are men, as well as other folks."

The extreme delicacy of Lindamira's virtue was cruelly hurt by those freedoms which Leonora allowed herself: she said, "It was an affront to her sex; that she did not imagine it consistent with any woman's honour to speak to the creature, or to be seen in her company; and that, for her part, she should always refuse to dance at an assembly with her, for fear of contamination by taking her by the hand."

But to return to my story: as soon as Bellarmine was recovered, which was somewhat within a month from his receiving the wound, he set out, according to agreement, for Leonora's father's, in order to propose the match, and settle all matters with him touching settlements, and the like.

A little before his arrival the old gentleman had received an intimation of the affair by the following letter, which I can repeat *verbatim*, and which, they say, was written neither by Leonora nor her aunt, though it was in a woman's hand. The letter was in these words:

SIR,

I am sorry to acquaint you that your daughter, Leonora, hath acted one of the basest as well as most simple parts with a young gentleman to whom she had engaged herself, and whom she hath (pardon the word) jilted for another of inferior fortune, notwithstanding his superior figure. You may take what measures you please on this occasion; I have performed what I thought my duty; as I have, though unknown to you, a very great respect for your family.

The old gentleman did not give himself the trouble to answer this kind epistle; nor did he take any notice of it, after he had read it, till he saw Bellarmine. He was, to say the truth, one of those fathers who look on children as an unhappy consequence of their youthful pleasures; which, as he would have been delighted not to have had attended them, so was he no less pleased with any opportunity to rid himself of the incumbrance. He passed, in the world's language, as an exceeding good father; being not only so rapacious as to rob and plunder all mankind to the utmost of his power, but even to deny himself the conveniences, and almost necessaries, of life; which his neighbours attributed to a desire of raising immense fortunes for his children: but in fact it was not so; he heaped up money for its own sake only, and looked on his children as his rivals, who were to enjoy his beloved mistress when he was incapable of possessing her, and which he would have been much more charmed with the power of carrying along with him; nor had his children any other security of being his heirs than that the law would constitute them such without a will, and that he had not affection enough for any one living to take the trouble of writing one.

To this gentleman came Bellarmine, on the errand I have

mentioned. His person, his equipage, his family, and his estate, seemed to the father to make him an advantageous match for his daughter: he therefore very readily accepted his proposals: but when Bellarmine imagined the principal affair concluded, and began to open the incidental matters of fortune, the old gentleman presently changed his countenance, saying, "He resolved never to marry his daughter on a Smithfield match; that whoever had love for her to take her would, when he died, find her share of his fortune in his coffers; but he had seen such examples of undutifulness happen from the too early generosity of parents, that he had made a vow never to part with a shilling whilst he lived." He commended the saying of Solomon, "He that spareth the rod spoileth the child"; but added, "he might have likewise asserted, That he that spareth the purse saveth the child." He then ran into a discourse on the extravagance of the youth of the age; whence he launched into a dissertation on horses; and came at length to commend those Bellarmine drove. That fine gentleman, who at another season would have been well enough pleased to dwell a little on that subject, was now very eager to resume the circumstances of fortune. He said, "He had a very high value for the young lady, and would receive her with less than he would any other whatever; but that even his love to her made some regard to worldly matters necessary; for it would be a most distracting sight for him to see her, when he had the honour to be her husband, in less than a coach and six." The old gentleman answered, "Four will do, four will do"; and then took a turn from horses to extravagance and from extravagance to horses, till he came round to the equipage again; whither he was no sooner arrived than Bellarmine brought him back to the point; but all to no purpose; he made his escape from that subject in a minute; till at last the lover declared, "That in the present situation of his affairs it was impossible for him, though he loved Leonora more than *tout le monde*, to marry her without any fortune." To which the father answered, "He was sorry that his daughter must lose so valuable a match; that, if he had an inclination, at present it was not in his power to advance a shilling: that he had had great losses, and been at great expenses on projects; which, though he had great expectation from them, had yet produced him nothing: that he did not know what might happen hereafter, as on the birth of a son, or such accident; but he would make no promise, or enter into any article, for he would not break his vow for all the daughters in the world."

In short, ladies, to keep you no longer in suspense, Bellarmine, having tried every argument and persuasion, which he could invent, and finding them all ineffectual, at length took his leave, but not in order to return to Leonora; he proceeded directly to his own seat, whence, after a few days' stay, he returned to Paris, to the great delight of the French and the honour of the English nation.

But as soon as he arrived at his home he presently despatched a messenger with the following epistle to Leonora:

ADORABLE AND CHARMANTE,
    I am sorry to have the honour to tell you I am not the *heureux* person destined for your divine arms. Your papa hath told me so with a *politesse* not often seen on this side Paris. You may perhaps guess his manner of refusing me. *Ah, mon Dieu!* You will certainly believe me, madam, incapable myself of delivering this *triste* message, which I intend to try the French air to cure the consequences of. *A jamais! Cœur! Ange! Au diable!* If your papa obliges you to a marriage, I hope we shall see you at Paris; till when, the wind that flows from thence will be the warmest *dans le monde*, for it will consist almost entirely of my sighs. *Adieu, ma princesse! Ah, l'amour!*   BELLARMINE.

I shall not attempt, ladies, to describe Leonora's condition when she received this letter. It is a picture of horror, which I should have as little pleasure in drawing as you in beholding. She immediately left the place where she was the subject of conversation and ridicule, and retired to that house I showed you when I began the story; where she hath ever since led a disconsolate life, and deserves, perhaps, pity for her misfortunes, more than our censure for a behaviour to which the artifices of her aunt very probably contributed, and to which very young women are often rendered too liable by that blameable levity in the education of our sex.

"If I was inclined to pity her," said a young lady in the coach, "it would be for the loss of Horatio; for I cannot discern any misfortune in her missing such a husband as Bellarmine."

"Why, I must own," says Slipslop, "the gentleman was a little false-hearted; but howsumever, it was hard to have two lovers, and get never a husband at all. But pray, madam, what became of *Our-asho?*"

He remains, said the lady, still unmarried, and hath applied himself so strictly to his business, that he hath raised, I hear, a very considerable fortune. And what is remarkable, they say he never hears the name of Leonora without a sigh, nor hath ever uttered one syllable to charge her with her ill-conduct towards him.

CHAPTER VII

A VERY SHORT CHAPTER, IN WHICH PARSON ADAMS WENT A GREAT WAY

THE lady, having finished her story, received the thanks of the company; and now Joseph, putting his head out of the coach, cried out, "Never believe me if yonder be not our parson Adams walking along without his horse!"—"On my word, and so he is," says Slipslop: "and as sure as twopence he hath left him behind at the inn." Indeed, true it is, the parson had exhibited a fresh instance of his absence of mind; for he was so pleased with having got Joseph into the coach, that he never once thought of the beast in the stable; and, finding his legs as nimble as he desired, he sallied out, brandishing a crabstick, and had kept on before the coach, mending and slackening his pace occasionally, so that he had never been much more or less than a quarter of a mile distant from it.

Mrs. Slipslop desired the coachman to overtake him, which he attempted, but in vain; for the faster he drove the faster ran the parson, often crying out, "Aye, aye, catch me if you can"; till at length the coachman swore he would as soon attempt to drive after a greyhound, and, giving the parson two or three hearty curses, he cry'd, "Softly, softly, boys," to his horses, which the civil beasts immediately obeyed.

But we will be more courteous to our reader than he was to Mrs. Slipslop; and, leaving the coach and its company to pursue their journey, we will carry our reader on after parson Adams, who stretched forwards without once looking behind him, till, having left the coach full three miles in his rear, he came to a place where, by keeping the extremest track to the right, it was just barely possible for a human creature to miss his way. This track, however, did he keep, as indeed he had a wonderful capacity at these kinds of bare possibilities, and, travelling in it about three miles over the plain, he arrived at the summit of a hill, whence looking a great way backwards, and perceiving no coach in sight, he sat himself down on the turf, and, pulling out his Æschylus, determined to wait here for its arrival.

He had not sat long here before a gun going off very near, a little startled him; and he looked up and saw a gentleman within a hundred paces taking up a partridge which he had just shot.

Adams stood up and presented a figure to the gentleman which would have moved laughter in many; for his cassock had just again fallen down below his greatcoat, that is to say, it reached his knees, whereas the skirts of his greatcoat descended no lower than half-way down his thighs; but the gentleman's mirth gave way to his surprise at beholding such a personage in such a place.

Adams, advancing to the gentleman, told him he hoped he had good sport, to which the other answered, "Very little."— "I see, sir," says Adams, "you have smote one partridge"; to which the sportsman made no reply, but proceeded to charge his piece.

Whilst the gun was charging, Adams remained in silence, which he at last broke by observing that it was a delightful evening. The gentleman, who had at first sight conceived a very distasteful opinion of the parson, began, on perceiving a book in his hand, and smoaking likewise the information of the cassock, to change his thoughts, and made a small advance to conversation on his side by saying, "Sir, I suppose you are not one of these parts?"

Adams immediately told him, "No; that he was a traveller, and invited by the beauty of the evening and the place to repose a little and amuse himself with reading."—"I may as well repose myself too," said the sportsman, "for I have been out this whole afternoon, and the devil a bird have I seen till I came hither."

"Perhaps then the game is not very plenty hereabouts?" cries Adams. "No, sir," said the gentleman: "the soldiers, who are quartered in the neighbourhood, have killed it all."— "It is very probable," cries Adams, "for shooting is their profession."—"Aye, shooting the game," answered the other; "but I don't see they are so forward to shoot our enemies. I don't like that affair of Carthagena; if I had been there, I believe I should have done other-guess things, d—n me: what's a man's life when his country demands it? a man who won't sacrifice his life for his country deserves to be hanged, d—n me." Which words he spoke with so violent a gesture, so loud a voice, so strong an accent, and so fierce a countenance, that he might have frightened a captain of trained bands at the head of his company; but Mr. Adams was not greatly subject to fear; he told him intrepidly that he very much approved his virtue, but disliked his swearing, and begged him not to addict himself to so bad a custom, without which he said he might fight as bravely as Achilles did. Indeed he was charmed with this discourse; he told the gentleman he would willingly have gone many miles to have met a man of his generous way of thinking; that, if he pleased to sit down, he should be greatly delighted to commune with him; for, though he was a clergyman, he would himself be ready, if thereto called, to lay down his life for his country.

The gentleman sat down, and Adams by him; and then the latter began, as in the following chapter, a discourse which we have placed by itself, as it is not only the most curious in this but perhaps in any other book.

CHAPTER VIII

A NOTABLE DISSERTATION BY MR. ABRAHAM ADAMS; WHEREIN
THAT GENTLEMAN APPEARS IN A POLITICAL LIGHT

"I DO assure you, sir" (says he, taking the gentleman by the hand), "I am heartily glad to meet with a man of your kidney; for, though I am a poor parson, I will be bold to say I am an honest man, and would not do an ill thing to be made a bishop; nay, though it hath not fallen in my way to offer so noble a sacrifice, I have not been without opportunities of suffering for the sake of my conscience, I thank Heaven for them; for I have had relations, though I say it, who made some figure in the world; particularly a nephew, who was a shopkeeper and an alderman of a corporation. He was a good lad, and was under my care when a boy; and I believe would do what I bade him to his dying day. Indeed, it looks like extreme vanity in me to affect being a man of such consequence as to have so great an interest in an alderman; but others have thought so too, as manifestly appeared by the rector, whose curate I formerly was, sending for me on the approach of an election, and telling me, if I expected to continue in his cure, that I must bring my nephew to vote for one Colonel Courtly, a gentleman whom I had never heard tidings of till that instant. I told the rector I had no power over my nephew's vote (God forgive me for such pre-varication!); that I supposed he would give it according to his conscience; that I would by no means endeavour to influence him to give it otherwise. He told me it was in vain to equivocate; that he knew I had already spoke to him in favour of esquire Fickle, my neighbour; and, indeed, it was true I had; for it was at a season when the church was in danger, and when all good men expected they knew not what would happen to us all. I then answered boldly, if he thought I had given my promise, he affronted me in proposing any breach of it. Not to be too prolix; I persevered, and so did my nephew, in the esquire's interest, who was chose chiefly through his means; and so I lost my curacy. Well, sir, but do you think the esquire ever mentioned a word of the church? *Ne verbum quidem, ut ita dicam:* within two years he got a place, and hath ever since lived in London; where I have been informed (but God forbid I should believe that), that he never so much as goeth to church. I remained, sir, a considerable time without any cure and lived a full month on one funeral sermon, which I preached on the indisposition of a clergyman; but this by the bye. At last, when Mr. Fickle got his place, Colonel Courtly stood again; and who should make interest for him but Mr. Fickle himself! that very identical Mr. Fickle, who had formerly told me the colonel was an enemy to both the church and state, had the confidence to sollicit my nephew for him; and the colonel himself offered me to make me chaplain to his regiment, which I refused in favour of Sir Oliver Hearty, who told us he would sacrifice everything to his country; and I believe he would, except his hunting, which he stuck so close to, that in five years together he went but twice up to parliament; and one of those times, I have been told, never was within sight of the House. However, he was a worthy man, and the best friend I ever had; for, by his interest with a bishop, he got me replaced into my curacy, and gave me eight pounds out of his own pocket to buy me a gown and cassock, and furnish my house. He had our interest while he lived, which was not many years. On his death I had fresh applications made to me; for all the world knew the interest I had with my good nephew, who now was a leading man in the corporation; and Sir Thomas Booby, buying the estate which had been Sir Oliver's, proposed himself a candidate. He was then a young gentleman just come from his travels; and it did me good to hear him discourse on affairs which, for my part, I knew nothing of. If I had been master of a thousand votes he should have had them all. I engaged my nephew in his interest, and he was elected; and a very fine parliament-man he was. They tell me he made speeches of an hour long, and, I have been told, very fine ones; but he could never persuade the parliament to be of his opinion. *Non omnia possumus omnes.* He promised me a living, poor man! and I believe I should have had it, but an accident happened, which was, that my lady had promised it before, unknown to him. This, indeed, I never heard till afterwards; for my nephew, who died about a month before the incumbent, always told me I might be assured of it. Since that time, Sir Thomas, poor man, had always so much business, that he never could find leisure to see me. I believe it was partly my lady's fault too, who did not think my dress good enough for the gentry at her table. However, I must do him the justice to say he never was ungrateful; and I have always found his kitchen, and his cellar too, open to me: many a time, after service on a Sunday—for I preach at four churches—have I recruited my spirits with a glass of his ale. Since my nephew's death, the corporation is in other hands; and I am not a man of that consequence I was formerly. I have now no longer any talents to lay out in the service of my country; and to whom nothing is given, of him can nothing be required. However, on all proper seasons, such as the approach of an election, I throw a suitable dash or two into my sermons; which I have the pleasure to hear is not disagreeable to Sir Thomas and the other honest gentlemen my neighbours, who have all promised me these five years to procure an ordination for a son of mine, who is now near thirty, hath an infinite stock of learning, and is, I thank Heaven, of an unexceptionable life; though, as he was never at an university, the bishop refuses to ordain him. Too much care cannot indeed be taken in admitting any to the sacred office; though I hope he will never act so as to be a disgrace to any order, but will serve his God and his country to the utmost of his power, as I have endeavoured to do before him; nay, and will lay down his life whenever called to that purpose. I am sure I have educated him in those principles; so that I have acquitted my duty, and shall have nothing to answer for on that account. But I do not distrust him, for he is a good boy; and if Providence should throw it in his way to be of as much consequence in a public light as his father once was, I can answer for him he will use his talents as honestly as I have done."

CHAPTER IX

IN WHICH THE GENTLEMAN DISCANTS ON BRAVERY AND HEROIC VIRTUE, TILL AN UNLUCKY ACCIDENT PUTS AN END TO THE DISCOURSE

THE gentleman highly commended Mr. Adams for his good resolutions, and told him, "He hoped his son would tread in his steps"; adding, "that if he would not die for his country, he would not be worthy to live in it. I'd make no more of shooting a man that would not die for his country, than——

"Sir," said he, "I have disinherited a nephew, who is in the army, because he would not exchange his commission and go to the West Indies. I believe the rascal is a coward, though he pretends to be in love forsooth. I would have all such fellows hanged, sir; I would have them hanged." Adams answered, "That would be too severe; that men did not make themselves; and if fear had too much ascendance in the mind, the man was rather to be pitied than abhorred; that reason and time might teach him to subdue it." He said, "A man might be a coward at one time, and brave at another. Homer," says he, "who so well understood and copied Nature, hath taught us this lesson; for Paris fights and Hector runs away. Nay, we have a mighty instance of this in the history of later ages, no longer ago than the 705th year of Rome, when the great Pompey, who had won so many battles and been honoured with so many triumphs, and of whose valour several authors, especially Cicero and Paterculus, have formed such eulogiums; this very Pompey left the battle of Pharsalia before he had lost it, and retreated to his tent, where he sat like the most pusillanimous rascal in a fit of despair, and yielded a victory, which was to determine the empire of the world, to Cæsar. I am not much travelled in the history of modern times, that is to say, these last thousand years; but those who are can, I make no question, furnish you with parallel instances." He concluded, therefore, that, had he taken any such hasty resolutions against his nephew, he hoped he would consider better, and retract them. The gentleman answered with great warmth, and talked much of courage and his country, till, perceiving it grew late, he asked Adams, "What place he intended for that night?" He told him, "He waited there for the stage-coach."—"The stage-coach, sir!" said the gentleman; "they are all passed by long ago. You may see the last yourself almost three miles before us."—"I protest and so they are," cries Adams; "then I must make haste and follow them." The gentleman told him, "he would hardly be able to overtake them; and that, if he did not know his way, he would be in danger of losing himself on the downs, for it would be presently dark; and he might ramble about all night, and perhaps find himself farther from his journey's end in the morning than he was now." He advised him, therefore, "to accompany him to his house, which was very little out of his way," assuring him "that he would find some country fellow in his parish who would conduct him for sixpence to the city where he was going." Adams accepted this proposal, and on they travelled, the gentleman renewing his discourse on courage, and the infamy of not being ready, at all times, to sacrifice our lives to our country. Night overtook them much about the same time as they arrived near some bushes; whence, on a sudden, they heard the most violent shrieks imaginable in a female voice. Adams offered to snatch the gun out of his companion's hand. "What are you doing?" said he. "Doing!" said Adams; "I am hastening to the assistance of the poor creature whom some villains are murdering."—"You are not mad enough, I hope," says the gentleman, trembling: "do you consider this gun is only charged with shot, and that the robbers are most probably furnished with pistols loaded with bullets? This is no business of ours; let us make as much haste as possible out of the way, or we may fall into their hands ourselves." The shrieks now increasing, Adams made no answer, but snapt his fingers, and, brandishing his crabstick, made directly to the place whence the voice issued; and the man of courage made as much expedition towards his own home, whither he escaped in a very short time without once looking behind him; where we will leave him, to contemplate his own bravery, and to censure the want of it in others, and return to the good Adams, who, on coming up to the place whence the noise proceeded, found a woman struggling with a man, who had thrown her on the ground, and had almost overpowered her. The great abilities of Mr. Adams were not necessary to have formed a right judgment of this affair on the first sight. He did not, therefore, want the entreaties of the poor wretch to assist her; but, lifting up his crabstick, he immediately levelled a blow at that part of the ravisher's head where, according to the opinion of the ancients, the brains of some persons are deposited, and which he had undoubtedly let forth, had not Nature (who, as wise men have observed, equips all creatures with what is most expedient for them) taken a provident care (as she always doth with those she intends for encounters) to make this part of the head three times as thick as those of ordinary men who are designed to exercise talents which are vulgarly called rational, and for whom, as brains are necessary, she is obliged to leave some room for them in the cavity of the skull; whereas, those ingredients being entirely useless to persons of the heroic calling, she hath an opportunity of thickening the bone, so as to make it less subject to any impression, or liable to be cracked or broken: and indeed, in some who are predestined to the command of armies and empires, she is supposed sometimes to make that part perfectly solid.

As a game cock, when engaged in amorous toying with a hen, if perchance he espies another cock at hand, immediately quits his female, and opposes himself to his rival, so did the ravisher, on the information of the crabstick, immediately leap from the woman and hasten to assail the man. He had no weapons but what Nature had furnished him with. However, he clenched his fist, and presently darted it at that part of Adams's breast where the heart is lodged. Adams staggered at the violence of the blow, when, throwing away his staff, he likewise clenched that fist which we have before commemorated, and would have discharged it full in the breast of his antagonist, had he not dexterously caught it with his left hand, at the same time darting his head (which some modern heroes of the lower class use, like the battering-ram of the ancients, for a weapon of offence; another reason to admire the cunningness of Nature, in composing it of those impenetrable materials); dashing his head, I say, into the stomach of Adams, he tumbled him on his back; and, not having any regard to the laws of heroism, which would have restrained him from any farther attack on his enemy till he was again on his legs, he threw himself upon him, and, laying hold on the ground with his left hand, he with his right belaboured the body of Adams till he was weary, and indeed till he concluded (to use the language of fighting) "that he had done his business"; or, in the language of poetry, "that he had sent him to the shades below"; in plain English, "that he was dead."

But Adams, who was no chicken, and could bear a drubbing as well as any boxing champion in the universe, lay still only to watch his opportunity; and now, perceiving his antagonist to pant with his labours, he exerted his utmost force at once, and with such success that he overturned him, and became his superior; when, fixing one of his knees in his breast, he cried out in an exulting voice, "It is my turn now"; and, after a few minutes' constant application, he gave him so dexterous a blow just under his chin that the fellow no longer retained any motion, and Adams began to fear he had struck him once too often; for he often asserted "he should be concerned to have the blood of even the wicked upon him."

Adams got up and called aloud to the young woman. "Be of good cheer, damsel," said he, "you are no longer in danger of your ravisher, who, I am terribly afraid, lies dead at my feet; but God forgive me what I have done in defence of innocence!" The poor wretch, who had been some time in recovering strength enough to rise, and had afterwards, during the engagement, stood trembling, being disabled by fear even from running away, hearing her champion was victorious, came up to him, but not without apprehensions even of her deliverer; which, however, she was soon relieved from by his courteous behaviour and gentle words. They were both standing by the body, which lay motionless on the ground, and which Adams wished to see stir much more than the woman did, when he earnestly begged her to tell him "by what misfortune she came, at such a time of night, into so lonely a place." She acquainted him, "She was travelling towards London, and had accidentally met with the person from whom he had delivered her, who told her he was likewise on his journey to the same place, and would keep her company; an offer which, suspecting no harm, she had accepted; that he told her they were at a small distance from an inn where she might take up her lodging that evening, and he would show her a nearer way to it than by following the road; that if she had suspected him (which she did not, he spoke so kindly to her), being alone on these downs in the dark, she had no human means to avoid him; that, therefore, she had put her whole trust in Providence, and walked on, expecting every moment to arrive at the inn; when on a sudden, being come to those bushes, he desired her to stop, and after some rude kisses, which she resisted, and some entreaties, which she rejected, he laid violent hands on her, and was attempting to execute his wicked will, when, she thanked G——, he timely came up and prevented him." Adams encouraged her for saying she had put her whole trust in Providence, and told her, "He doubted not but Providence had sent him to her deliverance, as a reward for that trust. He wished indeed he had not deprived the wicked wretch of life, but G——'s will be done"; said, "He hoped the goodness of his intention would excuse him in the next world, and he trusted in her evidence to acquit him in this." He was then silent, and began to consider with himself whether it would be proper to make his escape, or to deliver himself into the hands of justice; which meditation ended as the reader will see in the next chapter.

CHAPTER X

GIVING AN ACCOUNT OF THE STRANGE CATASTROPHE OF THE PRE
CEDING ADVENTURE, WHICH DREW POOR ADAMS INTO FRESH
CALAMITIES; AND WHO THE WOMAN WAS WHO OWED THE
PRESERVATION OF HER CHASTITY TO HIS VICTORIOUS ARM

THE silence of Adams, added to the darkness of the night and
loneliness of the place, struck dreadful apprehension into the
poor woman's mind; she began to fear as great an enemy in her
deliverer as he had delivered her from; and as she had not light
enough to discover the age of Adams, and the benevolence visible
in his countenance, she suspected he had used her as some very
honest men have used their country; and had rescued her out of
the hands of one rifler in order to rifle her himself. Such were
the suspicions she drew from his silence; but indeed they were
ill-grounded. He stood over his vanquished enemy, wisely
weighing in his mind the objections which might be made to
either of the two methods of proceeding mentioned in the last
chapter, his judgment sometimes inclining to the one, and sometimes to the other; for both seemed to him so equally advisable
and so equally dangerous, that probably he would have ended
his days, at least two or three of them, on that very spot, before
he had taken any resolution; at length he lifted up his eyes, and
spied a light at a distance, to which he instantly addressed himself with *Heus tu, traveller, heus tu!* He presently heard several
voices, and perceived the light approaching toward him. The
persons who attended the light began some to laugh, others to
sing, and others to hollow, at which the woman testified some
fear (for she had concealed her suspicions of the parson himself);
but Adams said, "Be of good cheer, damsel, and repose thy trust
in the same Providence which hath hitherto protected thee, and
never will forsake the innocent." These people, who now approached, were no other, reader, than a set of young fellows, who
came to these bushes in pursuit of a diversion which they call
bird-batting. This, if you are ignorant of it (as perhaps if thou
hast never travelled beyond Kensington, Islington, Hackney,
or the Borough, thou mayst be), I will inform thee, is performed
by holding a large clap-net before a lanthorn, and at the same
time beating the bushes; for the birds, when they are disturbed
from their places of rest, or roost, immediately make to the
light, and so are inticed within the net. Adams immediately

told them what happened, and desired them to hold the lanthorn to the face of the man on the ground, for he feared he had smote him fatally. But indeed his fears were frivolous; for the fellow, though he had been stunned by the last blow he received, had long since recovered his senses, and, finding himself quit of Adams, had listened attentively to the discourse between him and the young woman; for whose departure he had patiently waited, that he might likewise withdraw himself, having no longer hopes of succeeding in his desires, which were moreover almost as well cooled by Mr. Adams as they could have been by the young woman herself had he obtained his utmost wish. This fellow, who had a readiness at improving any accident, thought he might now play a better part than that of a dead man; and, accordingly, the moment the candle was held to his face he leapt up, and, laying hold on Adams, cried out, "No, villain, I am not dead, though you and your wicked whore might well think me so, after the barbarous cruelties you have exercised on me. Gentle-men," said he, "you are luckily come to the assistance of a poor traveller, who would otherwise have been robbed and murdered by this vile man and woman, who led me hither out of my way from the high-road, and both falling on me have used me as you see." Adams was going to answer, when one of the young fellows cried, "D—n them, let's carry them both before the justice." The poor woman began to tremble, and Adams lifted up his voice, but in vain. Three or four of them laid hands on him; and one holding the lanthorn to his face, they all agreed he had the most villainous countenance they ever beheld; and an attorney's clerk, who was of the company, declared he was sure he had remembered him at the bar. As to the woman, her hair was dishevelled in the struggle, and her nose had bled; so that they could not perceive whether she was handsome or ugly, but they said her fright plainly discovered her guilt. And searching her pockets, as they did those of Adams, for money, which the fellow said he had lost, they found in her pocket a purse with some gold in it, which abundantly convinced them, especially as the fellow offered to swear to it. Mr. Adams was found to have no more than one halfpenny about him. This the clerk said "was a great presumption that he was an old offender, by cunningly giving all the booty to the woman." To which all the rest readily assented.

This accident promising them better sport than what they had proposed, they quitted their intention of catching birds, and unanimously resolved to proceed to the justice with the offenders. Being informed what a desperate fellow Adams was, they tied his hands behind him; and, having hid their nets among the bushes, and the lanthorn being carried before them, they placed the two prisoners in their front, and then began their march; Adams not only submitting patiently to his own fate, but comforting and encouraging his companion under her sufferings.

Whilst they were on their way the clerk informed the rest that this adventure would prove a very beneficial one; for that they would all be entitled to their proportions of £80 for apprehending the robbers. This occasioned a contention concerning the parts which they had severally borne in taking them; one insisting he ought to have the greatest share, for he had first laid his hands on Adams; another claiming a superior part for having first held the lanthorn to the man's face on the ground, by which, he said, "the whole was discovered." The clerk claimed four-fifths of the reward for having proposed to search the prisoners, and likewise the carrying them before the justice: he said, "Indeed, in strict justice, he ought to have the whole." These claims, however, they at last consented to refer to a future decision, but seemed all to agree that the clerk was entitled to a moiety. They then debated what money should be allotted to the young fellow who had been employed only in holding the nets. He very modestly said, "That he did not apprehend any large proportion would fall to his share, but hoped they would allow him something; he desired them to consider that they had assigned their nets to his care, which prevented him from being as forward as any in laying hold of the robbers" (for so those innocent people were called); "that if he had not occupied the nets, some other must"; concluding, however, "that he should be contented with the smallest share imaginable, and should think that rather their bounty than his merit." But they were all unanimous in excluding him from any part whatever, the clerk particularly swearing, "If they gave him a shilling they might do what they pleased with the rest; for he would not concern himself with the affair." This contention was so hot, and so totally engaged the attention of all the parties, that a dexterous nimble thief, had he been in Mr. Adams's situation, would have taken care to have given the justice no trouble that evening. Indeed, it required not the art of a Sheppard to escape, especially as the darkness of the night would have so much befriended him; but Adams trusted rather to his innocence than his heels, and, without thinking of flight, which was easy, or resistance (which was impossible, as there were six lusty young fellows, besides the villain himself, present), he walked with perfect resignation the way they thought proper to conduct him.

Adams frequently vented himself in ejaculations during their journey; at last, poor Joseph Andrews occurring to his mind, he could not refrain sighing forth his name, which being heard by his companion in affliction, she cried with some vehemence, "Sure, I should know that voice; you cannot certainly, sir, be Mr. Abraham Adams?"—"Indeed, damsel," says he, "that is my name; there is something also in your voice which persuades me I have heard it before."—"La! sir," says she, "don't you remember poor Fanny?"—"How, Fanny!" answered Adams: "indeed I very well remember you; what can have brought you hither?"—"I have told you, sir," replied she, "I was travelling towards London; but I thought you mentioned Joseph Andrews; pray what is become of him?"—"I left him, child, this afternoon," said Adams, "in the stage-coach, in his way towards our parish, whither he is going to see you."—"To see me! La, sir," answered Fanny, "sure you jeer me; what should he be going to see me for?"—"Can you ask that?" replied Adams. "I hope, Fanny, you are not inconstant; I assure you he deserves much better of you."—"La! Mr. Adams," said she, "what is Mr. Joseph to me? I am sure I never had anything to say to him, but as one fellow-servant might to another."—"I am sorry to hear this," said Adams; "a virtuous passion for a young man is what no woman need be ashamed of. You either do not tell me the truth, or you are false to a very worthy man." Adams then told her what had happened at the inn, to which she listened very attentively; and a sigh often escaped from her, notwithstanding her utmost endeavours to the contrary; nor could she prevent herself from asking a thousand questions, which would have assured any one but Adams, who never saw farther into people than they desired to let him, of the truth of a passion she endeavoured to conceal. Indeed, the fact was, that this poor girl, having heard of Joseph's misfortune, by some of the servants belonging to the coach which we have formerly mentioned to have stopt at the inn while the poor youth was confined to his bed, that instant abandoned the cow she was milking, and, taking with her a little bundle of clothes under her arm, and all the money she was worth in her own purse, without consulting any one, immediately set forward in pursuit of one whom, notwithstanding her shyness to the parson, she loved with inexpressible violence, though with the purest and

most delicate passion. This shyness, therefore, as we trust it
will recommend her character to all our female readers, and not
greatly surprise such of our males as are well acquainted with
the younger part of the other sex, we shall not give ourselves
any trouble to vindicate.

CHAPTER XI

WHAT HAPPENED TO THEM WHILE BEFORE THE JUSTICE.
A CHAPTER VERY FULL OF LEARNING

THEIR fellow-travellers were so engaged in the hot dispute concerning the division of the reward for apprehending these
innocent people, that they attended very little to their discourse.
They were now arrived at the justice's house, and had sent one
of his servants in to acquaint his worship that they had taken
two robbers and brought them before him. The justice, who
was just returned from a fox-chase, and had not yet finished his
dinner, ordered them to carry the prisoners into the stable,
whither they were attended by all the servants in the house,
and all the people in the neighbourhood, who flocked together to
see them with as much curiosity as if there was something uncommon to be seen, or that a rogue did not look like other people.

The justice, now being in the height of his mirth and his cups,
bethought himself of the prisoners; and, telling his company he
believed they should have good sport in their examination, he
ordered them into his presence. They had no sooner entered
the room than he began to revile them, saying, "That robberies
on the highway were now grown so frequent, that people could
not sleep safely in their beds, and assured them they both should
be made examples of at the ensuing assizes." After he had gone
on some time in this manner, he was reminded by his clerk,
"That it would be proper to take the depositions of the witnesses
against them." Which he bid him do, and he would light his
pipe in the meantime. Whilst the clerk was employed in writing
down the deposition of the fellow who had pretended to be
robbed, the justice employed himself in cracking jests on poor
Fanny, in which he was seconded by all the company at table.
One asked, "Whether she was to be indicted for a highwayman?"
Another whispered in her ear, "If she had not provided herself a
great belly, he was at her service." A third said, "He warranted
she was a relation of Turpin." To which one of the company,

a great wit, shaking his head, and then his sides, answered, "He believed she was nearer related to Turpis"; at which there was an universal laugh. They were proceeding thus with the poor girl, when somebody, smoking the cassock peeping forth from under the greatcoat of Adams, cried out, "What have we here, a parson?" "How, sirrah," says the justice, "do you go robbing in the dress of a clergyman? let me tell you your habit will not entitle you to the benefit of the clergy." "Yes," said the witty fellow, "he will have one benefit of clergy, he will be exalted above the heads of the people"; at which there was a second laugh. And now the witty spark, seeing his jokes take, began to rise in spirits; and, turning to Adams, challenged him to cap verses, and, provoking him by giving the first blow, he repeated:

Molle meum levibus cord est vilebile telis.

Upon which Adams, with a look full of ineffable contempt, told him, "He deserved scourging for his pronunciation." The witty fellow answered, "What do you deserve, doctor, for not being able to answer the first time? Why, I'll give one, you blockhead, with an S.

Si licet, ut fulvum spectatur in ignibus haurum.

"What, canst not with an M neither? Thou art a pretty fellow for a parson! Why didst not steal some of the parson's Latin as well as his gown?" Another at the table then answered, "If he had, you would have been too hard for him; I remember you at the college a very devil at this sport; I have seen you catch a freshman, for nobody that knew you would engage with you." "I have forgot those things now," cried the wit. "I believe I could have done pretty well formerly. Let's see, what did I end with?—an M again—aye——

Mars, Bacchus, Apollo, virorum.

I could have done it once." "Ah! evil betide you, and so you can now," said the other: "nobody in this country will undertake you." Adams could hold no longer: "Friend," said he, "I have a boy not above eight years old who would instruct thee that the last verse runs thus:

Ut sunt Divorum, Mars, Bacchus, Apollo, virorum."

"I'll hold thee a guinea of that," said the wit, throwing the money on the table. "And I'll go your halves," cries the other. "Done," answered Adams; but upon applying to his pocket he was forced to retract, and own he had no money about him; which set them all a-laughing, and confirmed the triumph of his adversary, which was not moderate, any more than the approbation he met with from the whole company, who told Adams he must go a little longer to school before he attempted to attack that gentleman in Latin.

The clerk, having finished the depositions, as well of the fellow himself, as of those who apprehended the prisoners, delivered them to the justice; who, having sworn the several witnesses without reading a syllable, ordered his clerk to make the mittimus.

Adams then said, "He hoped he should not be condemned unheard." "No, no," cries the justice, "you will be asked what you have to say for yourself when you come on your trial: we are not trying you now; I shall only commit you to gaol: if you can prove your innocence at 'size, you will be found ignoramus, and so no harm done." "Is it no punishment, sir, for an innocent man to lie several months in gaol?" cries Adams: "I beg you would at least hear me before you sign the mittimus." "What signifies all you can say?" says the justice: "is it not here in black and white against you? I must tell you you are a very impertinent fellow to take up so much of my time. So make haste with his mittimus."

The clerk now acquainted the justice that among other suspicious things, as a penknife, &c., found in Adams's pocket, they had discovered a book written, as he apprehended, in cyphers; for no one could read a word in it. "Ay," says the justice, "the fellow may be more than a common robber, he may be in a plot against the Government. Produce the book." Upon which the poor manuscript of Æschylus, which Adams had transcribed with his own hand, was brought forth; and the justice, looking at it, shook his head, and, turning to the prisoner, asked the meaning of those cyphers. "Cyphers?" answered Adams, "it is a manuscript of Æschylus." "Who? who?" said the justice. Adams repeated, "Æschylus." "That is an outlandish name," cried the clerk. "A fictitious name rather, I believe," said the justice. One of the company declared it looked very much like Greek. "Greek?" said the justice; "why, 'tis all writing." "No," says the other, "I don't positively say it is so; for it is a very long time since I have seen any Greek." "There's one," says he, turning to the parson of the parish, who was present, "will tell us immediately." The parson, taking up the book, and putting on his spectacles and gravity together, muttered some words to himself, and then pronounced aloud—"Ay, indeed, it is a Greek manuscript; a very fine piece of antiquity. I make no doubt but it was stolen

from the same clergyman from whom the rogue took the cassock."
"What did the rascal mean by his Æschylus?" says the justice.
"Pooh!" answered the doctor, with a contemptuous grin, "do
you think that fellow knows anything of this book? Æschylus!
ho! ho! I see now what it is—a manuscript of one of the fathers.
I know a nobleman who would give a great deal of money for
such a piece of antiquity. Ay, ay, question and answer. The
beginning is the catechism in Greek. Ay, ay, *Pollaki toi*:
What's your name?"—"Ay, what's your name?" says the
justice to Adams; who answered, "It is Æschylus, and I will
maintain it."—"Oh! it is," says the justice: "make Mr. Æschylus
his mittimus. I will teach you to banter me with a false name."

One of the company, having looked steadfastly at Adams,
asked him, "If he did not know Lady Booby?" Upon which
Adams, presently calling him to mind, answered in a rapture,
"O squire! are you there? I believe you will inform his worship
I am innocent."—"I can indeed say," replied the squire, "that
I am very much surprised to see you in this situation": and then,
addressing himself to the justice, he said, "Sir, I assure you Mr.
Adams is a clergyman, as he appears, and a gentleman of a very
good character. I wish you would enquire a little farther into
this affair; for I am convinced of his innocence."—"Nay,"
says the justice, "if he is a gentleman, and you are sure he is
innocent, I don't desire to commit him, not I: I will commit the
woman by herself, and take your bail for the gentleman: look
into the book, clerk, and see how it is to take bail—come—and
make the mittimus for the woman as fast as you can."—"Sir,"
cries Adams, "I assure you she is as innocent as myself."—
"Perhaps," said the squire, "there may be some mistake! pray
let us hear Mr. Adams's relation."—"With all my heart,"
answered the justice; "and give the gentleman a glass to wet
his whistle before he begins. I know how to behave myself to
gentlemen as well as another. Nobody can say I have committed
a gentleman since I have been in the commission." Adams
then began the narrative, in which, though he was very prolix,
he was uninterrupted, unless by several hums and hahs of the
justice, and his desire to repeat those parts which seemed
to him most material. When he had finished, the justice,
who, on what the squire had said, believed every syllable
of his story on his bare affirmation, notwithstanding the depositions on oath to the contrary, began to let loose several
rogues and rascals against the witness, whom he ordered to
stand forth, but in vain; the said witness, long since finding

what turn matters were likely to take, had privily withdrawn, without attending the issue. The justice now flew into a violent passion, and was hardly prevailed with not to commit the innocent fellows who had been imposed on as well as himself. He swore, "They had best find out the fellow who was guilty of perjury, and bring him before him within two days, or he would bind them all over to their good behaviour." They all promised to use their best endeavours to that purpose, and were dismissed. Then the justice insisted that Mr. Adams should sit down and take a glass with him; and the parson of the parish delivered him back the manuscript without saying a word; nor would Adams, who plainly discerned his ignorance, expose it. As for Fanny, she was, at her own request, recommended to the care of a maid-servant of the house, who helped her to new dress and clean herself.

The company in the parlour had not been long seated before they were alarmed with a horrible uproar from without, where the persons who had apprehended Adams and Fanny had been regaling, according to the custom of the house, with the justice's strong beer. These were all fallen together by the ears, and were cuffing each other without any mercy. The justice himself sallied out, and with the dignity of his presence soon put an end to the fray. On his return into the parlour, he reported, "That the occasion of the quarrel was no other than a dispute to whom, if Adams had been convicted, the greater share of the reward for apprehending him had belonged." All the company laughed at this, except Adams, who, taking his pipe from his mouth, fetched a deep groan, and said, "He was concerned to see so litigious a temper in men. That he remembered a story something like it in one of the parishes where his cure lay:—There was," continued he, "a competition between three young fellows for the place of the clerk, which I disposed of, to the best of my abilities, according to merit; that is, I gave it to him who had the happiest knack at setting a psalm. The clerk was no sooner established in his place than a contention began between the two disappointed candidates concerning their excellence; each contending on whom, had they two been the only competitors, my election would have fallen. This dispute frequently disturbed the congregation, and introduced a discord into the psalmody, till I was forced to silence them both. But, alas! the litigious spirit could not be stifled; and, being no longer able to vent itself in singing, it now broke forth in fighting. It produced many battles (for they were very near a match), and

I believe would have ended fatally, had not the death of the clerk given me an opportunity to promote one of them to his place; which presently put an end to the dispute, and entirely reconciled the contending parties." Adams then proceeded to make some philosophical observations on the folly of growing warm in disputes in which neither party is interested. He then applied himself vigorously to smoking; and a long silence ensued, which was at length broke by the justice, who began to sing forth his own praises, and to value himself exceedingly on his nice discernment in the cause which had lately been before him. He was quickly interrupted by Mr. Adams, between whom and his worship a dispute now arose, whether he ought not, in strictness of law, to have committed him, the said Adams; in which the latter maintained he ought to have been committed, and the justice as vehemently held he ought not. This had most probably produced a quarrel (for both were very violent and positive in their opinions), had not Fanny accidentally heard that a young fellow was going from the justice's house to the very inn where the stage-coach in which Joseph was, put up. Upon this news, she immediately sent for the parson out of the parlour. Adams, when he found her resolute to go (though she would not own the reason, but pretended she could not bear to see the faces of those who had suspected her of such a crime), was as fully determined to go with her; he accordingly took leave of the justice and company: and so ended a dispute in which the law seemed shamefully to intend to set a magistrate and a divine together by the ears.

CHAPTER XII

A VERY DELIGHTFUL ADVENTURE, AS WELL TO THE PERSONS CONCERNED AS TO THE GOOD-NATURED READER

ADAMS, Fanny, and the guide, set out together about one in the morning, the moon being then just risen. They had not gone above a mile before a most violent storm of rain obliged them to take shelter in an inn, or rather alehouse, where Adams immediately procured himself a good fire, a toast and ale, and a pipe, and began to smoke with great content, utterly forgetting everything that had happened.

Fanny sat likewise down by the fire; but was much more impatient at the storm. She presently engaged the eyes of the host, his wife, the maid of the house, and the young fellow who was their guide; they all conceived they had never seen anything half so handsome; and indeed, reader, if thou art of an amorous hue, I advise thee to skip over the next paragraph; which, to render our history perfect, we are obliged to set down, humbly hoping that we may escape the fate of Pygmalion; for if it should happen to us, or to thee, to be struck with this picture, we should be perhaps in as helpless a condition as Narcissus, and might say to ourselves, *Quod petis est nusquam.* Or, if the finest features in it should set Lady ——'s image before our eyes, we should be still in as bad a situation, and might say to our desires, *Cælum ipsum petimus stultitia.*

Fanny was now in the nineteenth year of her age; she was tall and delicately shaped; but not one of those slender young women who seem rather intended to hang up in the hall of an anatomist than for any other purpose. On the contrary, she was so plump that she seemed bursting through her tight stays, especially in the part which confined her swelling breasts. Nor did her hips want the assistance of a hoop to extend them. The exact shape of her arms denoted the form of those limbs which she concealed; and though they were a little reddened by her labour, yet, if her sleeve slipped above her elbow, or her hand-kerchief discovered any part of her neck, a whiteness appeared which the finest Italian paint would be unable to reach. Her hair was of a chestnut brown, and nature had been extremely lavish to her of it, which she had cut, and on Sundays used to curl down her neck, in the modern fashion. Her forehead was high, her eyebrows arched, and rather full than otherwise. Her eyes black and sparkling; her nose just inclining to the Roman; her lips red and moist, and her underlip, according to the opinion of the ladies, too pouting. Her teeth were white, but not exactly even. The small-pox had left one only mark on her chin, which was so large, it might have been mistaken for a dimple, had not her left cheek produced one so near a neighbour to it, that the former served only for a foil to the latter. Her complexion was fair, a little injured by the sun, but overspread with such a bloom that the finest ladies would have exchanged all their white for it: add to these a countenance in which, though she was extremely bashful, a sensibility appeared almost incredible; and a sweet-ness, whenever she smiled, beyond either imitation or description. To conclude all, she had a natural gentility, superior to the acquisition of art, and which surprised all who beheld her.

This lovely creature was sitting by the fire with Adams, when her attention was suddenly engaged by a voice from an inner room, which sung the following song:

THE SONG

Say, Chloe, where must the swain stray
    Who is by thy beauties undone?
To wash their remembrance away,
    To what distant Lethe must run?
The wretch who is sentenced to die
    May escape, and leave justice behind;
From his country perhaps he may fly,
    But oh! can he fly from his mind?

O rapture! unthought of before,
    To be thus of Chloe possess'd;
Nor she, nor no tyrant's hard power,
    Her image can tear from my breast.
But felt not Narcissus more joy,
    With his eyes he beheld his loved charms,
Yet what he beheld the fond boy
    More eagerly wish'd in his arms.

How can it thy dear image be
    Which fills thus my bosom with woe?
Can aught bear resemblance to thee
    Which grief and not joy can bestow?
This counterfeit snatch from my heart,
    Ye pow'rs, tho' with torment I rave,
Tho' mortal will prove the fell smart:
    I then shall find rest in my grave.

Ah, see the dear nymph o'er the plain
    Come smiling and tripping along!
A thousand Loves dance in her train,
    The Graces around her all throng.
To meet her soft Zephyrus flies,
    And wafts all the sweets from the flowers,
Ah, rogue! whilst he kisses her eyes,
    More sweets from her breath he devours.

My soul, whilst I gaze, is on fire;
    But her looks were so tender and kind,
My hope almost reach'd my desire,
    And left lame despair far behind.
Transported with madness, I flew,
    And eagerly seized on my bliss;
Her bosom but half she withdrew,
    But half she refused my fond kiss.

Advances like these made me bold;
    I whisper'd her—Love, we're alone.—
The rest let immortals unfold;
    No language can tell but their own.
Ah, Chloe, expiring, I cried,
    How long I thy cruelty bore!
Ah, Strephon, she blushing replied,
    You ne'er was so pressing before.

Adams had been ruminating all this time on a passage in
Æschylus, without attending in the least to the voice, though
one of the most melodious that ever was heard, when, casting
his eyes on Fanny, he cried out, "Bless us, you look extremely
pale!"—"Pale! Mr. Adams," says she; "O Jesus!" and fell
backwards in her chair. Adams jumped up, flung his Æschylus
into the fire, and fell a-roaring to the people of the house for
help. He soon summoned every one into the room, and the song-
ster among the rest; but, O reader! when this nightingale, who
was no other than Joseph Andrews himself, saw his beloved
Fanny in the situation we have described her, canst thou conceive the agitations of his mind? If thou canst not, waive that
meditation to behold his happiness, when, clasping her in his
arms, he found life and blood returning to her cheeks: when he
saw her open her beloved eyes, and heard her with the softest
accent whisper, "Are you Joseph Andrews?"—"Art thou my
Fanny?" he answered eagerly: and, pulling her to his heart, he
imprinted numberless kisses on her lips, without considering
who were present.

If prudes are offended at the lusciousness of this picture, they
may take their eyes off from it, and survey parson Adams
dancing about the room in a rapture of joy. Some philosophers
may perhaps doubt whether he was not the happiest of the three:
for the goodness of his heart enjoyed the blessings which were
exulting in the breasts of both the other two, together with his
own. But we shall leave such disquisitions, as too deep for us,
to those who are building some favourite hypothesis, which
they will refuse no metaphysical rubbish to erect and support:
for our part, we give it clearly on the side of Joseph, whose
happiness was not only greater than the parson's, but of longer
duration: for as soon as the first tumults of Adams's rapture
were over he cast his eyes towards the fire, where Æschylus lay
expiring; and immediately rescued the poor remains, to wit, the
sheepskin covering, of his dear friend, which was the work of his
own hands, and had been his inseparable companion for upwards
of thirty years.

Fanny had no sooner perfectly recovered herself than she
began to restrain the impetuosity of her transports; and, reflecting on what she had done and suffered in the presence of so
many, she was immediately covered with confusion; and, push-
ing Joseph gently from her, she begged him to be quiet, nor would
admit of either kiss or embrace any longer. Then, seeing Mrs.
Slipslop, she curtsied, and offered to advance to her; but that

high woman would not return her curtsies; but, casting her eyes another way, immediately withdrew into another room, muttering, as she went, she wondered who the creature was.

CHAPTER XIII

A DISSERTATION CONCERNING HIGH PEOPLE AND LOW PEOPLE, WITH MRS. SLIPSLOP'S DEPARTURE IN NO VERY GOOD TEMPER OF MIND, AND THE EVIL PLIGHT IN WHICH SHE LEFT ADAMS AND HIS COMPANY

IT will doubtless seem extremely odd to many readers, that Mrs. Slipslop, who had lived several years in the same house with Fanny, should, in a short separation, utterly forget her. And indeed the truth is, that she remembered her very well. As we would not willingly, therefore, that anything should appear unnatural in this our history, we will endeavour to explain the reasons of her conduct; nor do we doubt being able to satisfy the most curious reader that Mrs. Slipslop did not in the least deviate from the common road in this behaviour; and, indeed, had she done otherwise, she must have descended below herself, and would have very justly been liable to censure.

Be it known then, that the human species are divided into two sorts of people, to wit, high people and low people. As by high people I would not be understood to mean persons literally born higher in their dimensions than the rest of their species, nor metaphorically those of exalted characters or abilities; so by low people I cannot be construed to intend the reverse. High people signify no other than people of fashion, and low people those of no fashion. Now, this word fashion hath by long use lost its original meaning, from which at present it gives us a very different idea; for I am deceived if by persons of fashion we do not generally include a conception of birth and accomplishments superior to the herd of mankind; whereas, in reality, nothing more was originally meant by a person of fashion than a person who dressed himself in the fashion of the times; and the word really and truly signifies no more at this day. Now, the world being thus divided into people of fashion and people of no fashion, a fierce contention arose between them; nor would those of one party, to avoid suspicion, be seen publicly to speak to those of the other, though they often held a very good correspondence in private. In this contention it is difficult to say which party succeeded; for, whilst the people of fashion seized several places to their own use, such as courts, assemblies, operas, balls, &c., the people of no fashion, besides one royal place, called his Majesty's Bear-garden, have been in constant possession of all hops, fairs, revels, &c. Two places have been agreed to be divided between them, namely, the church and the playhouse, where they segregate themselves from each other in a remarkable manner; for, as the people of fashion exalt themselves at church over the heads of the people of no fashion, so in the playhouse they abase themselves in the same degree under their feet. This distinction I have never met with any one able to account for: it is sufficient that, so far from looking on at each other as brethren in the Christian language, they seem scarce to regard each other as of the same species. This, the terms "strange persons, people one does not know, the creature, wretches, beasts, brutes," and many other appellations evidently demonstrate; which Mrs. Slipslop, having often heard her mistress use, thought she had also a right to use in her turn; and perhaps she was not mistaken; for these two parties, especially those bordering nearly on each other, to wit, the lowest of the high, and the highest of the low, often change their parties according to place and time; for those who are people of fashion in one place are often people of no fashion in another. And with regard to time, it may not be unpleasant to survey the picture of dependance like a kind of ladder; as, for instance: early in the morning arises the postillion, or some other boy, which great families, no more than great ships, are without, and falls to brushing the clothes and cleaning the shoes of John the footman; who, being drest himself, applies his hands to the same labours for Mr. Second-hand, the squire's gentleman; the gentleman in the like manner, a little later in the day, attends the squire; the squire is no sooner equipped than he attends the levee of my lord; which is no sooner over than my lord himself is seen at the levee of the favourite, who, after the hour of homage is at an end, appears himself to pay homage to the levee of his sovereign. Nor is there, perhaps, in this whole ladder of dependance, any one step at a greater distance from the other than the first from the second; so that to a philosopher the question might only seem, whether you would chuse to be a great man at six in the morning or at two in the afternoon. And yet there are scarce two of these who do not think the least familiarity with the persons below them a condescension, and, if they were to go one step farther, a degradation.

And now, reader, I hope thou wilt pardon this long digression, which seemed to me necessary to vindicate the great character of Mrs. Slipslop from what low people, who have never seen high people, might think an absurdity; but we who know them must have daily found very high persons know us in one place and not in another, to-day and not to-morrow; all which it is difficult to account for otherwise than I have here endeavoured; and perhaps, if the gods, according to the opinion of some, made men only to laugh at them, there is no part of our behaviour which answers the end of our creation better than this.

But to return to our history: Adams, who knew no more of this than the cat which sat on the table, imagining Mrs. Slipslop's memory had been much worse than it really was, followed her into the next room, crying out, "Madam Slipslop, here is one of your old acquaintance; do but see what a fine woman she is grown since she left Lady Booby's service."—"I think I reflect something of her," answered she, with great dignity, "but I can't remember all the inferior servants in our family." She then proceeded to satisfy Adams's curiosity, by telling him, "When she arrived at the inn, she found a chaise ready for her; that, her lady being expected very shortly in the country, she was obliged to make the utmost haste; and, in commensuration of Joseph's lameness, she had taken him with her"; and lastly, "that the excessive virulence of the storm had driven them into the house where he found them." After which, she acquainted Adams with his having left his horse, and exprest some wonder at his having strayed so far out of his way, and at meeting him, as she said, "in the company of that wench, who she feared was no better than she should be."

The horse was no sooner put into Adams's head but he was immediately driven out by this reflection on the character of Fanny. He protested, "He believed there was not a chaster damsel in the universe. I heartily wish, I heartily wish," cried he (snapping his fingers), "that all her betters were as good." He then proceeded to inform her of the accident of their meeting; but when he came to mention the circumstance of delivering her from the rape, she said, "She thought him properer for the army than the clergy; that it did not become a clergyman to lay violent hands on any one; that he should have rather prayed that she might be strengthened." Adams said, "He was very far from being ashamed of what he had done": she replied, "Want of shame was not the currycuristic of a clergyman." This dialogue might have probably grown warmer, had not

Joseph opportunely entered the room, to ask leave of Madam Slipslop to introduce Fanny: but she positively refused to admit any such trollops, and told him, "She would have been burnt before she would have suffered him to get into a chaise with her, if she had once suspected him of having his sluts waylaid on the road for him"; adding, "that Mr. Adams acted a very pretty part, and she did not doubt but to see him a bishop." He made the best bow he could, and cried out, "I thank you, madam, for that right-reverend appellation, which I shall take all honest means to deserve."—"Very honest means," returned she, with a sneer, "to bring people together." At these words Adams took two or three strides across the room, when the coachman came to inform Mrs. Slipslop, "That the storm was over, and the moon shone very bright." She then sent for Joseph, who was sitting without with his Fanny, and would have had him gone with her; but he peremptorily refused to leave Fanny behind, which threw the good woman into a violent rage. She said, "She would inform her lady what doings were carrying on, and did not doubt but she would rid the parish of all such people"; and concluded a long speech, full of bitterness and very hard words, with some reflections on the clergy not decent to repeat; at last, finding Joseph unmoveable, she flung herself into the chaise, casting a look at Fanny as she went, not unlike that which Cleopatra gives Octavia in the play. To say the truth, she was most disagreeably disappointed by the presence of Fanny: she had, from her first seeing Joseph at the inn, conceived hopes of something which might have been accomplished at an alehouse as well as a palace. Indeed, it is probable Mr. Adams had rescued more than Fanny from the danger of a rape that evening.

When the chaise had carried off the enraged Slipslop, Adams, Joseph, and Fanny assembled over the fire, where they had a great deal of innocent chat, pretty enough; but, as possibly it would not be very entertaining to the reader, we shall hasten to the morning; only observing that none of them went to bed that night. Adams, when he had smoked three pipes, took a comfortable nap in a great chair, and left the lovers, whose eyes were too well employed to permit any desire of shutting them, to enjoy by themselves, during some hours, an happiness which none of my readers who have never been in love are capable of the least conception of, though we had as many tongues as Homer desired, to describe it with, and which all true lovers will represent to their own minds without the least assistance from us.

Let it suffice then to say, that Fanny, after a thousand entreaties, at last gave up her whole soul to Joseph; and, almost
fainting in his arms, with a sigh infinitely softer and sweeter too
than any Arabian breeze, she whispered to his lips, which were
then close to hers, "O Joseph, you have won me: I will be yours
for ever." Joseph, having thanked her on his knees, and embraced her with an eagerness which she now almost returned,
leapt up in a rapture, and awakened the parson, earnestly
begging him "that he would that instant join their hands together." Adams rebuked him for his request, and told him,
"He would by no means consent to anything contrary to the
forms of the Church; that he had no licence, nor indeed would he
advise him to obtain one; that the Church had prescribed a
form—namely, the publication of banns—with which all good
Christians ought to comply, and to the omission of which he
attributed the many miseries which befell great folks in
marriage"; concluding, "As many as are joined together otherwise than G—'s word doth allow are not joined together by G—,
neither is their matrimony lawful." Fanny agreed with the
parson, saying to Joseph, with a blush, "She assured him she
would not consent to any such thing, and that she wondered at his
offering it." In which resolution she was comforted and commended by Adams; and Joseph was obliged to wait patiently
till after the third publication of the banns, which, however, he
obtained the consent of Fanny, in the presence of Adams, to put
in at their arrival.

The sun had now been risen some hours, when Joseph, finding
his leg surprisingly recovered, proposed to walk forwards; but
when they were all ready to set out, an accident a little retarded
them. This was no other than the reckoning, which amounted
to seven shillings; no great sum if we consider the immense
quantity of ale which Mr. Adams poured in. Indeed, they had
no objection to the reasonableness of the bill, but many to
the probability of paying it; for the fellow who had taken poor
Fanny's purse had unluckily forgot to return it. So that the
account stood thus:—

	£	s.	d.
Mr. Adams and company, Dr. . . .	0	7	0
In Mr. Adams's pocket	0	0	6½
In Mr. Joseph's	0	0	0
In Mrs. Fanny's	0	0	0
Balance	0	6	5½

They stood silent some few minutes, staring at each other, when Adams whipt out on his toes, and asked the hostess, "If there was no clergyman in that parish?" She answered, "There was."— "Is he wealthy?" replied he; to which she likewise answered in the affirmative. Adams then snapping his fingers returned overjoyed to his companions, crying out, "Heureka, Heureka"; which not being understood, he told them in plain English, "They need give themselves no trouble, for he had a brother in the parish who would defray the reckoning, and that he would just step to his house and fetch the money, and return to them instantly."

CHAPTER XIV

AN INTERVIEW BETWEEN PARSON ADAMS AND PARSON TRULLIBER

PARSON ADAMS came to the house of parson Trulliber, whom he found stript into his waistcoat, with an apron on, and a pail in his hand, just come from serving his hogs; for Mr. Trulliber was a parson on Sundays, but all the other six might more properly be called a farmer. He occupied a small piece of land of his own, besides which he rented a considerable deal more. His wife milked his cows, managed his dairy, and followed the markets with butter and eggs. The hogs fell chiefly to his care, which he carefully waited on at home, and attended to fairs; on which occasion he was liable to many jokes, his own size being, with much ale, rendered little inferior to that of the beasts he sold. He was indeed one of the largest men you should see, and could have acted the part of Sir John Falstaff without stuffing. Add to this that the rotundity of his belly was considerably increased by the shortness of his stature, his shadow ascending very near as far in height, when he lay on his back, as when he stood on his legs. His voice was loud and hoarse, and his accents extremely broad. To complete the whole, he had a stateliness in his gait, when he walked, not unlike that of a goose, only he stalked slower.

Mr. Trulliber, being informed that somebody wanted to speak with him, immediately slipt off his apron and clothed himself in an old night-gown, being the dress in which he always saw his company at home. His wife, who informed him of Mr. Adams's arrival, had made a small mistake; for she had told her husband, "She believed there was a man come for some of his hogs." This supposition made Mr. Trulliber hasten with the utmost expedition to attend his guest. He no sooner saw Adams than, not in the least doubting the cause of his errand to be what his wife had imagined, he told him, "He was come in very good time; that he expected a dealer that very afternoon"; and added, "they were all pure and fat, and upwards of twenty score a-piece." Adams answered, "He believed he did not know him." "Yes, yes," cried Trulliber, "I have seen you often at fair; why, we have dealt before now, mun, I warrant you. Yes, yes," cries he, "I remember thy face very well, but won't mention a word more till you have seen them, though I have never sold thee a flitch of such bacon as is now in the stye." Upon which he laid violent hands on Adams, and dragged him into the hog-stye, which was indeed but two steps from his parlour window. They were no sooner arrived here than he cry'd out, "Do but handle them! step in, friend! art welcome to handle them, whether dost buy or no." At which words, opening the gate, he pushed Adams into the pig-stye, insisting on it that he should handle them before he would talk one word with him.

Adams, whose natural complacence was beyond any artificial, was obliged to comply before he was suffered to explain himself; and, laying hold on one of their tails, the unruly beast gave such a sudden spring, that he threw poor Adams all along in the mire. Trulliber, instead of assisting him to get up, burst into a laughter, and, entering the stye, said to Adams, with some contempt, "Why, dost not know how to handle a hog?" and was going to lay hold of one himself, but Adams, who thought he had carried his complacence far enough, was no sooner on his legs than he escaped out of the reach of the animals, and cried out, "*Nihil habeo cum porcis*: I am a clergyman, sir, and am not come to buy hogs." Trulliber answered, "He was sorry for the mistake, but that he must blame his wife," adding, "she was a fool, and always committed blunders." He then desired him to walk in and clean himself, that he would only fasten up the stye and follow him. Adams desired leave to dry his greatcoat, wig, and hat by the fire, which Trulliber granted. Mrs. Trulliber would have brought him a basin of water to wash his face, but her husband bid her be quiet like a fool as she was, or she would commit more blunders, and then directed Adams to the pump. While Adams was thus employed, Trulliber, conceiving no great respect for the appearance of his guest, fastened the parlour door, and now conducted him into the kitchen, telling him he believed a cup of drink would do him no harm, and whispered his wife to draw a little of the worst ale. After a short silence Adams said, "I fancy, sir, you already perceive me to be a clergyman."—"Ay, ay," cries Trulliber, grinning, "I perceive you have some cassock; I will not venture to caale it a whole one." Adams answered, "It was indeed none of the best, but he had the misfortune to tear it about ten years ago in passing over a stile." Mrs. Trulliber, returning with the drink, told her husband, "She fancied the gentleman was a traveller, and that he would be glad to eat a bit." Trulliber bid her hold her impertinent tongue, and asked her, "If parsons used to travel without horses?" adding, "he supposed the gentleman had none by his having no boots on."— "Yes, sir, yes," says Adams; "I have a horse, but I have left him behind me."—"I am glad to hear you have one," says Trulliber; "for I assure you I don't love to see clergymen on foot; it is not seemly nor suiting the dignity of the cloth." Here Trulliber made a long oration on the dignity of the cloth (or rather gown) not much worth relating, till his wife had spread the table and set a mess of porridge on it for his breakfast. He then said to Adams, "I don't know, friend, how you came to caale on me; however, as you are here, if you think proper to eat a morsel, you may." Adams accepted the invitation, and the two parsons sat down together; Mrs. Trulliber waiting behind her husband's chair, as was, it seems, her custom. Trulliber eat heartily, but scarce put anything in his mouth without finding fault with his wife's cookery. All which the poor woman bore patiently. Indeed, she was so absolute an admirer of her husband's greatness and importance, of which she had frequent hints from his own mouth, that she almost carried her adoration to an opinion of his infallibility. To say the truth, the parson had exercised her more ways than one; and the pious woman had [been] so well edified by her husband's sermons, that she had resolved to receive the bad things of this world together with the good. She had indeed been at first a little contentious; but he had long since got the better; partly by her love for this, partly by her fear of that, partly by her religion, partly by the respect he paid himself, and partly by that which he received from the parish. She had, in short, absolutely submitted, and now worshipped her husband, as Sarah did Abraham, calling him (not lord, but) master. Whilst they were at table her husband gave her a fresh example of his greatness; for, as she had just delivered a cup of ale to Adams, he snatched it out of his hand, and, crying out, "I caal'd vurst," swallowed down the ale. Adams denied it; it was referred to the wife, who, though her conscience was on the side of Adams, durst not give it against her husband; upon which

he said, "No, sir, no; I should not have been so rude to have
taken it from you if you had caal'd vurst, but I'd have you
know I'm a better man than to suffer the best he in the kingdom
to drink before me in my own house when I caale vurst."

As soon as their breakfast was ended, Adams began in the
following manner: "I think, sir, it is high time to inform you of
the business of my embassy. I am a traveller, and am passing
this way in company with two young people, a lad and a damsel,
my parishioners, towards my own cure; we stopt at a house of
hospitality in the parish, where they directed me to you as having
the cure."—"Though I am but a curate," says Trulliber, "I
believe I am as warm as the vicar himself, or perhaps the rector
of the next parish too; I believe I could buy them both."—
"Sir," cries Adams, "I rejoice thereat. Now, sir, my business
is, that we are by various accidents stript of our money, and are
not able to pay our reckoning, being seven shillings. I therefore
request you to assist me with the loan of those seven shillings,
and also seven shillings more, which, peradventure, I shall return
to you; but if not, I am convinced you will joyfully embrace
such an opportunity of laying up a treasure in a better place than
any this world affords."

Suppose a stranger, who entered the chambers of a lawyer,
being imagined a client, when the lawyer was preparing his palm
for the fee, should pull out a writ against him. Suppose an
apothecary, at the door of a chariot containing some great doctor
of eminent skill, should, instead of directions to a patient, present
him with a potion for himself Suppose a minister should,
instead of a good round sum, treat my lord ——, or sir ——,
or esq. —— with a good broomstick. Suppose a civil companion, or a led captain, should, instead of virtue, and honour,
and beauty, and parts, and admiration, thunder vice, and infamy, and ugliness, and folly, and contempt in his patron's ears.
Suppose, when a tradesman first carries in his bill, the man of
fashion should pay it; or suppose, if he did so, the tradesman
should abate what he had overcharged, on the supposition of
waiting. In short—suppose what you will, you never can nor
will suppose anything equal to the astonishment which seized
on Trulliber, as soon as Adams had ended his speech. A
while he rolled his eyes in silence; sometimes surveying Adams,
then his wife; then casting them on the ground, then lifting them
up to heaven. At last he burst forth in the following accents:
"Sir, I believe I know where to lay up my little treasure as well
as another. I thank G—, if I am not so warm as some, I am

content; that is a blessing greater than riches; and he to whom that is given need ask no more. To be content with a little is greater than to possess the world; which a man may possess without being so. Lay up my treasure! what matters where a man's treasure is whose heart is in the Scriptures? there is the treasure of a Christian." At these words the water ran from Adams's eyes; and, catching Trulliber by the hand in a rapture, "Brother," says he, "heavens bless the accident by which I came to see you! I would have walked many a mile to have communed with you; and, believe me, I will shortly pay you a second visit; but my friends, I fancy, by this time, wonder at my stay; so let me have the money immediately." Trulliber then put on a stern look, and cried out, "Thou dost not intend to rob me?" At which the wife, bursting into tears, fell on her knees and roared out, "O dear sir! for Heaven's sake don't rob my master; we are but poor people." "Get up, for a fool as thou art, and go about thy business," said Trulliber; "dost think the man will venture his life? he is a beggar, and no robber." "Very true, indeed," answered Adams. "I wish, with all my heart, the tithing-man was here," cries Trulliber; "I would have thee punished as a vagabond for thy impudence. Fourteen shillings indeed! I won't give thee a farthing. I believe thou art no more a clergyman than the woman there" (pointing to his wife); "but if thou art, dost deserve to have thy gown stript over thy shoulders for running about the country in such a manner." "I forgive your suspicions," says Adams; "but suppose I am not a clergyman, I am nevertheless thy brother; and thou, as a Christian, much more as a clergyman, art obliged to relieve my distress." "Dost preach to me?" replied Trulliber, "dost pretend to instruct me in my duty?" "Ifacks, a good story," cries Mrs. Trulliber, "to preach to my master." "Silence, woman," cries Trulliber. "I would have thee know, friend" (addressing himself to Adams), "I shall not learn my duty from such as thee. I know what charity is, better than to give to vagabonds." "Besides, if we were inclined, the poor's rate obliges us to give so much charity," cries the wife. "Pugh! thou art a fool. Poor's rate! Hold thy nonsense," answered Trulliber; and then, turning to Adams, he told him, "he would give him nothing." "I am sorry," answered Adams, "that you do know what charity is, since you practise it no better: I must tell you, if you trust to your knowledge for your justification, you will find yourself deceived, though you should add faith to it, without good works." "Fellow," cries Trulliber, "dost thou speak against faith in my house? Get out of my doors: I will no longer remain under the same roof with a wretch who speaks wantonly of faith and the Scriptures." "Name not the Scriptures," says Adams. "How! not name the Scriptures! Do you disbelieve the Scriptures?" cries Trulliber. "No; but you do," answered Adams, "if I may reason from your practice; for their commands are so explicit, and their rewards and punishments so immense, that it is impossible a man should stedfastly believe without obeying. Now, there is no command more express, no duty more frequently enjoined, than charity. Whoever, therefore, is void of charity, I make no scruple of pronouncing that he is no Christian." "I would not advise thee," says Trulliber, "to say that I am no Christian: I won't take it of you; for I believe I am as good a man as thyself" (and indeed, though he was now rather too corpulent for athletic exercises, he had, in his youth, been one of the best boxers and cudgel-players in the county). His wife, seeing him clench his fist, interposed, and begged him not to fight, but show himself a true Christian, and take the law of him. As nothing could provoke Adams to strike, but an absolute assault on himself or his friend, he smiled at the angry look and gestures of Trulliber; and, telling him he was sorry to see such men in orders, departed without further ceremony.

CHAPTER XV

AN ADVENTURE, THE CONSEQUENCE OF A NEW INSTANCE WHICH PARSON ADAMS GAVE OF HIS FORGETFULNESS

WHEN he came back to the inn he found Joseph and Fanny sitting together. They were so far from thinking his absence long, as he had feared they would, that they never once missed or thought of him. Indeed, I have been often assured by both, that they spent these hours in a most delightful conversation; but, as I never could prevail on either to relate it, so I cannot communicate it to the reader.

Adams acquainted the lovers with the ill success of his enterprise. They were all greatly confounded, none being able to propose any method of departing, till Joseph at last advised calling in the hostess, and desiring her to trust them; which Fanny said she despaired of her doing, as she was one of the sourest-faced women she had ever beheld.

But she was agreeably disappointed; for the hostess was no sooner asked the question than she readily agreed; and, with a curtsy and smile, wished them a good journey. However, lest Fanny's skill in physiognomy should be called in question, we will venture to assign one reason which might probably incline her to this confidence and good-humour. When Adams said he was going to visit his brother, he had unwittingly imposed on Joseph and Fanny, who believed he had meant his natural brother, and not his brother in divinity, and had so informed the hostess, on her enquiry after him. Now Mr. Trulliber had, by his professions of piety, by his gravity, austerity, reserve, and the opinion of his great wealth, so great an authority in his parish, that they all lived in the utmost fear and apprehension of him. It was therefore no wonder that the hostess, who knew it was in his option whether she should ever sell another mug of drink, did not dare to affront his supposed brother by denying him credit.

They were now just on their departure when Adams recollected he had left his greatcoat and hat at Mr. Trulliber's. As he was not desirous of renewing his visit, the hostess herself, having no servant at home, offered to fetch it.

This was an unfortunate expedient; for the hostess was soon undeceived in the opinion she had entertained of Adams, whom Trulliber abused in the grossest terms, especially when he heard he had had the assurance to pretend to be his near relation.

At her return, therefore, she entirely changed her note. She said, "Folks might be ashamed of travelling about, and pretending to be what they were not. That taxes were high, and for her part she was obliged to pay for what she had; she could not therefore possibly, nor would she, trust anybody; no, not her own father. That money was never scarcer, and she wanted to make up a sum. That she expected, therefore, they should pay their reckoning before they left the house."

Adams was now greatly perplexed; but, as he knew that he could easily have borrowed such a sum in his own parish, and as he knew he would have lent it himself to any mortal in distress, so he took fresh courage, and sallied out all round the parish, but to no purpose; he returned as pennyless as he went, groaning and lamenting that it was possible, in a country professing Christianity, for a wretch to starve in the midst of his fellow-creatures who abounded.

Whilst he was gone, the hostess, who stayed as a sort of guard with Joseph and Fanny, entertained them with the goodness of parson Trulliber. And, indeed, he had not only a very good character as to other qualities in the neighbourhood, but was reputed a man of great charity; for, though he never gave a farthing, he had always that word in his mouth.

Adams was no sooner returned the second time than the storm grew exceedingly high, the hostess declaring, among other things, that, if they offered to stir without paying her, she would soon overtake them with a warrant.

Plato and Aristotle, or somebody else, hath said, *that when the most exquisite cunning fails, chance often hits the mark, and that by means the least expected.* Virgil expresses this very boldly:

> *Turne, quod optanti divum promittere nemo*
> *Auderet, volvenda dies, en ! attulit ultro.*

I would quote more great men if I could; but my memory not permitting me, I will proceed to exemplify these observations by the following instance:

There chanced (for Adams had not cunning enough to contrive it) to be at that time in the alehouse a fellow who had been formerly a drummer in an Irish regiment, and now travelled the country as a pedlar. This man, having attentively listened to the discourse of the hostess, at last took Adams aside, and asked him what the sum was for which they were detained. As soon as he was informed, he sighed, and said, "He was sorry it was so much; for that he had no more than six shillings and sixpence in his pocket, which he would lend them with all his heart." Adams gave a caper, and cry'd out, "It would do; for that he had sixpence himself." And thus these poor people, who could not engage the compassion of riches and piety, were at length delivered out of their distress by the charity of a poor pedlar.

I shall refer it to my reader to make what observations he pleases on this incident: it is sufficient for me to inform him that, after Adams and his companions had returned him a thousand thanks, and told him where he might call to be repaid, they all sallied out of the house without any compliments from their hostess, or indeed without paying her any; Adams declaring he would take particular care never to call there again; and she on her side assuring them she wanted no such guests.

CHAPTER XVI

A VERY CURIOUS ADVENTURE, IN WHICH MR. ADAMS GAVE A MUCH GREATER INSTANCE OF THE HONEST SIMPLICITY OF HIS HEART, THAN OF HIS EXPERIENCE IN THE WAYS OF THIS WORLD

OUR travellers had walked about two miles from that inn, which they had more reason to have mistaken for a castle than Don Quixote ever had any of those in which he sojourned, seeing they had met with such difficulty in escaping out of its walls, when they came to a parish, and beheld a sign of invitation hanging out. A gentleman sat smoking a pipe at the door, of whom Adams inquired the road, and received so courteous and obliging an answer, accompanied with so smiling a countenance, that the good parson, whose heart was naturally disposed to love and affection, began to ask several other questions; particularly the name of the parish, and who was the owner of a large house whose front they then had in prospect. The gentleman answered as obligingly as before; and as to the house, acquainted him it was his own. He then proceeded in the following manner: "Sir, I presume by your habit you are a clergyman; and as you are travelling on foot I suppose a glass of good beer will not be disagreeable to you; and I can recommend my landlord's within as some of the best in all this country. What say you, will you halt a little and let us take a pipe together? there is no better tobacco in the kingdom." This proposal was not displeasing to Adams, who had allayed his thirst that day with no better liquor than what Mrs. Trulliber's cellar had produced; and which was indeed little superior, either in richness or in flavour, to that which distilled from those grains her generous husband bestowed on his hogs. Having, therefore, abundantly thanked the gentleman for his kind invitation, and bid Joseph and Fanny follow him, he entered the alehouse, where a large loaf and cheese and a pitcher of beer, which truly answered the character given of it, being set before them, the three travellers fell to eating, with appetites infinitely more voracious than are to be found at the most exquisite eating-houses in the parish of St. James's.

The gentleman expressed great delight in the hearty and cheerful behaviour of Adams; and particularly in the familiarity with which he conversed with Joseph and Fanny, whom he often called his children; a term he explained to mean no more than his parishioners; saying, "He looked on all those whom God had intrusted to his cure to stand to him in that relation." The gentleman, shaking him by the hand, highly applauded those sentiments. "They are, indeed," says he, "the true principles of a Christian divine; and I heartily wish they were universal; but, on the contrary, I am sorry to say the parson of our parish, instead of esteeming his poor parishioners as a part of his family, seems rather to consider them as not of the same species with himself. He seldom speaks to any, unless some few of the richest of us; nay, indeed, he will not move his hat to the others. I often laugh when I behold him on Sundays strutting along the churchyard like a turkey-cock through rows of his parishioners, who bow to him with as much submission, and are as unregarded, as a set of servile courtiers by the proudest prince in Christendom. But if such temporal pride is ridiculous, surely the spiritual is odious and detestable; if such a puffed-up empty human bladder, strutting in princely robes, justly moves one's derision, surely in the habit of a priest it must raise our scorn."

"Doubtless," answered Adams, "your opinion is right; but I hope such examples are rare. The clergy whom I have the honour to know maintain a different behaviour; and you will allow me, sir, that the readiness which too many of the laity show to contemn the order may be one reason of their avoiding too much humility."—"Very true, indeed," says the gentleman; "I find, sir, you are a man of excellent sense, and am happy in this opportunity of knowing you; perhaps our accidental meeting may not be disadvantageous to you neither. At present I shall only say to you that the incumbent of this living is old and infirm, and that it is in my gift. Doctor, give me your hand; and assure yourself of it at his decease." Adams told him, "He was never more confounded in his life than at his utter incapacity to make any return to such noble and unmerited generosity."—"A mere trifle, sir," cries the gentleman, "scarce worth your acceptance; a little more than three hundred a year. I wish it was double the value for your sake." Adams bowed, and cried from the emotions of his gratitude; when the other asked him, "If he was married, or had any children, besides those in the spiritual sense he had mentioned."—"Sir," replied the parson, "I have a wife and six at your service."—"That is unlucky," says the gentleman; "for I would otherwise have taken you into my own house as my chaplain; however, I have another in the parish (for the parsonage-house is not good enough), which I will furnish for you. Pray, does your wife understand a dairy?"—"I can't profess she does," says Adams. "I am sorry for it," quoth the gentleman; "I would have given you half-a-dozen cows, and very good grounds to have maintained them."—"Sir," said Adams, in an ecstasy, "you are too liberal; indeed you are."— "Not at all," cries the gentleman: "I esteem riches only as they give me an opportunity of doing good; and I never saw one whom I had a greater inclination to serve." At which words he shook him heartily by the hand, and told him he had sufficient room in his house to entertain him and his friends. Adams begged he might give him no such trouble; that they could be very well accommodated in the house where they were; forgetting they had not a sixpenny piece among them. The gentleman would not be denied; and, informing himself how far they were travelling, he said it was too long a journey to take on foot, and begged that they would favour him by suffering him to lend them a servant and horses; adding, withal, that, if they would do him the pleasure of their company only two days, he would furnish them with his coach and six. Adams, turning to Joseph, said, "How lucky is this gentleman's goodness to you, who I am afraid would be scarce able to hold out on your lame leg!" and then, addressing the person who made him these liberal promises, after much bowing, he cried out, "Blessed be the hour which first introduced me to a man of your charity! you are indeed a Christian of the true primitive kind, and an honour to the country wherein you live. I would willingly have taken a pilgrimage to the Holy Land to have beheld you; for the advantages which we draw from your goodness give me little pleasure, in comparison of what I enjoy for your own sake when I consider the treasures you are by these means laying up for yourself in a country that passeth not away. We will therefore, most generous sir, accept your goodness, as well the entertainment you have so kindly offered us at your house this evening, as the accommodation of your horses to-morrow morning." He then began to search for his hat, as did Joseph for his; and both they and Fanny were in order of departure, when the gentleman, stopping short, and seeming to meditate by himself for the space of about a minute, exclaimed thus: "Sure never anything was so unlucky; I had forgot that my housekeeper was gone abroad, and hath locked up all my rooms; indeed, I would break them open for you, but shall not be able to furnish you with a bed; for she has likewise put away all my linen. I am glad it entered into my head before I had given you the trouble of walking there;

besides, I believe you will find better accommodations here than you expected.—Landlord, you can provide good beds for these people, can't you?"—"Yes, and please your worship," cries the host, "and such as no lord or justice of the peace in the kingdom need be ashamed to lie in."—"I am heartily sorry," says the gentleman, "for this disappointment. I am resolved I will never suffer her to carry away the keys again."—"Pray, sir, let it not make you uneasy," cries Adams; "we shall do very well here; and the loan of your horses is a favour we shall be incapable of making any return to."—"Ay!" said the squire, "the horses shall attend you here at what hour in the morning you please"; and now, after many civilities too tedious to enumerate, many squeezes by the hand, with most affectionate looks and smiles at each other, and after appointing the horses at seven the next morning, the gentleman took his leave of them, and departed to his own house. Adams and his companions returned to the table, where the parson smoked another pipe, and then they all retired to rest.

Mr. Adams rose very early, and called Joseph out of his bed, between whom a very fierce dispute ensued whether Fanny should ride behind Joseph, or behind the gentleman's servant; Joseph insisting on it that he was perfectly recovered, and was as capable of taking care of Fanny as any other person could be. But Adams would not agree to it, and declared he would not trust her behind him; for that he was weaker than he imagined himself to be.

This dispute continued a long time, and had begun to be very hot, when a servant arrived from their good friend, to acquaint them that he was unfortunately prevented from lending them any horses; for that his groom had, unknown to him, put his whole stable under a course of physic.

This advice presently struck the two disputants dumb: Adams cried out, "Was ever anything so unlucky as this poor gentleman? I protest I am more sorry on his account than my own. You see, Joseph, how this good-natured man is treated by his servants; one locks up his linen, another physics his horses, and I suppose, by his being at this house last night, the butler had locked up his cellar. Bless us! how good-nature is used in this world! I protest I am more concerned on his account than my own."—"So am not I," cries Joseph; "not that I am much troubled about walking on foot; all my concern is, how we shall get out of the house, unless God sends another pedlar to redeem us. But certainly this gentleman has such an affection for you, that he would lend you a larger sum than we owe here, which is not above four or five shillings."—"Very true, child," answered Adams; "I will write a letter to him, and will even venture to solicit him for three half-crowns; there will be no harm in having two or three shillings in our pockets; as we have full forty miles to travel, we may possibly have occasion for them."

Fanny being now risen, Joseph paid her a visit, and left Adams to write his letter, which having finished, he despatched a boy with it to the gentleman, and then seated himself by the door, lighted his pipe, and betook himself to meditation.

The boy staying longer than seemed to be necessary, Joseph, who with Fanny was now returned to the parson, expressed some apprehensions that the gentleman's steward had locked up his purse too. To which Adams answered, "It might very possibly be, and he should wonder at no liberties which the devil might put into the head of a wicked servant to take with so worthy a master"; but added, "that, as the sum was so small, so noble a gentleman would be easily able to procure it in the parish, though he had it not in his own pocket. Indeed," says he, "if it was four or five guineas, or any such large quantity of money, it might be a different matter."

They were now sat down to breakfast over some toast and ale, when the boy returned and informed them that the gentleman was not at home. "Very well!" cries Adams; "but why, child, did you not stay till his return? Go back again, my good boy, and wait for his coming home; he cannot be gone far, as his horses are all sick; and besides, he had no intention to go abroad, for he invited us to spend this day and to-morrow at his house. Therefore go back, child, and tarry till his return home." The messenger departed, and was back again with great expedition, bringing an account that the gentleman was gone on a long journey, and would not be at home again this month. At these words Adams seemed greatly confounded, saying, "This must be a sudden accident, as the sickness or death of a relation or some such unforeseen misfortune"; and then, turning to Joseph, cried, "I wish you had reminded me to have borrowed this money last night." Joseph, smiling, answered, "He was very much deceived if the gentleman would not have found some excuse to avoid lending it.—I own," says he, "I was never much pleased with his professing so much kindness for you at first sight; for I have heard the gentlemen of our cloth in London tell many such stories of their masters. But when the boy brought the message back of his not being at home, I presently knew what would follow; for, whenever a man of fashion doth not care to fulfil his promises, the custom is to order his servants that he will never be at home to the person so promised. In London they call it denying him. I have myself denied Sir Thomas Booby above a hundred times, and when the man hath danced attendance for about a month or sometimes longer, he is acquainted in the end that the gentleman is gone out of town and could do nothing in the business."—"Good Lord!" says Adams, "what wickedness is there in the Christian world! I profess almost equal to what I have read of the heathens. But surely, Joseph, your suspicions of this gentleman must be unjust, for what a silly fellow must he be who would do the devil's work for nothing! and canst thou tell me any interest he could possibly propose to himself by deceiving us in his professions?"—"It is not for me," answered Joseph, "to give reasons for what men do, to a gentleman of your learning."—"You say right," quoth Adams; "knowledge of men is only to be learned from books; Plato and Seneca for that; and those are authors, I am afraid, child, you never read."—"Not I, sir, truly," answered Joseph; "all I know is, it is a maxim among the gentlemen of our cloth, that those masters who promise the most perform the least; and I have often heard them say they have found the largest vails in those families where they were not promised any. But, sir, instead of considering any farther these matters, it would be our wisest way to contrive some method of getting out of this house; for the generous gentleman, instead of doing us any service, hath left us the whole reckoning to pay." Adams was going to answer, when their host came in, and, with a kind of jeering smile, said, "Well, masters! the squire hath not sent his horses for you yet. Laud help me! how easily some folks make promises!"—"How!" says Adams; "have you ever known him do anything of this kind before?"—"Ay! marry have I," answered the host: "it is no business of mine, you know, sir, to say anything to a gentleman to his face; but now he is not here, I will assure you, he hath not his fellow within the three next market-towns. I own I could not help laughing when I heard him offer you the living, for thereby hangs a good jest. I thought he would have offered you my house next, for one is no more his to dispose of than the other." At these words Adams, blessing himself, declared, "He had never read of such a monster. But what vexes me most," says he, "is, that he hath decoyed us into running up a long debt with you, which we are not able to pay, for we have no money about us, and, what is worse, live at such a distance, that if you should trust us, I am afraid you would lose your money for want of our finding any conveniency of sending it."—"Trust you, master!" says the host, "that I will with all my heart. I honour the clergy too much to deny trusting one of them for such a trifle; besides, I like your fear of never paying me. I have lost many a debt in my lifetime, but was promised to be paid them all in a very short time. I will score this reckoning for the novelty of it. It is the first, I do assure you, of its kind. But what say you, master, shall we have t'other pot before we part? It will waste but little chalk more, and if you never pay me a shilling the loss will not ruin me." Adams liked the invitation very well, especially as it was delivered with so hearty an accent. He shook his host by the hand, and thanking him, said, "He would tarry another pot rather for the pleasure of such worthy company than for the liquor"; adding, "he was glad to find some Christians left in the kingdom, for that he almost began to suspect that he was sojourning in a country inhabited only by Jews and Turks."

The kind host produced the liquor, and Joseph with Fanny retired into the garden, where, while they solaced themselves with amorous discourse, Adams sat down with his host; and, both filling their glasses, and lighting their pipes, they began that dialogue which the reader will find in the next chapter.

CHAPTER XVII

A DIALOGUE BETWEEN MR. AERAHAM ADAMS AND HIS HOST, WHICH, BY THE DISAGREEMENT IN THEIR OPINIONS, SEEMED TO THREATEN AN UNLUCKY CATASTROPHE, HAD IT NOT BEEN TIMELY PREVENTED BY THE RETURN OF THE LOVERS

"Sir," said the host, "I assure you you are not the first to whom our squire hath promised more than he hath performed. He is so famous for this practice, that his word will not be taken for much by those who know him. I remember a young fellow whom he promised his parents to make an exciseman. The poor people, who could ill afford it, bred their son to writing and accounts, and other learning to qualify him for the place; and the boy held up his head above his condition with these hopes; nor would he go to plough, nor to any other kind of work, and went constantly drest as fine as could be, with two clean Holland shirts a week, and this for several years; till at last he followed the squire up to London, thinking there to mind him of his promises; but he could never get sight of him. So that, being out of money and business, he fell into evil company and wicked courses; and in the end came to a sentence of transportation, the news of which broke the mother's heart.—I will tell you another true story of him. There was a neighbour of mine, a farmer, who had two sons whom he bred up to the business. Pretty lads they were. Nothing would serve the squire but that the youngest must be made a parson. Upon which he persuaded the father to send him to school, promising that he would afterwards maintain him at the university, and, when he was of a proper age, give him a living. But after the lad had been seven years at school, and his father brought him to the squire, with a letter from his master that he was fit for the university, the squire, instead of minding his promise, or sending him thither at his expense, only told his father that the young man was a fine scholar, and it was a pity he could not afford to keep him at Oxford for four or five years more, by which time, if he could get him a curacy, he might have him ordained. The farmer said, 'He was not a man sufficient to do any such thing.' —'Why, then,' answered the squire, 'I am very sorry you have given him so much learning; for, if he cannot get his living by that, it will rather spoil him for anything else; and your other son, who can hardly write his name, will do more at ploughing and sowing, and is in a better condition, than he.' And indeed so it proved; for the poor lad, not finding friends to maintain him in his learning, as he had expected, and being unwilling to work, fell to drinking, though he was a very sober lad before; and in a short time, partly with grief, and partly with good liquor, fell into a consumption, and died.—Nay, I can tell you more still: there was another, a young woman, and the handsomest in all this neighbourhood, whom he enticed up to London, promising to make her a gentlewoman to one of your women of quality; but, instead of keeping his word, we have since heard, after having a child by her himself, she became a common whore; then kept a coffee-house in Covent Garden; and a little after died of the French distemper in a gaol.—I could tell you many more stories; but how do you imagine he served me myself? You must know, sir, I was bred a seafaring man, and have been many voyages; till at last I came to be master of a ship myself, and was in a fair way of making a fortune, when I was attacked by one of those cursed guarda-costas who took our ships before the beginning of the war; and after a fight, wherein I lost the greater part of my crew, my rigging being all demolished, and two shots received between wind and water, I was forced to strike. The villains carried off my ship, a brigantine of 150 tons—a pretty creature she was—and put me, a man, and a boy, into a little bad pink, in which, with much ado, we at last made Falmouth; though I believe the Spaniards did not imagine she could possibly live a day at sea. Upon my return hither, where my wife, who was of this country, then lived, the squire told me he was so pleased with the defence I had made against the enemy, that he did not fear of getting me promoted to a lieutenancy of a man-of-war, if I would accept of it; which I thankfully assured him I would. Well, sir, two or three years passed, during which I had many repeated promises, not only from the squire, but (as he told me) from the lords of the admiralty. He never returned from London but I was assured I might be satisfied now, for I was certain of the first vacancy; and, what surprises me still, when I reflect on it, these assurances were given me with no less confidence, after so many disappointments, than at first. At last, sir, growing weary, and somewhat suspicious, after so much delay, I wrote to a friend in London, who I knew had some acquaintance at the best house in the admiralty, and desired him to back the squire's interest; for indeed I feared he had solicited the affair with more coldness than he pretended. And what answer do you think my friend sent me? Truly, sir, he acquainted me that the squire had never mentioned my name at the admiralty in his life; and, unless I had much faithfuller interest, advised me to give over my pretensions; which I immediately did, and, with the concurrence of my wife, resolved to set up an alehouse, where you are heartily welcome; and so my service to you; and may the squire, and all such sneaking rascals, go to the devil together."—"O fie!" says Adams, "O fie! He is indeed a wicked man; but G— will, I hope, turn his heart to repentance. Nay, if he could but once see the meanness of this detestable vice; would he but once reflect that he is one of the most scandalous as well as pernicious lyars; sure he must despise himself to so intolerable a degree, that it would be impossible for him to continue a moment in such a course. And to confess the truth, notwithstanding the baseness of this character, which he hath too well deserved, he hath in his countenance sufficient symptoms of that *bona indoles*, that sweetness of disposition, which furnishes out a good Christian."—"Ah, master! master!" says the host, "if you had travelled as far as I have, and conversed with the many nations where I have traded, you would not give any credit to a man's countenance. Symptoms in his countenance, quotha! I would look there, perhaps, to see whether a man had the small-pox, but for nothing else." He spoke this with so little regard to the parson's observation, that it a good deal nettled him; and, taking his pipe hastily from his mouth, he thus answered: "Master of mine, perhaps I have travelled a great deal farther than you without the assistance of a ship. Do you imagine sailing by different cities or countries is travelling? No.

Cælum non animum mutant qui trans mare currunt.

I can go farther in an afternoon than you in a twelvemonth. What, I suppose you have seen the Pillars of Hercules, and perhaps the walls of Carthage. Nay, you may have heard Scylla, and seen Charybdis; you may have entered the closet where Archimedes was found at the taking of Syracuse. I suppose you have sailed among the Cyclades, and passed the famous straits which take their name from the unfortunate Helle, whose fate is sweetly described by Apollonius Rhodius; you have passed the very spot, I conceive, where Dædalus fell into that sea, his waxen wings being melted by the sun; you have traversed the Euxine sea, I make no doubt; nay, you may have been on the banks of the Caspian, and called at Colchis, to see if there is ever another golden fleece."—"Not I, truly, master," answered the host: "I never touched at any of these places."—"But I have been at all these," replied Adams. "Then, I suppose," cries the host, "you have been at the East Indies; for there are no such, I will be sworn, either in the West or the Levant."—"Pray where's the Levant?" quoth Adams; "that should be in the East Indies by right."—"Oho! you are a pretty traveller," cries the host, "and not know the Levant! My service to you, master; you must not talk of these things with me! you must not tip us the traveller; it won't go here."—"Since thou art so dull to misunderstand me still," quoth Adams, "I will inform thee; the travelling I mean is in books, the only way of travelling by which any knowledge is to be acquired. From them I learn what I asserted just now, that nature generally imprints such a portraiture of the mind in the countenance, that a skilful physiognomist will rarely be deceived. I presume you have never read the story of Socrates to this purpose, and therefore I will tell it you. A certain physiognomist asserted of Socrates, that he plainly discovered by his features that he was a rogue in his nature.

A character so contrary to the tenour of all this great man's
actions, and the generally received opinion concerning him,
incensed the boys of Athens so that they threw stones at the
physiognomist, and would have demolished him for his ignorance, had not Socrates himself prevented them by confessing
the truth of his observations, and acknowledging that, though
he corrected his disposition by philosophy, he was indeed
naturally as inclined to vice as had been predicated of him.
Now, pray resolve me—How should a man know this story if he
had not read it?"—"Well, master," said the host, "and what
signifies it whether a man knows it or no?   He who goes abroad,
as I have done, will always have opportunities enough of knowing
the world without troubling his head with Socrates, or any such
fellows."—"Friend," cries Adams, "if a man should sail round
the world, and anchor in every harbour of it, without learning,
he would return home as ignorant as he went out."—"Lord help
you!" answered the host; "there was my boatswain, poor fellow!
he could scarce either write or read, and yet he would navigate a
ship with any master of a man-of-war; and a very pretty knowledge of trade he had too."—"Trade," answered Adams, "as
Aristotle proves in his first chapter of Politics, is below a philosopher, and unnatural as it is managed now."   The host looked
stedfastly at Adams, and after a minute's silence asked him,
"If he was one of the writers of the Gazetteers? for I have heard,"
says he, "they are writ by parsons."—"Gazetteers!" answered
Adams, "what is that?"—"It is a dirty newspaper," replied the
host, "which hath been given away all over the nation for these
many years, to abuse trade and honest men, which I would not
suffer to lye on my table, though it hath been offered me for
nothing."—"Not I truly," said Adams; "I never write anything
but sermons; and I assure you I am no enemy to trade, whilst
it is consistent with honesty; nay, I have always looked on the
tradesman as a very valuable member of society, and, perhaps,
inferior to none but the man of learning."—"No, I believe he is
not, nor to him neither," answered the host.   "Of what use
would learning be in a country without trade?   What would all
you parsons do to clothe your backs and feed your bellies?   Who
fetches you your silks, and your linens, and your wines, and all
the other necessaries of life?   I speak chiefly with regard to the
sailors."—"You should say the extravagances of life," replied
the parson; "but admit they were the necessaries, there is something which is more necessary than life itself, which is provided
by learning; I mean the learning of the clergy.   Who clothes

you with piety, meekness, humility, charity, patience, and all the other Christian virtues? Who feeds your souls with the milk of brotherly love, and diets them with all the dainty food of holiness, which at once cleanses them of all impure carnal affections, and fattens them with the truly rich spirit of grace? Who doth this?"—"Ay, who, indeed?" cries the host; "for I do not remember ever to have seen any such clothing or such feeding. And so, in the mean time, master, my service to you." Adams was going to answer with some severity, when Joseph and Fanny returned and pressed his departure so eagerly that he would not refuse them; and so, grasping his crabstick, he took leave of his host (neither of them being so well pleased with each other as they had been at their first sitting down together), and with Joseph and Fanny, who both expressed much impatience, departed, and now all together renewed their journey.

BOOK III

CHAPTER I

MATTER PREFATORY IN PRAISE OF BIOGRAPHY

NOTWITHSTANDING the preference which may be vulgarly given to the authority of those romance writers who entitle their books "the History of England, the History of France, of Spain, &c.," it is most certain that truth is to be found only in the works of those who celebrate the lives of great men, and are commonly called biographers, as the others should indeed be termed topographers, or chorographers; words which might well mark the distinction between them; it being the business of the latter chiefly to describe countries and cities, which, with the assistance of maps, they do pretty justly, and may be depended upon; but as to the actions and characters of men, their writings are not quite so authentic; of which there needs no other proof than those eternal contradictions occurring between two topographers who undertake the history of the same country: for instance, between my Lord Clarendon and Mr. Whitelocke, between Mr. Echard and Rapin, and many others; where, facts being set forth in a different light, every reader believes as he pleases; and, indeed, the more judicious and suspicious very justly esteem the whole as no other than a romance, in which the writer hath indulged a happy and fertile invention. But though these widely differ in the narrative of facts; some ascribing victory to the one, and others to the other party; some representing the same man as a rogue, while others give him a great and honest character; yet all agree in the scene where the fact is supposed to have happened, and where the person, who is both a rogue and an honest man, lived. Now with us biographers the case is different; the facts we deliver may be relied on, though we often mistake the age and country wherein they happened: for, though it may be worth the examination of critics, whether the shepherd Chrysostom, who, as Cervantes informs us, died for love of the fair Marcella, who hated him, was ever in Spain, will any one doubt but that such a silly fellow hath really existed? Is there in the world such a sceptic as to disbelieve the madness of Cardenio, the perfidy of Ferdinand, the impertinent curiosity of Anselmo, the weakness of Camilla, the irresolute friendship of Lothario? though perhaps, as to the time and place where those several persons lived, that good historian may be deplorably deficient. But the most known instance of this kind is in the true history of Gil Blas, where the inimitable biographer hath made a notorious blunder in the country of Dr. Sangrado, who used his patients as a vintner doth his wine vessels, by letting out their blood, and filling them up with water. Doth not every one, who is the least versed in physical history, know that Spain was not the country in which this doctor lived? The same writer hath likewise erred in the country of his archbishop, as well as that of those great personages whose understandings were too sublime to taste anything but tragedy, and in many others. The same mistakes may likewise be observed in Scarron, the Arabian Nights, the History of Marianne and le Paisan Parvenu, and perhaps some few other writers of this class, whom I have not read, or do not at present recollect; for I would by no means be thought to comprehend those persons of surprising genius, the authors of immense romances, or the modern novel and Atalantis writers; who, without any assistance from nature or history, record persons who never were, or will be, and facts which never did, nor possibly can, happen; whose heroes are of their own creation, and their brains the chaos whence all their materials are selected. Not that such writers deserve no honour; so far otherwise, that perhaps they merit the highest; for what can be nobler than to be as an example of the wonderful extent of human genius? One may apply to them what Balzac says of Aristotle, that they are a second nature (for they have no communication with the first; by which, authors of an inferior class, who cannot stand alone, are obliged to support themselves as with crutches); but these of whom I am now speaking seem to be possessed of those stilts, which the excellent Voltaire tells us, in his letters, "carry the genius far off, but with a regular pace." Indeed, far out of the sight of the reader,

> Beyond the realm of Chaos and old Night.

But to return to the former class, who are contented to copy nature, instead of forming originals from the confused heap of matter in their own brains, is not such a book as that which records the achievements of the renowned Don Quixote more worthy the name of a history than even Mariana's: for, whereas the latter is confined to a particular period of time, and to a particular nation, the former is the history of the world in general, at least that part which is polished by laws, arts, and sciences; and of that from the time it was first polished to this day; nay, and forwards as long as it shall so remain?

I shall now proceed to apply these observations to the work before us; for indeed I have set them down principally to obviate some constructions which the good-nature of mankind, who are always forward to see their friends' virtues recorded, may put to particular parts. I question not but several of my readers will know the lawyer in the stage-coach the moment they hear his voice. It is likewise odds but the wit and the prude meet with some of their acquaintance, as well as all the rest of my characters. To prevent, therefore, any such malicious applications, I declare here, once for all, I describe not men, but manners; not an individual, but a species. Perhaps it will be answered, Are not the characters then taken from life? To which I answer in the affirmative; nay, I believe I might aver that I have writ little more than I have seen. The lawyer is not only alive, but hath been so these four thousand years; and I hope G— will indulge his life as many yet to come. He hath not indeed confined himself to one profession, one religion, or one country; but when the first mean selfish creature appeared on the human stage, who made self the centre of the whole creation, would give himself no pain, incur no danger, advance no money, to assist or preserve his fellow-creatures; then was our lawyer born; and, whilst such a person as I have described exists on earth, so long shall he remain upon it. It is, therefore, doing him little honour to imagine he endeavours to mimick some little obscure fellow, because he happens to resemble him in one particular feature, or perhaps in his profession; whereas his appearance in the world is calculated for much more general and noble purposes; not to expose one pitiful wretch to the small and contemptible circle of his acquaintance; but to hold the glass to thousands in their closets, that they may contemplate their deformity, and endeavour to reduce it, and thus by suffering private mortification may avoid public shame. This places the boundary between, and distinguishes the satirist from the libeller: for the former privately corrects the fault for the benefit of the person, like a parent; the latter publickly exposes the person himself, as an example to others, like an executioner.

There are, besides, little circumstances to be considered; as the drapery of a picture, which though fashion varies at different times the resemblance of the countenance is not by those means diminished. Thus I believe we may venture to say Mrs. Tow-wouse is coeval with our lawyer: and, though perhaps, during the changes which so long an existence must have passed through, she may in her turn have stood behind the bar at an inn, I will not scruple to affirm she hath likewise in the revolution of ages sat on a throne. In short, where extreme turbulency of temper, avarice, and an insensibility of human misery, with a degree of hypocrisy, have united in a female composition, Mrs. Tow-wouse was that woman; and where a good inclination, eclipsed by a poverty of spirit and understanding, hath glimmered forth in a man, that man hath been no other than her sneaking husband.

I shall detain my reader no longer than to give him one caution more of an opposite kind: for, as in most of our particular characters we mean not to lash individuals, but all of the like sort, so, in our general descriptions, we mean not universals, but would be understood with many exceptions: for instance, in our description of high people, we cannot be intended to include such as, whilst they are an honour to their high rank, by a well-guided condescension make their superiority as easy as possible to those whom fortune chiefly hath placed below them. Of this number I could name a peer no less elevated by nature than by fortune; who, whilst he wears the noblest signs of honour on his person, bears the truest stamp of dignity on his mind, adorned with greatness, enriched with knowledge, and embellished with genius. I have seen this man relieve with generosity, while he hath conversed with freedom, and be to the same person a patron and a companion. I could name a commoner, raised higher above the multitude by superior talents than is in the power of his prince to exalt him, whose behaviour to those he hath obliged is more amiable than the obligation itself; and who is so great a master of affability, that, if he could divest himself of an in-herent greatness in his manner, would often make the lowest of his acquaintance forget who was the master of that palace in which they are so courteously entertained. These are pictures which must be, I believe, known: I declare they are taken from the life, and not intended to exceed it. By those high people, therefore, whom I have described, I mean a set of wretches, who, while they are a disgrace to their ancestors, whose honours and fortunes they inherit (or perhaps a greater to their mother, for such degeneracy is scarce credible), have the insolence to treat those with disregard who are at least equal to the founders of their own splendour. It is, I fancy, impossible to conceive a spectacle more worthy of our indignation, than that of a fellow.

who is not only a blot in the escutcheon of a great family, but a scandal to the human species, maintaining a supercilious behaviour to men who are an honour to their nature and a disgrace to their fortune.

And now, reader, taking these hints along with you, you may, if you please, proceed to the sequel of this our true history.

CHAPTER II

A NIGHT SCENE, WHEREIN SEVERAL WONDERFUL ADVENTURES BEFEL ADAMS AND HIS FELLOW-TRAVELLERS

It was so late when our travellers left the inn or alehouse (for it might be called either), that they had not travelled many miles before night overtook them, or met them, which you please. The reader must excuse me if I am not particular as to the way they took; for, as we are now drawing near the seat of the Boobies, and as that is a ticklish name, which malicious persons may apply, according to their evil inclinations, to several worthy country squires, a race of men whom we look upon as entirely inoffensive, and for whom we have an adequate regard, we shall lend no assistance to any such malicious purposes.

Darkness had now overspread the hemisphere, when Fanny whispered Joseph "that she begged to rest herself a little; for that she was so tired she could walk no farther." Joseph immediately prevailed with parson Adams, who was as brisk as a bee, to stop. He had no sooner seated himself than he lamented the loss of his dear Æschylus, but was a little comforted when reminded that, if he had it in his possession, he could not see to read.

The sky was so clouded that not a star appeared. It was indeed, according to Milton, darkness visible. This was a circumstance, however, very favourable to Joseph; for Fanny, not suspicious of being overseen by Adams, gave a loose to her passion which she had never done before, and, reclining her head on his bosom, threw her arm carelessly round him, and suffered him to lay his cheek close to hers. All this infused such happiness into Joseph, that he would not have changed his turf for the finest down in the finest palace in the universe.

Adams sat at some distance from the lovers, and, being unwilling to disturb them, applied himself to meditation; in which he had not spent much time before he discovered a light at some

distance that seemed approaching towards him. He immediately hailed it; but, to his sorrow and surprise, it stopped for
a moment, and then disappeared. He then called to Joseph,
asking him, "if he had not seen the light?" Joseph answered,
"he had."—"And did you not mark how it vanished?" returned
he: "though I am not afraid of ghosts, I do not absolutely
disbelieve them."

He then entered into a meditation on those unsubstantial
beings; which was soon interrupted by several voices, which he
thought almost at his elbow, though in fact they were not so
extremely near. However, he could distinctly hear them agree
on the murder of any one they met; and a little after heard one
of them say, "he had killed a dozen since that day fortnight."

Adams now fell on his knees, and committed himself to the
care of Providence; and poor Fanny, who likewise heard those
terrible words, embraced Joseph so closely, that had not he,
whose ears were also open, been apprehensive on her account,
he would have thought no danger which threatened only himself
too dear a price for such embraces.

Joseph now drew forth his penknife, and Adams, having
finished his ejaculations, grasped his crabstick, his only weapon,
and, coming up to Joseph, would have had him quit Fanny, and
place her in the rear; but his advice was fruitless; she clung
closer to him, not at all regarding the presence of Adams, and in
a soothing voice declared, "she would die in his arms." Joseph,
clasping her with inexpressible eagerness, whispered her, "that
he preferred death in hers to life out of them." Adams, brandishing his crabstick, said, "he despised death as much as any
man," and then repeated aloud:

> *Est hic, est animus lucis contemptor et illum,*
> *Qui vita bene credat emi quo tendis, honorem.*

Upon this the voices ceased for a moment, and then one of
them called out, "D—n you, who is there?" To which Adams
was prudent enough to make no reply; and of a sudden he observed half-a-dozen lights, which seemed to rise all at once from
the ground and advance briskly towards him. This he immediately concluded to be an apparition; and now, beginning to
conceive that the voices were of the same kind, he called out,
"In the name of the L—d, what wouldst thou have?" He had
no sooner spoke than he heard one of the voices cry out, "D—n
them, here they come"; and soon after heard several hearty
blows, as if a number of men had been engaged at quarterstaff.

He was just advancing towards the place of combat, when Joseph, catching him by the skirts, begged him that they might take the opportunity of the dark to convey away Fanny from the danger which threatened her. He presently complied, and, Joseph lifting up Fanny, they all three made the best of their way; and without looking behind them, or being overtaken, they had travelled full two miles, poor Fanny not once complaining of being tired, when they saw afar off several lights scattered at a small distance from each other, and at the same time found themselves on the descent of a very steep hill. Adams's foot slipping, he instantly disappeared, which greatly frightened both Joseph and Fanny; indeed, if the light had permitted them to see it, they would scarce have refrained laughing to see the parson rolling down the hill; which he did from top to bottom, without receiving any harm. He then hollowed as loud as he could, to inform them of his safety, and relieve them from the fears which they had conceived for him. Joseph and Fanny halted some time, considering what to do; at last, they advanced a few paces, where the declivity seemed least steep; and then Joseph, taking his Fanny in his arms, walked firmly down the hill, without making a false step, and at length landed her at the bottom, where Adams soon came to them.

Learn hence, my fair countrywomen, to consider your own weakness, and the many occasions on which the strength of a man may be useful to you; and, duly weighing this, take care that you match not yourselves with the spindle-shanked beaus and *petit-maîtres* of the age, who, instead of being able, like Joseph Andrews, to carry you in lusty arms through the rugged ways and downhill steeps of life, will rather want to support their feeble limbs with your strength and assistance.

Our travellers now moved forwards where the nearest light presented itself; and, having crossed a common field, they came to a meadow, where they seemed to be at a very little distance from the light, when, to their grief, they arrived at the banks of a river. Adams here made a full stop, and declared he could swim, but doubted how it was possible to get Fanny over: to which Joseph answered, "If they walked along its banks, they might be certain of soon finding a bridge, especially as by the number of lights they might be assured a parish was near." "Odso, that's true indeed," said Adams; "I did not think of that."

Accordingly, Joseph's advice being taken, they passed over two meadows, and came to a little orchard, which led them to a house. Fanny begged of Joseph to knock at the door, assuring him, "she was so weary that she could hardly stand on her feet." Adams, who was foremost, performed this ceremony; and, the door being immediately opened, a plain kind of man appeared at it: Adams acquainted him, "that they had a young woman with them who was so tired with her journey that he should be much obliged to him if he would suffer her to come in and rest herself." The man, who saw Fanny by the light of the candle which he held in his hand, perceiving her innocent and modest look, and having no apprehensions from the civil behaviour of Adams, presently answered, "That the young woman was very welcome to rest herself in his house, and so were her company." He then ushered them into a very decent room, where his wife was sitting at a table: she immediately rose up and assisted them in setting forth chairs, and desired them to sit down; which they had no sooner done than the man of the house asked them if they would have anything to refresh themselves with? Adams thanked him, and answered he should be obliged to him for a cup of his ale, which was likewise chosen by Joseph and Fanny. Whilst he was gone to fill a very large jug with this liquor, his wife told Fanny she seemed greatly fatigued, and desired her to take something stronger than ale; but she refused with many thanks, saying it was true she was very much tired, but a little rest she hoped would restore her. As soon as the company were all seated, Mr. Adams, who had filled himself with ale, and by public permission had lighted his pipe, turned to the master of the house, asking him, "If evil spirits did not use to walk in that neighbourhood?" To which receiving no answer, he began to inform him of the adventure which they met with on the downs; nor had he proceeded far in the story when somebody knocked very hard at the door. The company expressed some amazement, and Fanny and the good woman turned pale: her husband went forth, and whilst he was absent, which was some time, they all remained silent, looking at one another, and heard several voices discoursing pretty loudly. Adams was fully persuaded that spirits were abroad, and began to meditate some exorcisms; Joseph a little inclined to the same opinion; Fanny was more afraid of men; and the good woman herself began to suspect her guests, and imagined those without were rogues belonging to their gang. At length the master of the house returned, and laughing, told Adams he had discovered his apparition; that the murderers were sheep-stealers, and the twelve persons murdered were no other than twelve sheep;

adding, that the shepherds had got the better of them, had secured two, and were proceeding with them to a justice of peace. This account greatly relieved the fears of the whole company; but Adams muttered to himself, "He was convinced of the truth of apparitions for all that."

They now sat chearfully round the fire, till the master of the house, having surveyed his guests, and conceiving that the cassock, which, having fallen down, appeared under Adams's greatcoat, and the shabby livery on Joseph Andrews, did not well suit with the familiarity between them, began to entertain some suspicions not much to their advantage: addressing himself therefore to Adams, he said, "He perceived he was a clergyman by his dress, and supposed that honest man was his footman." "Sir," answered Adams, "I am a clergyman at your service; but as to that young man, whom you have rightly termed honest, he is at present in nobody's service; he never lived in any other family than that of Lady Booby, from whence he was discharged, I assure you, for no crime." Joseph said, "He did not wonder the gentleman was surprised to see one of Mr. Adams's character condescend to so much goodness with a poor man."—"Child," said Adams, "I should be ashamed of my cloth if I thought a poor man, who is honest, below my notice or my familiarity. I know not how those who think otherwise can profess themselves followers and servants of Him who made no distinction, unless, peradventure, by preferring the poor to the rich.—Sir," said he, addressing himself to the gentleman, "these two poor young people are my parishioners, and I look on them and love them as my children. There is something singular enough in their history, but I have not now time to recount it." The master of the house, notwithstanding the simplicity which discovered itself in Adams, knew too much of the world to give a hasty belief to professions. He was not yet quite certain that Adams had any more of the clergyman in him than his cassock. To try him therefore further, he asked him, "If Mr. Pope had lately published anything new?" Adams answered, "He had heard great commendations of that poet, but that he had never read nor knew any of his works."—"Ho! ho!" says the gentleman to himself, "have I caught you? What!" said he, "have you never seen his Homer?" Adams answered, "he had never read any translation of the classicks."—"Why, truly," reply'd the gentleman, "there is a dignity in the Greek language which I think no modern tongue can reach."—"Do you understand Greek, sir?" said Adams hastily. "A little, sir," answered the gentleman. "Do you know, sir," cry'd Adams, "where I can buy an Æschylus? an unlucky misfortune lately happened to mine." Æschylus was beyond the gentleman, though he knew him very well by name; he therefore, returning back to Homer, asked Adams, "What part of the Iliad he thought most excellent?" Adams returned, "His question would be properer, What kind of beauty was the chief in poetry? for that Homer was equally excellent in them all. And, indeed," continued he, "what Cicero says of a complete orator may well be applied to a great poet: 'He ought to comprehend all perfections.' Homer did this in the most excellent degree; it is not without reason, therefore, that the philosopher, in the twenty-second chapter of his Poeticks, mentions him by no other appellation than that of the Poet. He was the father of the drama as well as the epic; not of tragedy only, but of comedy also; for his Margites, which is deplorably lost, bore, says Aristotle, the same analogy to comedy as his Odyssey and Iliad to tragedy. To him, therefore, we owe Aristophanes as well as Euripides, Sophocles, and my poor Æschylus. But if you please we will confine ourselves (at least for the present) to the Iliad, his noblest work; though neither Aristotle nor Horace give it the preference, as I remember, to the Odyssey. First, then, as to his subject, can anything be more simple, and at the same time more noble? He is rightly praised by the first of those judicious critics for not chusing the whole war, which, though he says it hath a complete beginning and end, would have been too great for the understanding to comprehend at one view. I have, therefore, often wondered why so correct a writer as Horace should, in his epistle to Lollius, call him the Trojani Belli Scriptorem. Secondly, his action, termed by Aristotle, Pragmaton Systasis; is it possible for the mind of man to conceive an idea of such perfect unity, and at the same time so replete with greatness? And here I must observe, what I do not remember to have seen noted by any, the Harmotton, that agreement of his action to his subject: for, as the subject is anger, how agreeable is his action, which is war; from which every incident arises and to which every episode immediately relates. Thirdly, his manners, which Aristotle places second in his description of the several parts of tragedy, and which he says are included in the action; I am at a loss whether I should rather admire the exactness of his judgment in the nice distinction or the immensity of his imagination in their variety. For, as to the former of these, how accurately is the sedate, injured resentment of Achilles, distinguished from the hot, insulting passion of

Agamemnon! How widely doth the brutal courage of Ajax differ from the amiable bravery of Diomedes; and the wisdom of Nestor, which is the result of long reflection and experience, from the cunning of Ulysses, the effect of art and subtlety only! If we consider their variety, we may cry out, with Aristotle in his 24th chapter, that no part of this divine poem is destitute of manners. Indeed, I might affirm that there is scarce a character in human nature untouched in some part or other. And, as there is no passion which he is not able to describe, so is there none in his reader which he cannot raise. If he hath any superior excellence to the rest, I have been inclined to fancy it is in the pathetic. I am sure I never read with dry eyes the two episodes where Andromache is introduced in the former lamenting the danger, and in the latter the death, of Hector. The images are so extremely tender in these, that I am convinced the poet had the worthiest and best heart imaginable. Nor can I help observing how Sophocles falls short of the beauties of the original, in that imitation of the dissuasive speech of Andromache which he hath put into the mouth of Tecmessa. And yet Sophocles was the greatest genius who ever wrote tragedy; nor have any of his successors in that art, that is to say, neither Euripides nor Seneca the tragedian, been able to come near him. As to his sentiments and diction, I need say nothing: the former are particularly remarkable for the utmost perfection on that head, namely, propriety; and as to the latter, Aristotle, whom doubtless you have read over and over, is very diffuse. I shall mention but one thing more, which that great critic in his division of tragedy calls Opsis, or the scenery; and which is as proper to the epic as to the drama, with this difference, that in the former it falls to the share of the poet, and in the latter to that of the painter. But did ever painter imagine a scene like that in the 13th and 14th Iliads? where the reader sees at one view the prospect of Troy, with the army drawn up before it; the Grecian army, camp, and fleet; Jupiter sitting on Mount Ida, with his head wrapt in a cloud, and a thunderbolt in his hand, looking towards Thrace; Neptune driving through the sea, which divides on each side to permit his passage, and then seating himself on Mount Samos; the heavens opened, and the deities all seated on their thrones. This is sublime! This is poetry!" Adams then rapt out a hundred Greek verses, and with such a voice, emphasis, and action, that he almost frightened the women; and as for the gentleman, he was so far from entertaining any further suspicion of Adams, that he now doubted whether he had not

a bishop in his house. He ran into the most extravagant encomiums on his learning; and the goodness of his heart began to
dilate to all the strangers. He said he had great compassion for
the poor young woman, who looked pale and faint with her
journey; and in truth he conceived a much higher opinion of her
quality than it deserved. He said he was sorry he could not
accommodate them all; but if they were contented with his
fireside, he would sit up with the men; and the young woman
might, if she pleased, partake his wife's bed, which he advised
her to; for that they must walk upwards of a mile to any house
of entertainment, and that not very good neither. Adams, who
liked his seat, his ale, his tobacco, and his company, persuaded
Fanny to accept this kind proposal, in which sollicitation he was
seconded by Joseph. Nor was she very difficultly prevailed
on; for she had slept little the last night and not at all the preceding; so that love itself was scarce able to keep her eyes open
any longer. The offer, therefore, being kindly accepted, the
good woman produced everything eatable in her house on the
table, and the guests, being heartily invited, as heartily regaled
themselves, especially parson Adams. As to the other two, they
were examples of the truth of that physical observation, that
love, like other sweet things, is no whetter of the stomach.

Supper was no sooner ended, than Fanny at her own request
retired, and the good woman bore her company. The man of
the house, Adams, and Joseph, who would modestly have withdrawn, had not the gentleman insisted on the contrary, drew
round the fireside, where Adams (to use his own words) replen-
ished his pipe, and the gentleman produced a bottle of excellent
beer, being the best liquor in his house.

The modest behaviour of Joseph, with the gracefulness of
his person, the character which Adams gave of him, and the
friendship he seemed to entertain for him, began to work on the
gentleman's affections, and raised in him a curiosity to know the
singularity which Adams had mentioned in his history. This
curiosity Adams was no sooner informed of than, with Joseph's
consent, he agreed to gratify it; and accordingly related all he
knew, with as much tenderness as was possible for the character
of Lady Booby; and concluded with the long, faithful, and mutual
passion between him and Fanny, not concealing the meanness
of her birth and education. These latter circumstances entirely
cured a jealousy which had lately risen in the gentleman's mind,
that Fanny was the daughter of some person of fashion, and that
Joseph had run away with her, and Adams was concerned in the

plot. He was now enamoured of his guests, drank their healths with great chearfulness, and returned many thanks to Adams, who had spent much breath, for he was a circumstantial teller of a story.

Adams told him it was now in his power to return that favour; for his extraordinary goodness, as well as that fund of literature he was master of,[1] which he did not expect to find under such a roof, had raised in him more curiosity than he had ever known. "Therefore," said he, "if it be not too troublesome, sir, your history, if you please."

The gentleman answered, he could not refuse him what he had so much right to insist on; and after some of the common apologies, which are the usual preface to a story, he thus began.

CHAPTER III

IN WHICH THE GENTLEMAN RELATES THE HISTORY OF HIS LIFE

SIR, I am descended of a good family, and was born a gentleman. My education was liberal, and at a public school, in which I proceeded so far as to become a master of the Latin, and to be tolerably versed in the Greek language. My father died when I was sixteen, and left me master of myself. He bequeathed me a moderate fortune, which he intended I should not receive till I attained the age of twenty-five: for he constantly asserted that was full early enough to give up any man entirely to the guidance of his own discretion. However, as this intention was so obscurely worded in his will that the lawyers advised me to contest the point with my trustees, I own I paid so little regard to the inclinations of my dead father, which were sufficiently certain to me, that I followed their advice, and soon succeeded, for the trustees did not contest the matter very obstinately on their side. "Sir," said Adams, "may I crave

---

[1] The author hath by some been represented to have made a blunder here: for Adams had indeed shown some learning (say they), perhaps all the author had; but the gentleman hath shown none, unless his approbation of Mr. Adams be such: but surely it would be preposterous in him to call it so. I have, however, notwithstanding this criticism, which I am told came from the mouth of a great orator in a public coffee-house, left this blunder as it stood in the first edition. I will not have the vanity to apply to anything in this work the observation which M. Dacier makes in her preface to her Aristophanes: *Je tiens pour une maxime constante, qu'une beauté médiocre plaît plus généralement qu'une beauté sans défaut.* Mr. Congreve hath made such another blunder in his Love for Love, where Tattle tells Miss Prue, "She should admire him as much for the beauty he commends in her as if he himself was possessed of it."

the favour of your name?" The gentleman answered his name was Wilson, and then proceeded.

I stayed a very little while at school after his death; for, being a forward youth, I was extremely impatient to be in the world, for which I thought my parts, knowledge, and manhood thoroughly qualified me. And to this early introduction into life, without a guide, I impute all my future misfortunes; for, besides the obvious mischiefs which attend this, there is one which hath not been so generally observed: the first impression which mankind receives of you will be very difficult to eradicate. How unhappy, therefore, must it be to fix your character in life, before you can possibly know its value, or weigh the consequences of those actions which are to establish your future reputation!

A little under seventeen I left my school, and went to London with no more than six pounds in my pocket; a great sum, as I then conceived; and which I was afterwards surprised to find so soon consumed.

The character I was ambitious of attaining was that of a fine gentleman; the first requisites to which I apprehended were to be supplied by a taylor, a periwig-maker, and some few more tradesmen, who deal in furnishing out the human body. Notwithstanding the lowness of my purse, I found credit with them more easily than I expected, and was soon equipped to my wish. This I own then agreeably surprised me; but I have since learned that it is a maxim among many tradesmen at the polite end of the town to deal as largely as they can, reckon as high as they can, and arrest as soon as they can.

The next qualifications, namely, dancing, fencing, riding the great horse, and music, came into my head: but, as they required expense and time, I comforted myself, with regard to dancing, that I had learned a little in my youth, and could walk a minuet genteelly enough; as to fencing, I thought my good-humour would preserve me from the danger of a quarrel; as to the horse, I hoped it would not be thought of; and for music, I imagined I could easily acquire the reputation of it; for I had heard some of my schoolfellows pretend to knowledge in operas, without being able to sing or play on the fiddle.

Knowledge of the town seemed another ingredient; this I thought I should arrive at by frequenting public places. Accordingly I paid constant attendance to them all; by which means I was soon master of the fashionable phrases, learned to cry up the fashionable diversions, and knew the names and faces of the most fashionable men and women.

Nothing now seemed to remain but an intrigue, which I was resolved to have immediately; I mean the reputation of it; and indeed I was so successful, that in a very short time I had half-a-dozen with the finest women in town.

At these words Adams fetched a deep groan, and then, blessing himself, cried out, "Good Lord! what wicked times these are!"

Not so wicked as you imagine, continued the gentleman; for I assure you they were all vestal virgins for anything which I knew to the contrary. The reputation of intriguing with them was all I sought, and was what I arrived at: and perhaps I only flattered myself even in that; for very probably the persons to whom I showed their billets knew as well as I that they were counterfeits, and that I had written them to myself. "Write letters to yourself!" said Adams, staring. O sir, answered the gentleman, it is the very error of the times. Half our modern plays have one of these characters in them. It is incredible the pains I have taken, and the absurd methods I employed, to traduce the character of women of distinction. When another had spoken in raptures of any one, I have answered, "D—n her, she! We shall have her at H——d's very soon." When he hath replied, "He thought her virtuous," I have answered, "Ay, thou wilt always think a woman virtuous, till she is in the streets; but you and I, Jack or Tom (turning to another in company), know better." At which I have drawn a paper out of my pocket, perhaps a taylor's bill, and kissed it, crying at the same time, "By Gad, I was once fond of her."

"Proceed, if you please, but do not swear any more," said Adams.

Sir, said the gentleman, I ask your pardon. Well, sir, in this course of life I continued full three years.—"What course of life?" answered Adams; "I do not remember you have mentioned any."—Your remark is just, said the gentleman, smiling; I should rather have said, in this course of doing nothing. I remember some time afterwards I wrote the journal of one day, which would serve, I believe, as well for any other during the whole time. I will endeavour to repeat it to you.

In the morning I arose, took my great stick, and walked out in my green frock, with my hair in papers (a groan from Adams), and sauntered about till ten. Went to the auction; told lady —— she had a dirty face; laughed heartily at something captain —— said, I can't remember what, for I did not very well hear it; whispered lord ——; bowed to the duke of ——; and was going to bid for a snuff-box, but did not, for fear I should have had it.

From 2 to 4, drest myself.	*A groan.*
4 to 6, dined.	*A groan.*
6 to 8, coffee-house.	
8 to 9, Drury-lane playhouse.	
9 to 10, Lincoln's Inn Fields.	
10 to 12, Drawing-room.	*A great groan.*

At all which places nothing happened worth remark.

At which Adams said, with some vehemence, "Sir, this is below the life of an animal, hardly above vegetation: and I am surprised what could lead a man of your sense into it." What leads us into more follies than you imagine, doctor, answered the gentleman—vanity; for as contemptible a creature as I was, and I assure you, yourself cannot have more contempt for such a wretch than I now have, I then admired myself, and should have despised a person of your present appearance (you will pardon me), with all your learning and those excellent qualities which I have remarked in you. Adams bowed, and begged him to proceed. After I had continued two years in this course of life, said the gentleman, an accident happened which obliged me to change the scene. As I was one day at St. James's coffee-house, making very free with the character of a young lady of quality, an officer of the guards, who was present, thought proper to give me the lye. I answered I might possibly be mistaken, but I intended to tell no more than the truth. To which he made no reply but by a scornful sneer. After this I observed a strange coldness in all my acquaintance; none of them spoke to me first, and very few returned me even the civility of a bow. The company I used to dine with left me out, and within a week I found myself in as much solitude at St. James's as if I had been in a desert. An honest elderly man, with a great hat and long sword, at last told me he had a compassion for my youth, and therefore advised me to show the world I was not such a rascal as they thought me to be. I did not at first understand him; but he explained himself, and ended with telling me, if I would write a challenge to the captain, he would, out of pure charity, go to him with it. "A very charitable person, truly!" cried Adams. I desired till the next day, continued the gentleman, to consider on it, and, retiring to my lodgings, I weighed the consequences on both sides as fairly as I could. On the one, I saw the risk of this alternative, either losing my own life, or having on my hands the blood of a man with whom I was not in the least angry. I soon determined that the good which appeared on the other was not worth this hazard. I therefore resolved to quit the scene, and presently retired to the Temple, where I took chambers. Here I soon got a fresh set of acquaintance, who knew nothing of what had happened to me. Indeed, they were not greatly to my approbation; for the beaus of the Temple are only the shadows of the others. They are the affectation of affectation. The vanity of these is still more ridiculous, if possible, than of the others. Here I met with smart fellows who drank with lords they did not know, and intrigued with women they never saw. Covent Garden was now the farthest stretch of my ambition; where I shone forth in the balconies at the playhouses, visited whores, made love to orange-wenches, and damned plays. This career was soon put a stop to by my surgeon, who convinced me of the necessity of confining myself to my room for a month. At the end of which, having had leisure to reflect, I resolved to quit all farther conversation with beaus and smarts of every kind, and to avoid, if possible, any occasion of returning to this place of confinement. "I think," said Adams, "the advice of a month's retirement and reflection was very proper; but I should rather have expected it from a divine than a surgeon." The gentleman smiled at Adams's simplicity, and, without explaining himself farther on such an odious subject, went on thus: I was no sooner perfectly restored to health than I found my passion for women, which I was afraid to satisfy as I had done, made me very uneasy; I determined, therefore, to keep a mistress. Nor was I long before I fixed my choice on a young woman, who had before been kept by two gentlemen, and to whom I was recommended by a celebrated bawd. I took her home to my chambers, and made her a settlement during cohabitation. This would, perhaps, have been very ill paid: however, she did not suffer me to be perplexed on that account; for, before quarter-day, I found her at my chambers in too familiar conversation with a young fellow who was drest like an officer, but was indeed a city apprentice. Instead of excusing her inconstancy, she rapped out half-a-dozen oaths, and, snapping her fingers at me, swore she scorned to confine herself to the best man in England. Upon this we parted, and the same bawd presently provided her another keeper. I was not so much concerned at our separation as I found, within a day or two, I had reason to be for our meeting; for I was obliged to pay a second visit to my surgeon. I was now forced to do penance for some weeks, during which time I contracted an acquaintance with a beautiful young girl, the daughter of a gentleman who, after having been forty years in the army, and in all the campaigns under the Duke of Marlborough, died a lieutenant on half-pay, and had left a widow, with this only child, in very distrest circumstances: they had only a small pension from the government, with what little the daughter could add to it by her work, for she had great excellence at her needle. This girl was, at my first acquaintance with her, solicited in marriage by a young fellow in good circumstances. He was apprentice to a linendraper, and had a little fortune, sufficient to set up his trade. The mother was greatly pleased with this match, as indeed she had sufficient reason. However, I soon prevented it. I represented him in so low a light to his mistress, and made so good an use of flattery, promises, and presents, that, not to dwell longer on this subject than is necessary, I prevailed with the poor girl, and conveyed her away from her mother! In a word, I debauched her.—(At which words Adams started up, fetched three strides across the room, and then replaced himself in his chair.) You are not more affected with this part of my story than myself; I assure you it will never be sufficiently repented of in my own opinion: but, if you already detest it, how much more will your indignation be raised when you hear the fatal consequences of this barbarous, this villanous action! If you please, therefore, I will here desist.—"By no means," cries Adams; "go on, I beseech you; and Heaven grant you may sincerely repent of this and many other things you have related!" —I was now, continued the gentleman, as happy as the possession of a fine young creature, who had a good education, and was endued with many agreeable qualities, could make me. We lived some months with vast fondness together, without any company or conversation, more than we found in one another: but this could not continue always; and, though I still preserved great affection for her, I began more and more to want the relief of other company, and consequently to leave her by degrees—at last whole days to herself. She failed not to testify some uneasiness on these occasions, and complained of the melancholy life she led; to remedy which, I introduced her into the acquaintance of some other kept mistresses, with whom she used to play at cards, and frequent plays and other diversions. She had not lived long in this intimacy before I perceived a visible alteration in her behaviour; all her modesty and innocence vanished by degrees, till her mind became thoroughly tainted. She affected the company of rakes, gave herself all manner of airs, was never easy but abroad, or when she had a party at my chambers. She was rapacious of money, extravagant to excess, loose in her conversation; and, if ever I demurred to any of her demands, oaths, tears, and fits were the immediate consequences. As the first raptures of fondness were long since over, this behaviour soon estranged my affections from her; I began to reflect with pleasure that she was not my wife, and to conceive an intention of parting with her; of which, having given her a hint, she took care to prevent me the pains of turning her out of doors, and accordingly departed herself, having first broken open my escrutore, and taken with her all she could find, to the amount of about £200. In the first heat of my resentment I resolved to pursue her with all the vengeance of the law: but, as she had the good luck to escape me during that ferment, my passion afterwards cooled; and, having reflected that I had been the first aggressor, and had done her an injury for which I could make her no reparation, by robbing her of the innocence of her mind; and hearing at the same time that the poor old woman her mother had broke her heart on her daughter's elopement from her, I, concluding myself her murderer ("As you very well might," cries Adams with a groan), was pleased that God Almighty had taken this method of punishing me, and resolved quietly to submit to the loss. Indeed, I could wish I had never heard more of the poor creature, who became in the end an abandoned profligate; and, after being some years a common prostitute, at last ended her miserable life in Newgate. —Here the gentleman fetched a deep sigh, which Mr. Adams echoed very loudly; and both continued silent, looking on each other for some minutes. At last the gentleman proceeded thus: I had been perfectly constant to this girl during the whole time I kept her: but she had scarce departed before I discovered more marks of her infidelity to me than the loss of my money. In short, I was forced to make a third visit to my surgeon, out of whose hands I did not get a hasty discharge.

I now forswore all future dealings with the sex, complained loudly that the pleasure did not compensate the pain, and railed at the beautiful creatures in as gross language as Juvenal himself formerly reviled them in. I looked on all the town harlots with a detestation not easy to be conceived, their persons appeared to me as painted palaces, inhabited by Disease and Death: nor could their beauty make them more desirable objects in my eyes than gilding could make me covet a pill, or golden plates a coffin. But though I was no longer the absolute slave, I found some reasons to own myself still the subject, of love. My hatred for women decreased daily; and I am not positive but time might

have betrayed me again to some common harlot, had I not been
secured by a passion for the charming Sapphira, which, having
once entered upon, made a violent progress in my heart. Sapphira was wife to a man of fashion and gallantry, and one who
seemed, I own, every way worthy of her affections; which, however, he had not the reputation of having. She was indeed a
coquette *achevée*. "Pray, sir," says Adams, "what is a coquette? I have met with the word in French authors, but never
could assign any idea to it. I believe it is the same with *une
sotte*, Anglicè, a fool." Sir, answered the gentleman, perhaps
you are not much mistaken; but, as it is a particular kind of folly,
I will endeavour to describe it. Were all creatures to be ranked
in the order of creation according to their usefulness, I know few
animals that would not take place of a coquette; nor indeed
hath this creature much pretence to anything beyond instinct;
for, though sometimes we might imagine it was animated by the
passion of vanity, yet far the greater part of its actions fall
beneath even that low motive; for instance, several absurd
gestures and tricks, infinitely more foolish than what can be
observed in the most ridiculous birds and beasts, and which
would persuade the beholder that the silly wretch was aiming
at our contempt. Indeed its characteristic is affectation, and
this led and governed by whim only: for as beauty, wisdom,
wit, good-nature, politeness, and health are sometimes affected
by this creature, so are ugliness, folly, nonsense, ill-nature, ill-
breeding, and sickness likewise put on by it in their turn. Its
life is one constant lie; and the only rule by which you can form
any judgment of them is, that they are never what they seem.
If it was possible for a coquette to love (as it is not, for if ever it
attains this passion the coquette ceases instantly), it would wear
the face of indifference, if not of hatred, to the beloved object;
you may therefore be assured, when they endeavour to persuade
you of their liking, that they are indifferent to you at least.
And indeed this was the case of my Sapphira, who no sooner saw
me in the number of her admirers than she gave me what is
commonly called encouragement: she would often look at me,
and, when she perceived me meet her eyes, would instantly take
them off, discovering at the same time as much surprise and
emotion as possible. These arts failed not of the success she
intended; and, as I grew more particular to her than the rest of
her admirers, she advanced, in proportion, more directly to me
than to the others. She affected the low voice, whisper, lisp,
sigh, start, laugh, and many other indications of passion which

daily deceive thousands. When I played at whist with her, she would look earnestly at me, and at the same time lose deal or revoke; then burst into a ridiculous laugh and cry, "La! I can't imagine what I was thinking of." To detain you no longer, after I had gone through a sufficient course of gallantry, as I thought, and was thoroughly convinced I had raised a violent passion in my mistress, I sought an opportunity of coming to an eclair-cissement with her. She avoided this as much as possible; however, great assiduity at length presented me one. I will not describe all the particulars of this interview; let it suffice that, when she could no longer pretend not to see my drift, she first affected a violent surprise, and immediately after as violent a passion: she wondered what I had seen in her conduct which could induce me to affront her in this manner; and, breaking from me the first moment she could, told me I had no other way to escape the consequence of her resentment than by never seeing, or at least speaking to her more. I was not contented with this answer; I still pursued her, but to no purpose; and was at length convinced that her husband had the sole possession of her person, and that neither he nor any other had made any impression on her heart. I was taken off from following this *ignis fatuus* by some advances which were made me by the wife of a citizen, who, though neither very young nor handsome, was yet too agreeable to be rejected by my amorous constitution. I accordingly soon satisfied her that she had not cast away her hints on a barren or cold soil: on the contrary, they instantly produced her an eager and desiring lover. Nor did she give me any reason to complain; she met the warmth she had raised with equal ardour. I had no longer a coquette to deal with, but one who was wiser than to prostitute the noble passion of love to the ridiculous lust of vanity. We presently understood one another; and, as the pleasures we sought lay in a mutual gratifi-cation, we soon found and enjoyed them. I thought myself at first greatly happy in the possession of this new mistress, whose fondness would have quickly surfeited a more sickly appetite; but it had a different effect on mine: she carried my passion higher by it than youth or beauty had been able. But my happi-ness could not long continue uninterrupted. The apprehen-sions we lay under from the jealousy of her husband gave us great uneasiness. "Poor wretch! I pity him," cried Adams. He did indeed deserve it, said the gentleman; for he loved his wife with great tenderness; and, I assure you, it is a great satisfaction to me that I was not the man who first seduced her affections from him. These apprehensions appeared also too well grounded, for in the end he discovered us, and procured witnesses of our caresses. He then prosecuted me at law, and recovered £3000 damages, which much distressed my fortune to pay; and, what was worse, his wife, being divorced, came upon my hands. I led a very uneasy life with her; for, besides that my passion was now much abated, her excessive jealousy was very troublesome. At length death rid me of an inconvenience which the consideration of my having been the author of her misfortunes would never suffer me to take any other method of discarding.

I now bade adieu to love, and resolved to pursue other less dangerous and expensive pleasures. I fell into the acquaintance of a set of jolly companions, who slept all day and drank all night; fellows who might rather be said to consume time than to live. Their best conversation was nothing but noise: singing, hollowing, wrangling, drinking, toasting, sp—wing, smoking were the chief ingredients of our entertainment. And yet, bad as these were, they were more tolerable than our graver scenes, which were either excessive tedious narratives of dull common matters of fact, or hot disputes about trifling matters, which commonly ended in a wager. This way of life the first serious reflection put a period to; and I became member of a club frequented by young men of great abilities. The bottle was now only called in to the assistance of our conversation, which rolled on the deepest points of philosophy. These gentlemen were engaged in a search after truth, in the pursuit of which they threw aside all the prejudices of education, and governed themselves only by the infallible guide of human reason. This great guide, after having shown them the falsehood of that very ancient but simple tenet, that there is such a being as a Deity in the universe, helped them to establish in his stead a certain rule of right, by adhering to which they all arrived at the utmost purity of morals. Reflection made me as much delighted with this society as it had taught me to despise and detest the former. I began now to esteem myself a being of a higher order than I had ever before conceived; and was the more charmed with this rule of right, as I really found in my own nature nothing repugnant to it. I held in utter contempt all persons who wanted any other inducement to virtue besides her intrinsic beauty and excellence; and had so high an opinion of my present companions, with regard to their morality, that I would have trusted them with whatever was nearest and dearest to me. Whilst I was engaged in this delightful dream, two or three accidents happened successively, which at first much surprised me; for one of our greatest philosophers, or rule-of-right men, withdrew himself from us, taking with him the wife of one of his most intimate friends. Secondly, another of the same society left the club without remembering to take leave of his bail. A third, having borrowed a sum of money of me, for which I received no security, when I asked him to repay it, absolutely denied the loan. These several practices, so inconsistent with our golden rule, made me begin to suspect its infallibility; but when I communicated my thoughts to one of the club, he said, "There was nothing absolutely good or evil in itself; that actions were denominated good or bad by the circumstances of the agent. That possibly the man who ran away with his neighbour's wife might be one of very good inclinations, but over-prevailed on by the violence of an unruly passion; and, in other particulars, might be a very worthy member of society; that if the beauty of any woman created in him an uneasiness, he had a right from nature to relieve himself;"—with many other things, which I then detested so much, that I took leave of the society that very evening and never returned to it again. Being now reduced to a state of solitude which I did not like, I became a great frequenter of the playhouses, which indeed was always my favourite diversion; and most evenings passed away two or three hours behind the scenes, where I met with several poets, with whom I made engagements at the taverns. Some of the players were likewise of our parties. At these meetings we were generally entertained by the poets with reading their performances, and by the players with repeating their parts: upon which occasions, I observed the gentleman who furnished our entertainment was commonly the best pleased of the company; who, though they were pretty civil to him to his face, seldom failed to take the first opportunity of his absence to ridicule him. Now I made some remarks which probably are too obvious to be worth relating. "Sir," says Adams, "your remarks if you please." First then, says he, I concluded that the general observation, that wits are most inclined to vanity, is not true. Men are equally vain of riches, strength, beauty, honours, &c. But these appear of themselves to the eyes of the beholders, whereas the poor wit is obliged to produce his performance to show you his perfection; and on his readiness to do this that vulgar opinion I have before mentioned is grounded; but doth not the person who expends vast sums in the furniture of his house or the ornaments of his person, who consumes much time and employs great pains in dressing himself, or who thinks himself paid for self-denial, labour, or even villany, by a title or a ribbon, sacrifice as much to vanity as the poor wit who is desirous to read you his poem or his play? My second remark was, that vanity is the worst of passions, and more apt to contaminate the mind than any other: for, as selfishness is much more general than we please to allow it, so it is natural to hate and envy those who stand between us and the good we desire. Now, in lust and ambition these are few; and even in avarice we find many who are no obstacles to our pursuits; but the vain man seeks pre-eminence; and everything which is excellent or praiseworthy in another renders him the mark of his antipathy. Adams now began to fumble in his pockets, and soon cried out, "O la! I have it not about me." Upon this, the gentleman asking him what he was searching for, he said he searched after a sermon, which he thought his master-piece, against vanity. "Fie upon it, fie upon it!" cries he, "why do I ever leave that sermon out of my pocket? I wish it was within five miles; I would willingly fetch it, to read it you." The gentleman answered that there was no need, for he was cured of the passion. "And for that very reason," quoth Adams, "I would read it, for I am confident you would admire it: indeed, I have never been a greater enemy to any passion than that silly one of vanity." The gentleman smiled, and proceeded—From this society I easily passed to that of the gamesters, where nothing remarkable happened but the finish-ing my fortune, which those gentlemen soon helped me to the end of. This opened scenes of life hitherto unknown; poverty and distress, with their horrid train of duns, attorneys, bailiffs, haunted me day and night. My clothes grew shabby, my credit bad, my friends and acquaintance of all kinds cold. In this situation the strangest thought imaginable came into my head; and what was this but to write a play? for I had sufficient leisure: fear of bailiffs confined me every day to my room: and, having always had a little inclination and something of a genius that way, I set myself to work, and within a few months pro-duced a piece of five acts, which was accepted of at the theatre. I remembered to have formerly taken tickets of other poets for their benefits, long before the appearance of their performances; and, resolving to follow a precedent which was so well suited to my present circumstances, I immediately provided myself with a large number of little papers. Happy indeed would be the state of poetry, would these tickets pass current at the bakehouse, the alehouse, and the chandler's shop: but alas! far otherwise; no taylor will take them in payment for buckram, canvas, stay-tape; nor no bailiff for civility money. They are, indeed, no more than a passport to beg with; a certificate that the owner wants five shillings, which induces well-disposed Christians to charity. I now experienced what is worse than poverty, or rather what is the worst consequence of poverty— I mean attendance and dependance on the great. Many a morning have I waited hours in the cold parlours of men of quality; where, after seeing the lowest rascals in lace and embroidery, the pimps and buffoons in fashion, admitted, I have been sometimes told, on sending in my name, that my lord could not possibly see me this morning; a sufficient assurance that I should never more get entrance into that house. Sometimes I have been at last admitted; and the great man hath thought proper to excuse himself, by telling me he was tied up. "Tied up," says Adams, "pray what's that?" Sir, says the gentleman, the profit which booksellers allowed authors for the best works was so very small, that certain men of birth and fortune some years ago, who were the patrons of wit and learning, thought fit to encourage them farther by entering into voluntary subscriptions for their encouragement. Thus Prior, Rowe, Pope, and some other men of genius, received large sums for their labours from the public. This seemed so easy a method of getting money, that many of the lowest scribblers of the times ventured to publish their works in the same way; and many had the assurance to take in subscriptions for what was not writ, nor ever intended. Subscriptions in this manner growing infinite, and a kind of tax on the publick, some persons, finding it not so easy a task to discern good from bad authors, or to know what genius was worthy encouragement and what was not, to prevent the expense of subscribing to so many, invented a method to excuse themselves from all subscriptions whatever; and this was to receive a small sum of money in consideration of giving a large one if ever they subscribed; which many have done, and many more have pretended to have done, in order to silence all solicitation. The same method was likewise taken with playhouse tickets, which were no less a public grievance; and this is what they call being tied up from subscribing. "I can't say but the term is apt enough, and somewhat typical," said Adams; "for a man of large fortune, who ties himself up, as you call it, from the encouragement of men of merit, ought to be tied up in reality." Well, sir, says the gentleman, to return to my story. Sometimes I have received a guinea from a man of quality, given with as ill a grace as alms are generally to the meanest beggar; and purchased too with as much time spent in attendance as, if it had been spent in honest industry, might have brought me more profit with infinitely more satisfaction. After about two months spent in this disagreeable way, with the utmost mortification, when I was pluming my hopes on the prospect of a plentiful harvest from my play, upon applying to the prompter to know when it came into rehearsal, he informed me he had received orders from the managers to return me the play again, for that they could not possibly act it that season; but, if I would take it and revise it against the next, they would be glad to see it again. I snatched it from him with great indignation, and retired to my room, where I threw myself on the bed in a fit of despair. "You should rather have thrown yourself on your knees," says Adams, "for despair is sinful." As soon, continued the gentleman, as I had indulged the first tumult of my passion, I began to consider coolly what course I should take, in a situation without friends, money, credit, or reputation of any kind. After revolving many things in my mind, I could see no other possibility of furnishing myself with the miserable necessaries of life than to retire to a garret near the Temple, and commence hackney-writer to the lawyers, for which I was well qualified, being an excellent penman. This purpose I resolved on, and immediately put it in execution. I had an acquaintance with an attorney who had formerly transacted affairs for me, and to him I applied; but, instead of furnishing me with any business, he laughed at my undertaking, and told me, "He was afraid I should turn his deeds into plays, and he should expect to see them on the stage." Not to tire you with instances of this kind from others, I found that Plato himself did not hold poets in greater abhorrence than these men of business do. Whenever I durst venture to a coffee-house, which was on Sundays only, a whisper ran round the room, which was constantly attended with a sneer—That's poet Wilson; for I know not whether you have observed it, but there is a malignity in the nature of man, which, when not weeded out, or at least covered by a good education and politeness, delights in making another uneasy or dissatisfied with himself. This abundantly appears in all assemblies, except those which are filled by people of fashion, and especially among the younger people of both sexes whose birth and fortunes place them just without the polite circles; I mean the lower class of the gentry, and the higher of the mercantile world, who are, in reality, the worst-bred part of mankind. Well, sir, whilst I continued in this miserable state, with scarce sufficient business to keep me from starving, the reputation of a poet being my bane, I accidentally became acquainted with a bookseller, who told me, "It was a pity a man of my learning and genius should be obliged to such a method of getting his livelihood; that he had a compassion for me, and, if I would engage with him, he would undertake to provide handsomely for me." A man in my circumstances, as he very well knew, had no choice. I accordingly accepted his proposal with his conditions, which were none of the most favourable, and fell to translating with all my might. I had no longer reason to lament the want of business; for he furnished me with so much, that in half a year I almost writ myself blind. I likewise contracted a distemper by my sedentary life, in which no part of my body was exercised but my right arm, which rendered me incapable of writing for a long time. This un-luckily happening to delay the publication of a work, and my last performance not having sold well, the bookseller declined any further engagement, and aspersed me to his brethren as a careless idle fellow. I had, however, by having half worked and half starved myself to death during the time I was in his service, saved a few guineas, with which I bought a lottery-ticket, resolving to throw myself into Fortune's lap, and try if she would make me amends for the injuries she had done me at the gaming-table. This purchase, being made, left me almost pennyless; when, as if I had not been sufficiently miserable, a bailiff in woman's clothes got admittance to my chamber, whither he was directed by the bookseller. He arrested me at my taylor's suit for thirty-five pounds; a sum for which I could not procure bail; and was therefore conveyed to his house, where I was locked up in an upper chamber. I had now neither health (for I was scarce recovered from my indisposition), liberty, money, or friends; and had abandoned all hopes, and even the desire, of life. "But this could not last long," said Adams; "for doubtless the taylor released you the moment he was truly acquainted with your affairs, and knew that your circumstances would not permit you to pay him." "Oh, sir," answered the gentleman, "he knew that before he arrested me; nay, he knew that nothing but incapacity could prevent me paying my debts; for I had been his customer many years, had spent vast sums of money with him, and had always paid

most punctually in my prosperous days; but when I reminded
him of this, with assurances that, if he would not molest my
endeavours, I would pay him all the money I could by my
utmost labour and industry procure, reserving only what was
sufficient to preserve me alive, he answered, his patience was
worn out; that I had put him off from time to time; that he
wanted the money; that he had put it into a lawyer's hands;
and if I did not pay him immediately, or find security, I must
die in gaol and expect no mercy." "He may expect mercy,"
cries Adams, starting from his chair, "where he will find none!
How can such a wretch repeat the Lord's Prayer; where the
word, which is translated, I know not for what reason, trespasses,
is in the original, debts? And as surely as we do not forgive
others their debts, when they are unable to pay them, so surely
shall we ourselves be unforgiven when we are in no condition of
paying." He ceased, and the gentleman proceeded. While I
was in this deplorable situation, a former acquaintance, to whom
I had communicated my lottery-ticket, found me out, and,
making me a visit, with great delight in his countenance, shook
me heartily by the hand, and wished me joy of my good fortune:
for, says he, your ticket is come up a prize of £3000. Adams
snapped his fingers at these words in an ecstasy of joy; which,
however, did not continue long; for the gentleman thus proceeded:—Alas! sir, this was only a trick of Fortune to sink me
the deeper; for I had disposed of this lottery-ticket two days
before to a relation, who refused lending me a shilling without
it, in order to procure myself bread. As soon as my friend
was acquainted with my unfortunate sale he began to revile
me and remind me of all the ill-conduct and miscarriages of my
life. He said I was one whom Fortune could not save if she
would; that I was now ruined without any hopes of retrieval,
nor must expect any pity from my friends; that it would be
extreme weakness to compassionate the misfortunes of a man
who ran headlong to his own destruction. He then painted to
me, in as lively colours as he was able, the happiness I should
have now enjoyed, had I not foolishly disposed of my ticket.
I urged the plea of necessity; but he made no answer to that,
and began again to revile me, till I could bear it no longer, and
desired him to finish his visit. I soon exchanged the bailiff's
house for a prison; where, as I had not money sufficient to
procure me a separate apartment, I was crouded in with a great
number of miserable wretches, in common with whom I was
destitute of every convenience of life, even that which all the

brutes enjoy, wholesome air. In these dreadful circumstances I applied by letter to several of my old acquaintance, and such to whom I had formerly lent money without any great prospect of its being returned, for their assistance; but in vain. An excuse, instead of a denial, was the gentlest answer I received. Whilst I languished in a condition too horrible to be described, and which, in a land of humanity, and, what is much more, Christianity, seems a strange punishment for a little inadvertency and indiscretion; whilst I was in this condition, a fellow came into the prison, and, enquiring me out, delivered me the following letter:

SIR,
My father, to whom you sold your ticket in the last lottery, died the same day in which it came up a prize, as you have possibly heard, and left me sole heiress of all his fortune. I am so much touched with your present circumstances, and the uneasiness you must feel at having been driven to dispose of what might have made you happy, that I must desire your acceptance of the enclosed, and am your humble servant,

HARRIET HEARTY.

And what do you think was enclosed? "I don't know," cried Adams; "not less than a guinea, I hope." Sir, it was a bank-note for £200.—"£200?" says Adams, in a rapture. No less, I assure you, answered the gentleman; a sum I was not half so delighted with as with the dear name of the generous girl that sent it me; and who was not only the best but the handsomest creature in the universe, and for whom I had long had a passion which I never durst disclose to her. I kissed her name a thousand times, my eyes overflowing with tenderness and gratitude; I repeated—But not to detain you with these raptures, I immediately acquired my liberty; and, having paid all my debts, departed, with upwards of fifty pounds in my pocket, to thank my kind deliverer. She happened to be then out of town, a circumstance which, upon reflection, pleased me; for by that means I had an opportunity to appear before her in a more decent dress. At her return to town, within a day or two, I threw myself at her feet with the most ardent acknowledgments, which she rejected with an unfeigned greatness of mind, and told me I could not oblige her more than by never mentioning, or if possible thinking on, a circumstance which must bring to my mind an accident that might be grievous to me to think on. She proceeded thus: "What I have done is in my own eyes a trifle, and perhaps infinitely less than would have become me to do. And if you think of engaging in any business where a larger sum may be serviceable to you, I shall not be over-rigid either as to the security or interest." I endeavoured to express all the gratitude in my power to this profusion of goodness, though perhaps it was my enemy, and began to afflict my mind with more agonies than all the miseries I had underwent; it affected me with severer reflections than poverty, distress, and prisons united had been able to make me feel; for, sir, these acts and professions of kindness, which were sufficient to have raised in a good heart the most violent passion of friendship to one of the same, or to age and ugliness in a different sex, came to me from a woman, a young and beautiful woman; one whose perfections I had long known, and for whom I had long conceived a violent passion, though with a despair which made me endeavour rather to curb and con-ceal, than to nourish or acquaint her with it. In short, they came upon me united with beauty, softness, and tenderness: such bewitching smiles!—O Mr. Adams, in that moment I lost myself, and, forgetting our different situations, nor considering what return I was making to her goodness by desiring her, who had given me so much, to bestow her all, I laid gently hold on her hand, and, conveying it to my lips, I prest it with incon-ceivable ardour; then, lifting up my swimming eyes, I saw her face and neck overspread with one blush; she offered to with-draw her hand, yet not so as to deliver it from mine, though I held it with the gentlest force. We both stood trembling; her eyes cast on the ground, and mine stedfastly fixed on her. Good G—d, what was then the condition of my soul! burning with love, desire, admiration, gratitude, and every tender passion, all bent on one charming object. Passion at last got the better of both reason and respect, and, softly letting go her hand, I offered madly to clasp her in my arms; when, a little recovering herself, she started from me, asking me, with some show of anger, "If she had any reason to expect this treatment from me?" I then fell prostrate before her, and told her, if I had offended, my life was absolutely in her power, which I would in any manner lose for her sake. Nay, madam, said I, you shall not be so ready to punish me as I to suffer. I own my guilt. I detest the reflection that I would have sacrificed your happiness to mine. Believe me, I sincerely repent my ingratitude; yet, believe me too, it was my passion, my unbounded passion for you, which hurried me so far: I have loved you long and tenderly, and the goodness you have shown me hath innocently weighed down a wretch undone before. Acquit me of all mean, mercenary views; and, before I take my leave of you for ever, which I am resolved instantly to do, believe me that Fortune could have raised me to no height to which I could not have gladly lifted you. O, curst be Fortune!—"Do not," says she, interrupting me with the sweetest voice, "do not curse Fortune, since she hath made me happy; and, if she hath put your happiness in my power, I have told you you shall ask nothing in reason which I will refuse." Madam, said I, you mistake me if you imagine, as you seem, my happiness is in the power of Fortune now. You have obliged me too much already; if I have any wish, it is for some blest accident, by which I may contribute with my life to the least augmentation of your felicity. As for myself, the only happiness I can ever have will be hearing of yours; and if Fortune will make that complete, I will forgive her all her wrongs to me. "You may, indeed," answered she, smiling, "for your own happiness must be included in mine. I have long known your worth; nay, I must confess," said she, blushing, "I have long discovered that passion for me you profess, not-withstanding those endeavours, which I am convinced were unaffected, to conceal it; and if all I can give with reason will not suffice, take reason away; and now I believe you cannot ask me what I will deny."—She uttered these words with a sweetness not to be imagined. I immediately started; my blood, which lay freezing at my heart, rushed tumultuously through every vein. I stood for a moment silent; then, flying to her, I caught her in my arms, no longer resisting, and softly told her she must give me then herself. O, sir! can I describe her look? She remained silent, and almost motionless, several minutes. At last, recovering herself a little, she insisted on my leaving her, and in such a manner that I instantly obeyed: you may imagine, however, I soon saw her again.—But I ask pardon: I fear I have detained you too long in relating the particulars of the former interview. "So far otherwise," said Adams, licking his lips, "that I could willingly hear it over again." Well, sir, continued the gentleman, to be as concise as possible, within a week she consented to make me the happiest of mankind. We were married shortly after; and when I came to examine the circumstances of my wife's fortune (which, I do assure you, I was not presently at leisure enough to do), I found it amounted to about six thousand pounds, most part of which lay in effects; for her father had been a wine merchant, and she seemed willing, if I liked it, that I should carry on the same trade. I readily, and too inconsiderately, undertook it; for, not having been bred up to the secrets of the business, and endeavouring to deal with the utmost honesty and uprightness, I soon found our fortune in a declining way, and my trade decreasing by little and little; for my wines, which I never adulterated after their importation, and were sold as neat as they came over, were universally decried by the vintners, to whom I could not allow them quite as cheap as those who gained double the profit by a less price. I soon began to despair of improving our fortune by these means; nor was I at all easy at the visits and familiarity of many who had been my acquaintance in my prosperity, but had denied and shunned me in my adversity, and now very forwardly renewed their acquaintance with me. In short, I had sufficiently seen that the pleasures of the world are chiefly folly, and the business of it mostly knavery, and both nothing better than vanity; the men of pleasure tearing one another to pieces from the emulation of spending money, and the men of business from envy in getting it. My happiness consisted entirely in my wife, whom I loved with an inexpressible fondness, which was perfectly returned; and my prospects were no other than to provide for our growing family; for she was now big of her second child: I therefore took an opportunity to ask her opinion of entering into a retired life, which, after hearing my reasons and perceiving my affection for it, she readily embraced. We soon put our small fortune, now reduced under three thousand pounds, into money, with part of which we purchased this little place, whither we retired soon after her delivery, from a world full of bustle, noise, hatred, envy, and ingratitude, to ease, quiet, and love. We have here lived almost twenty years, with little other conversation than our own, most of the neighbourhood taking us for very strange people; the squire of the parish representing me as a madman, and the parson as a presbyterian, because I will not hunt with the one nor drink with the other. "Sir," says Adams, "Fortune hath, I think, paid you all her debts in this sweet retirement." Sir, replied the gentleman, I am thankful to the great Author of all things for the blessings I here enjoy. I have the best of wives, and three pretty children, for whom I have the true tenderness of a parent. But no blessings are pure in this world: within three years of my arrival here I lost my eldest son. (Here he sighed bitterly.) "Sir," says Adams, "we must submit to Providence,

and consider death as common to all." We must submit,
indeed, answered the gentleman; and if he had died I could
have borne the loss with patience; but alas! sir, he was stolen
away from my door by some wicked travelling people whom
they call gipsies; nor could I ever, with the most diligent
search, recover him. Poor child! he had the sweetest look—
the exact picture of his mother; at which some tears unwittingly dropt from his eyes, as did likewise from those of
Adams, who always sympathised with his friends on those
occasions. Thus, sir, said the gentleman, I have finished my
story, in which if I have been too particular, I ask your pardon;
and now, if you please, I will fetch you another bottle: which
proposal the parson thankfully accepted.

CHAPTER IV

A DESCRIPTION OF MR. WILSON'S WAY OF LIVING. THE TRAGICAL
ADVENTURE OF THE DOG, AND OTHER GRAVE MATTERS

THE gentleman returned with the bottle; and Adams and he
sat some time silent, when the former started up, and cried,
"No, that won't do." The gentleman inquired into his meaning; he answered, "He had been considering that it was possible
the late famous king Theodore might have been that very son
whom he had lost"; but added, "that his age could not answer
that imagination. However," says he, "G— disposes all things
for the best; and very probably he may be some great man, or
duke, and may, one day or other, revisit you in that capacity."
The gentleman answered, he should know him amongst ten
thousand, for he had a mark on his left breast of a strawberry,
which his mother had given him by longing for that fruit.

That beautiful young lady the Morning now rose from her bed,
and with a countenance blooming with fresh youth and sprightliness, like Miss ——,[1] with soft dews hanging on her pouting lips,
began to take her early walk over the eastern hills; and presently
after, that gallant person the sun stole softly from his wife's
chamber to pay his addresses to her; when the gentleman asked
his guest if he would walk forth and survey his little garden,
which he readily agreed to, and Joseph at the same time awaking
from a sleep in which he had been two hours buried, went with
them. No parterres, no fountains, no statues, embellished this

[1] Whoever the reader pleases.

little garden. Its only ornament was a short walk, shaded on each side by a filbert-hedge, with a small alcove at one end, whither in hot weather the gentleman and his wife used to retire and divert themselves with their children, who played in the walk before them. But, though vanity had no votary in this little spot, here was variety of fruit and everything useful for the kitchen, which was abundantly sufficient to catch the admiration of Adams, who told the gentleman he had certainly a good gardener. Sir, answered he, that gardener is now before you: whatever you see here is the work solely of my own hands. Whilst I am providing necessaries for my table, I likewise procure myself an appetite for them. In fair seasons I seldom pass less than six hours of the twenty-four in this place, where I am not idle; and by these means I have been able to preserve my health ever since my arrival here, without assistance from physic. Hither I generally repair at the dawn, and exercise myself whilst my wife dresses her children and prepares our breakfast; after which we are seldom asunder during the residue of the day, for, when the weather will not permit them to accompany me here, I am usually within with them; for I am neither ashamed of conversing with my wife nor of playing with my children: to say the truth, I do not perceive that inferiority of understanding which the levity of rakes, the dulness of men of business, or the austerity of the learned, would persuade us of in women. As for my woman, I declare I have found none of my own sex capable of making juster observations on life, or of delivering them more agreeably; nor do I believe any one possessed of a faithfuller or braver friend. And sure as this friendship is sweetened with more delicacy and tenderness, so is it confirmed by dearer pledges than can attend the closest male alliance; for what union can be so fast as our common interest in the fruits of our embraces? Perhaps, sir, you are not yourself a father; if you are not, be assured you cannot conceive the delight I have in my little ones. Would you not despise me if you saw me stretched on the ground, and my children playing round me? "I should reverence the sight," quoth Adams; "I myself am now the father of six, and have been of eleven, and I can say I never scourged a child of my own, unless as his schoolmaster, and then have felt every stroke on my own posteriors. And as to what you say concerning women, I have often lamented my own wife did not understand Greek."—The gentleman smiled, and answered, he would not be apprehended to insinuate that his own had an understanding above the care of her family; on the contrary, says he, my Harriet, I assure you, is a notable housewife, and few gentlemen's housekeepers understand cookery or confectionery better; but these are arts which she hath no great occasion for now: however, the wine you commended so much last night at supper was of her own making, as is indeed all the liquor in my house, except my beer, which falls to my province. "And I assure you it is as excellent," quoth Adams, "as ever I tasted." We formerly kept a maid-servant, but since my girls have been growing up she is unwilling to indulge them in idleness; for as the fortunes I shall give them will be very small, we intend not to breed them above the rank they are likely to fill hereafter, nor to teach them to despise or ruin a plain husband. Indeed, I could wish a man of my own temper, and a retired life, might fall to their lot; for I have experienced that calm serene happiness, which is seated in content, is inconsistent with the hurry and bustle of the world. He was proceeding thus when the little things, being just risen, ran eagerly towards him and asked his blessing. They were shy to the strangers, but the eldest acquainted her father, that her mother and the young gentlewoman were up, and that breakfast was ready. They all went in, where the gentleman was surprised at the beauty of Fanny, who had now recovered herself from her fatigue, and was entirely clean drest; for the rogues who had taken away her purse had left her her bundle. But if he was so much amazed at the beauty of this young creature, his guests were no less charmed at the tenderness which appeared in the behaviour of the husband and wife to each other, and to their children, and at the dutiful and affectionate behaviour of these to their parents. These instances pleased the well-disposed mind of Adams equally with the readiness which they exprest to oblige their guests, and their forwardness to offer them the best of everything in their house; and what delighted him still more was an instance or two of their charity; for whilst they were at breakfast the good woman was called for to assist her sick neighbour, which she did with some cordials made for the public use, and the good man went into his garden at the same time to supply another with something which he wanted thence, for they had nothing which those who wanted it were not welcome to. These good people were in the utmost cheerfulness, when they heard the report of a gun, and immediately afterwards a little dog, the favourite of the eldest daughter, came limping in all bloody and laid himself at his mistress's feet: the poor girl, who was about eleven years old, burst into tears at the sight; and presently one of the neighbours

JOSEPH ANDREWS 177

came in and informed them that the young squire, the son of the
lord of the manor, had shot him as he past by, swearing at the
same time he would prosecute the master of him for keeping a
spaniel, for that he had given notice he would not suffer one in
the parish. The dog, whom his mistress had taken into her lap,
died in a few minutes, licking her hand. She exprest great agony
at his loss, and the other children began to cry for their sister's
misfortune; nor could Fanny herself refrain. Whilst the father
and mother attempted to comfort her, Adams grasped his crabstick and would have sallied out after the squire had not Joseph
withheld him. He could not however bridle his tongue—he
pronounced the word rascal with great emphasis; said he deserved
to be hanged more than a highwayman, and wished he had the
scourging him. The mother took her child, lamenting and carrying the dead favourite in her arms, out of the room, when the
gentleman said this was the second time this squire had endeavoured to kill the little wretch, and had wounded him smartly
once before; adding, he could have no motive but ill-nature, for
the little thing, which was not near as big as one's fist, had never
been twenty yards from the house in the six years his daughter
had had it. He said he had done nothing to deserve this usage,
but his father had too great a fortune to contend with: that he
was as absolute as any tyrant in the universe, and had killed
all the dogs and taken away all the guns in the neighbourhood;
and not only that, but he trampled down hedges and rode over
corn and gardens, with no more regard than if they were the
highway. "I wish I could catch him in my garden," said Adams,
"though I would rather forgive him riding through my house
than such an ill-natured act as this."

The cheerfulness of their conversation being interrupted by
this accident, in which the guests could be of no service to their
kind entertainer; and as the mother was taken up in administer-
ing consolation to the poor girl, whose disposition was too good
hastily to forget the sudden loss of her little favourite, which
had been fondling with her a few minutes before; and as Joseph
and Fanny were impatient to get home and begin those previous
ceremonies to their happiness which Adams had insisted on, they
now offered to take their leave. The gentleman importuned them
much to stay dinner; but when he found their eagerness to
depart he summoned his wife; and accordingly, having performed
all the usual ceremonies of bows and curtsies more pleasant to be
seen than to be related, they took their leave, the gentleman and
his wife heartily wishing them a good journey, and they as

*G 467

heartily thanking them for their kind entertainment. They then departed, Adams declaring that this was the manner in which the people had lived in the golden age.

CHAPTER V

A DISPUTATION ON SCHOOLS HELD ON THE ROAD BETWEEN MR. ABRAHAM ADAMS AND JOSEPH; AND A DISCOVERY NOT UNWELCOME TO THEM BOTH

OUR travellers, having well refreshed themselves at the gentleman's house, Joseph and Fanny with sleep, and Mr. Abraham Adams with ale and tobacco, renewed their journey with great alacrity; and pursuing the road into which they were directed, travelled many miles before they met with any adventure worth relating. In this interval we shall present our readers with a very curious discourse, as we apprehend it, concerning public schools, which passed between Mr. Joseph Andrews and Mr. Abraham Adams.

They had not gone far before Adams, calling to Joseph, asked him, "If he had attended to the gentleman's story?" He answered, "To all the former part."—"And don't you think," says he, "he was a very unhappy man in his youth?"—"A very unhappy man, indeed," answered the other. "Joseph," cries Adams, screwing up his mouth, "I have found it; I have discovered the cause of all the misfortunes which befel him; a public school, Joseph, was the cause of all the calamities which he afterwards suffered. Public schools are the nurseries of all vice and immorality. All the wicked fellows whom I remember at the university were bred at them.—Ah, Lord! I can remember as well as if it was but yesterday, a knot of them; they called them King's scholars, I forget why—very wicked fellows! Joseph, you may thank the Lord you were not bred at a public school; you would never have preserved your virtue as you have. The first care I always take is of a boy's morals; I had rather he should be a blockhead than an atheist or a presbyterian. What is all the learning in the world compared to his immortal soul? What shall a man take in exchange for his soul? But the masters of great schools trouble themselves about no such thing. I have known a lad of eighteen at the university, who hath not been able to say his catechism; but for my own part, I always scourged a lad sooner for missing that than any other lesson. Believe me, child, all that gentleman's misfortunes arose from his being educated at a public school."

"It doth not become me," answered Joseph, "to dispute anything, sir, with you, especially a matter of this kind; for to be sure you must be allowed by all the world to be the best teacher of a school in all our county."—"Yes, that," says Adams, "I believe, is granted me; that I may without much vanity pretend to—nay, I believe I may go to the next county too—but *gloriari non est meum.*"—"However, sir, as you are pleased to bid me speak," says Joseph, "you know my late master, Sir Thomas Booby, was bred at a public school, and he was the finest gentleman in all the neighbourhood. And I have often heard him say, if he had a hundred boys he would breed them all at the same place. It was his opinion, and I have often heard him deliver it, that a boy taken from a public school and carried into the world, will learn more in one year there than one of a private education will in five. He used to say the school itself initiated him a great way (I remember that was his very expression), for great schools are little societies, where a boy of any observation may see in epitome what he will afterwards find in the world at large."—"*Hinc illæ lachrymæ:* for that very reason," quoth Adams, "I prefer a private school, where boys may be kept in innocence and ignorance; for, according to that fine passage in the play of Cato, the only English tragedy I ever read:

> If knowledge of the world must make men villains
> May Juba ever live in ignorance!

Who would not rather preserve the purity of his child than wish him to attain the whole circle of arts and sciences? which, by the bye, he may learn in the classes of a private school; for I would not be vain, but I esteem myself to be second to none, *nulli secundum*, in teaching these things; so that a lad may have as much learning in a private as in a public education."—"And, with submission," answered Joseph, "he may get as much vice: witness several country gentlemen, who were educated within five miles of their own houses, and are as wicked as if they had known the world from their infancy. I remember when I was in the stable, if a young horse was vicious in his nature, no correction would make him otherwise: I take it to be equally the same among men: if a boy be of a mischievous wicked inclination, no school, though ever so private, will ever make him good: on the contrary, if he be of a righteous temper, you may trust him to London, or wherever else you please—he will be in no danger of being corrupted. Besides, I have often heard my master say that the discipline practised in public schools was much better than that in private."—"You talk like a jackanapes," said Adams, "and so did your master. Discipline indeed! Because one man scourges twenty or thirty boys more in a morning than another, is he therefore a better disciplinarian? I do presume to confer in this point with all who have taught from Chiron's time to this day; and, if I was master of six boys only, I would preserve as good discipline amongst them as the master of the greatest school in the world. I say nothing, young man; remember I say nothing; but if Sir Thomas himself had been educated nearer home, and under the tuition of somebody—remember I name nobody—it might have been better for him:—but his father must institute him in the knowledge of the world. *Nemo mortalium omnibus horis sapit.*" Joseph, seeing him run on in this manner, asked pardon many times, assuring him he had no intention to offend. "I believe you had not, child," said he, "and I am not angry with you; but for maintaining good discipline in a school; for this."—And then he ran on as before, named all the masters who are recorded in old books, and preferred himself to them all. Indeed, if this good man had an enthusiasm, or what the vulgar call a blind side, it was this: he thought a schoolmaster the greatest character in the world, and himself the greatest of all schoolmasters: neither of which points he would have given up to Alexander the Great at the head of his army.

Adams continued his subject till they came to one of the beautifullest spots of ground in the universe. It was a kind of natural amphitheatre, formed by the winding of a small rivulet, which was planted with thick woods, and the trees rose gradually above each other by the natural ascent of the ground they stood on; which ascent as they hid with their boughs, they seemed to have been disposed by the design of the most skilful planter. The soil was spread with a verdure which no paint could imitate; and the whole place might have raised romantic ideas in elder minds than those of Joseph and Fanny, without the assistance of love.

Here they arrived about noon, and Joseph proposed to Adams that they should rest awhile in this delightful place, and refresh themselves with some provisions which the good-nature of Mrs. Wilson had provided them with. Adams made no objection to the proposal; so down they sat, and, pulling out a cold fowl and a bottle of wine, they made a repast with a cheerfulness which might have attracted the envy of more splendid tables. I should not omit that they found among their provision a little paper containing a piece of gold, which Adams imagining had been put there by mistake, would have returned back to restore it; but he was at last convinced by Joseph that Mr. Wilson had taken this handsome way of furnishing them with a supply for their journey, on his having related the distress which they had been in, when they were relieved by the generosity of the pedlar. Adams said he was glad to see such an instance of goodness, not so much for the conveniency which it brought them as for the sake of the doer, whose reward would be great in heaven. He likewise comforted himself with a reflection that he should shortly have an opportunity of returning it him; for the gentleman was within a week to make a journey into Somersetshire, to pass through Adams's parish, and had faithfully promised to call on him; a circumstance which we thought too immaterial to mention before; but which those who have as great an affection for that gentleman as ourselves will rejoice at, as it may give them hopes of seeing him again. Then Joseph made a speech on charity which the reader, if he is so disposed, may see in the next chapter; for we scorn to betray him into any such reading, without first giving him warning.

CHAPTER VI

MORAL REFLECTIONS BY JOSEPH ANDREWS; WITH THE HUNTING
ADVENTURE, AND PARSON ADAMS'S MIRACULOUS ESCAPE

"I HAVE often wondered, sir," said Joseph, "to observe so few instances of charity among mankind; for though the goodness of a man's heart did not incline him to relieve the distresses of his fellow-creatures, methinks the desire of honour should move him to it. What inspires a man to build fine houses, to purchase fine furniture, pictures, clothes, and other things, at a great expense, but an ambition to be respected more than other people? Now, would not one great act of charity, one instance of redeeming a poor family from all the miseries of poverty, restoring an unfortunate tradesman by a sum of money to the means of procuring a livelihood by his industry, discharging an undone debtor from his debts or a gaol, or any suchlike example of goodness, create a man more honour and respect than he could acquire by the finest house, furniture, pictures, or clothes, that were ever beheld? For not only the object himself who was thus relieved, but all who heard the name of such a person, must, I imagine, reverence him infinitely more than the possessor of all those other things; which when we so admire, we rather praise the builder, the workman, the painter, the lace-maker, the taylor, and the rest, by whose ingenuity they are produced, than the person who by his money makes them his own. For my own part, when I have waited behind my lady in a room hung with fine pictures, while I have been looking at them I have never once thought of their owner, nor hath any one else, as I ever observed; for when it hath been asked whose picture that was, it was never once answered the master's of the house; but Ammyconni, Paul Varnish, Hannibal Scratchi, or Hogarthi, which I suppose were the names of the painters; but if it was asked—Who redeemed such a one out of prison? Who lent such a ruined tradesman money to set up? Who clothed that family of poor small children? it is very plain what must be the answer. And besides, these great folks are mistaken if they imagine they get any honour at all by these means; for I do not remember I ever was with my lady at any house where she commended the house or furniture but I have heard her at her return home make sport and jeer at whatever she had before commended; and I have been told by other gentlemen in livery that it is the same in their families: but I defy the wisest man in the world to turn a true good action into ridicule. I defy him to do it. He who should endeavour it would be laughed at himself, instead of making others laugh. Nobody scarce doth any good, yet they all agree in praising those who do. Indeed, it is strange that all men should consent in commending goodness, and no man endeavour to deserve that commendation; whilst, on the contrary, all rail at wickedness, and all are as eager to be what they abuse. This I know not the reason of; but it is as plain as daylight to those who converse in the world, as I have done these three years." "Are all the great folks wicked then?" says Fanny. "To be sure there are some exceptions," answered Joseph. "Some gentlemen of our cloth report charitable actions done by their lords and masters; and I have heard Squire Pope, the great poet, at my lady's table, tell stories of a man that lived at a place called Ross, and another at the Bath, one Al— Al— I forget his name, but it is in the book of verses. This gentleman hath built up a stately house too, which the squire likes very well; but his charity is seen farther than his house, though it stands on a hill,—ay, and brings him more honour too. It was his charity that put him in the book, where the squire says he puts all those who deserve it; and to be sure, as he lives among all the great people, if there were any such, he would know them." This was all of Mr. Joseph Andrews's speech which I could get him to recollect, which I have delivered as near as was possible in his own words, with a very small embellishment. But I believe the reader hath not been a little surprised at the long silence of parson Adams, especially as so many occasions offered themselves to exert his curiosity and observation. The truth is, he was fast asleep, and had so been from the beginning of the preceding narrative; and, indeed, if the reader considers that so many hours had passed since he had closed his eyes, he will not wonder at his repose, though even Henley himself, or as great an orator (if any such be), had been in his rostrum or tub before him.

Joseph, who whilst he was speaking had continued in one attitude, with his head reclining on one side, and his eyes cast on the ground, no sooner perceived, on looking up, the position of Adams, who was stretched on his back, and snored louder than the usual braying of the animal with long ears, than he turned towards Fanny, and, taking her by the hand, began a dalliance, which, though consistent with the purest innocence and decency, neither he would have attempted nor she permitted before any witness. Whilst they amused themselves in this harmless and delightful manner they heard a pack of hounds approaching in full cry towards them, and presently afterwards saw a hare pop forth from the wood, and, crossing the water, land within a few yards of them in the meadows. The hare was no sooner on shore than it seated itself on its hinder legs, and listened to the sound of the pursuers. Fanny was wonderfully pleased with the little wretch, and eagerly longed to have it in her arms that she might preserve it from the dangers which seemed to threaten it; but the rational part of the creation do not always aptly distinguish their friends from their foes; what wonder then if this silly creature, the moment it beheld her, fled from the friend who would have protected it, and, traversing the meadows again, passed the little rivulet on the opposite side? It was, however, so spent and weak, that it fell down twice or thrice in its way. This affected the tender heart of Fanny, who exclaimed, with tears in her eyes, against the barbarity of worrying a poor innocent defenceless animal out of its life, and putting it to the extremest torture for diversion.

She had not much time to make reflections of this kind, for on a sudden the hounds rushed through the wood, which resounded with their throats and the throats of their retinue, who attended on them on horseback. The dogs now past the rivulet, and pursued the footsteps of the hare; five horsemen attempted to leap over, three of whom succeeded, and two were in the attempt thrown from their saddles into the water; their companions, and their own horses too, proceeded after their sport, and left their friends and riders to invoke the assistance of Fortune, or employ the more active means of strength and agility for their deliverance. Joseph, however, was not so unconcerned on this occasion; he left Fanny for a moment to herself, and ran to the gentlemen, who were immediately on their legs, shaking their ears, and easily, with the help of his hand, obtained the bank (for the rivulet was not at all deep); and, without staying to thank their kind assister, ran dripping across the meadow, calling to their brother sportsmen to stop their horses; but they heard them not.

The hounds were now very little behind their poor reeling, staggering prey, which, fainting almost at every step, crawled through the wood, and had almost got round to the place where Fanny stood, when it was overtaken by its enemies, and being driven out of the covert, was caught, and instantly torn to pieces before Fanny's face, who was unable to assist it with any aid more powerful than pity; nor could she prevail on Joseph, who had been himself a sportsman in his youth, to attempt anything contrary to the laws of hunting in favour of the hare, which he said was killed fairly.

The hare was caught within a yard or two of Adams, who lay asleep at some distance from the lovers; and the hounds, in devouring it, and pulling it backwards and forwards, had drawn it so close to him, that some of them (by mistake perhaps for the hare's skin) laid hold of the skirts of his cassock; others at the same time applying their teeth to his wig, which he had with a handkerchief fastened to his head, began to pull him about; and had not the motion of his body had more effect on him than seemed to be wrought by the noise, they must certainly have tasted his flesh, which delicious flavour might have been fatal to him; but being roused by these tuggings, he instantly awaked, and with a jerk delivering his head from his wig, he with most admirable dexterity recovered his legs, which now seemed the only members he could entrust his safety to. Having, therefore, escaped likewise from at least a third part of his cassock, which he willingly left as his *exuviæ* or spoils to the enemy, he fled with the utmost speed he could summon to his assistance. Nor let this be any detraction from the bravery of his character: let the number of the enemies, and the surprise in which he was taken, be considered; and if there be any modern so outrageously brave that he cannot admit of flight in any circumstance whatever, I say (but I whisper that softly, and I solemnly declare without any intention of giving offence to any brave man in the nation), I say, or rather I whisper, that he is an ignorant fellow, and hath never read Homer nor Virgil, nor knows he anything of Hector or Turnus; nay, he is unacquainted with the history of some great men living, who, though as brave as lions, ay, as tigers, have run away, the Lord knows how far, and the Lord knows why, to the surprise of their friends and the entertainment of their enemies. But if persons of such heroic disposition are a little offended at the behaviour of Adams, we assure them they shall be as much pleased with what we shall immediately relate of Joseph Andrews. The master of the pack was just arrived, or, as the sportsmen call it, come in, when Adams set out, as we have before mentioned. This gentleman was generally said to be a great lover of humour; but, not to mince the matter, especially as we are upon this subject, he was a great hunter of men; indeed, he had hitherto followed the sport only with dogs of his own species; for he kept two or three couple of barking curs for that use only. However, as he thought he had now found a man nimble enough, he was willing to indulge himself with other sport, and accordingly, crying out, "Stole away," encouraged the hounds to pursue Mr. Adams, swearing it was the largest jack-hare he ever saw; at the same time hallooing and hooping as if a conquered foe was flying before him; in which he was imitated by these two or three couple of human or rather two-legged curs on horseback which we have mentioned before.

Now, thou, whoever thou art, whether a muse, or by what other name soever thou choosest to be called, who presidest over biography, and hast inspired all the writers of lives in these our times: thou who didst infuse such wonderful humour into the pen of immortal Gulliver; who hast carefully guided the judgment whilst thou hast exalted the nervous manly style of thy Mallet: thou who hadst no hand in that dedication and preface, or the translations, which thou wouldst willingly have struck out of the life of Cicero: lastly, thou who, without the assistance of the least spice of literature, and even against his inclination, hast, in some pages of his book, forced Colley Cibber to write English; do thou assist me in what I find myself unequal to.   Do thou introduce on the plain the young, the gay, the brave Joseph Andrews, whilst men shall view him with admiration and envy, tender virgins with love and anxious concern for his safety.

No sooner did Joseph Andrews perceive the distress of his friend, when first the quick-scenting dogs attacked him, than he grasped his cudgel in his right hand—a cudgel which his father had of his grandfather, to whom a mighty strong man of Kent had given it for a present in that day when he broke three heads on the stage.   It was a cudgel of mighty strength and wonderful art, made by one of Mr. Deard's best workmen, whom no other artificer can equal, and who hath made all those sticks which the beaus have lately walked with about the Park in a morning; but this was far his master-piece.   On its head was engraved a nose and chin, which might have been mistaken for a pair of nut-crackers.   The learned have imagined it designed to represent the Gorgon; but it was in fact copied from the face of a certain long English baronet, of infinite wit, humour, and gravity.   He did intend to have engraved here many histories: as the first night of Captain B——'s play, where you would have seen critics in embroidery transplanted from the boxes to the pit, whose ancient inhabitants were exalted to the galleries, where they played on catcalls.   He did intend to have painted an auction room, where Mr. Cock would have appeared aloft in his pulpit, trumpeting forth the praises of a china basin, and with astonishment wondering that "Nobody bids more for that fine, that superb——"   He did intend to have engraved many other things, but was forced to leave all out for want of room.

No sooner had Joseph grasped his cudgel in his hands than lightning darted from his eyes; and the heroick youth, swift of foot, ran with the utmost speed to his friend's assistance.   He overtook him just as Rockwood had laid hold of the skirt of his cassock, which, being torn, hung to the ground.   Reader, we would make a simile on this occasion, but for two reasons: the first is, it would interrupt the description, which should be rapid in this part; but that doth not weigh much, many precedents occurring for such an interruption: the second and much the greater reason is, that we could find no simile adequate to our purpose: for indeed, what instance could we bring to set before our reader's eyes at once the idea of friendship, courage, youth, beauty, strength, and swiftness? all which blazed in the person of Joseph Andrews. Let those, therefore, that describe lions and tigers, and heroes fiercer than both, raise their poems or plays with the simile of Joseph Andrews, who is himself above the reach of any simile.

Now Rockwood had laid fast hold on the parson's skirts, and stopt his flight; which Joseph no sooner perceived than he levelled his cudgel at his head and laid him sprawling. Jowler and Ringwood then fell on his greatcoat, and had undoubtedly brought him to the ground, had not Joseph, collecting all his force, given Jowler such a rap on the back, that, quitting his hold, he ran howling over the plain. A harder fate remained for thee, O Ringwood! Ringwood the best hound that ever pursued a hare, who never threw his tongue but where the scent was undoubtedly true; good at trailing, and sure in a highway; no babler, no overrunner; respected by the whole pack, who, whenever he opened, knew the game was at hand. He fell by the stroke of Joseph. Thunder and Plunder, and Wonder and Blunder, were the next victims of his wrath, and measured their lengths on the ground. Then Fairmaid, a bitch which Mr. John Temple had bred up in his house, and fed at his own table, and lately sent the squire fifty miles for a present, ran fiercely at Joseph and bit him by the leg: no dog was ever fiercer than she, being descended from an Amazonian breed, and had worried bulls in her own country, but now waged an unequal fight, and had shared the fate of those we have mentioned before, had not Diana (the reader may believe it or not if he pleases) in that instant interposed, and, in the shape of the huntsman, snatched her favourite up in her arms.

The parson now faced about, and with his crabstick felled many to the earth, and scattered others, till he was attacked by Cæsar and pulled to the ground. Then Joseph flew to his rescue, and with such might fell on the victor, that, O eternal blot to his name! Cæsar ran yelping away.

The battle now raged with the most dreadful violence, when lo! the huntsman, a man of years and dignity, lifted his voice, and called his hounds from the fight, telling them, in a language they understood, that it was in vain to contend longer, for that fate had decreed the victory to their enemies.

Thus far the muse hath with her usual dignity related this prodigious battle, a battle we apprehend never equalled by any poet, romance or life writer whatever, and, having brought it to a conclusion, she ceased; we shall therefore proceed in our ordinary style with the continuation of this history. The squire and his companions, whom the figure of Adams and the gallantry of Joseph had at first thrown into a violent fit of laughter, and who had hitherto beheld the engagement with more delight than any chase, shooting-match, race, cock-fighting, bull or bear baiting, had ever given them, began now to apprehend the danger of their hounds, many of which lay sprawling in the fields. The squire, therefore, having first called his friends about him, as guards for safety of his person, rode manfully up to the combatants, and, summoning all the terror he was master of into his countenance, demanded with an authoritative voice of Joseph what he meant by assaulting his dogs in that manner? Joseph answered, with great intrepidity, that they had first fallen on his friend; and if they had belonged to the greatest man in the kingdom, he would have treated them in the same way; for, whilst his veins contained a single drop of blood, he would not stand idle by and see that gentleman (pointing to Adams) abused either by man or beast; and, having so said, both he and Adams brandished their wooden weapons, and put themselves into such a posture, that the squire and his company thought proper to preponderate before they offered to revenge the cause of their four-footed allies.

At this instant Fanny, whom the apprehension of Joseph's danger had alarmed so much that, forgetting her own, she had made the utmost expedition, came up. The squire and all the horsemen were so surprised with her beauty, that they immediately fixed both their eyes and thoughts solely on her, every one declaring he had never seen so charming a creature. Neither mirth nor anger engaged them a moment longer, but all sat in silent amaze. The huntsman only was free from her attraction, who was busy in cutting the ears of the dogs, and endeavouring to recover them to life; in which he succeeded so well, that only two of no great note remained slaughtered on the field of action. Upon this the huntsman declared, "'Twas well it was no worse; for his part he could not blame the gentleman, and wondered his master would encourage the dogs to hunt Christians; that it was the surest way to spoil them, to make them follow vermin instead of sticking to a hare."

The squire, being informed of the little mischief that had been done, and perhaps having more mischief of another kind in his head, accosted Mr. Adams with a more favourable aspect than before: he told him he was sorry for what had happened;

that he had endeavoured all he could to prevent it the moment he was acquainted with his cloth, and greatly commended the courage of his servant, for so he imagined Joseph to be. He then invited Mr. Adams to dinner, and desired the young woman might come with him. Adams refused a long while; but the invitation was repeated with so much earnestness and courtesy, that at length he was forced to accept it. His wig and hat, and other spoils of the field, being gathered together by Joseph (for otherwise probably they would have been forgotten), he put himself into the best order he could; and then the horse and foot moved forward in the same pace towards the squire's house, which stood at a very little distance.

Whilst they were on the road the lovely Fanny attracted the eyes of all: they endeavoured to outvie one another in encomiums on her beauty; which the reader will pardon my not relating, as they had not anything new or uncommon in them: so must he likewise my not setting down the many curious jests which were made on Adams; some of them declaring that parson-hunting was the best sport in the world; others commending his standing at bay, which they said he had done as well as any badger; with such like merriment, which, though it would ill become the dignity of this history, afforded much laughter and diversion to the squire and his facetious companions.

CHAPTER VII

A SCENE OF ROASTING, VERY NICELY ADAPTED TO THE PRESENT TASTE AND TIMES

THEY arrived at the squire's house just as his dinner was ready. A little dispute arose on the account of Fanny, whom the squire, who was a bachelor, was desirous to place at his own table; but she would not consent, nor would Mr. Adams permit her to be parted from Joseph; so that she was at length with him consigned over to the kitchen, where the servants were ordered to make him drunk; a favour which was likewise intended for Adams; which design being executed, the squire thought he should easily accomplish what he had when he first saw her intended to perpetrate with Fanny.

It may not be improper, before we proceed farther, to open a little the character of this gentleman, and that of his friends. The master of this house, then, was a man of a very considerable

fortune; a bachelor, as we have said, and about forty years of
age: he had been educated (if we may use the expression) in
the country, and at his own home, under the care of his mother,
and a tutor who had orders never to correct him, nor to compel
him to learn more than he liked, which it seems was very little,
and that only in his childhood; for from the age of fifteen he
addicted himself entirely to hunting and other rural amusements, for which his mother took care to equip him with horses,
hounds, and all other necessaries; and his tutor, endeavouring
to ingratiate himself with his young pupil, who would, he knew,
be able handsomely to provide for him, became his companion,
not only at these exercises, but likewise over a bottle, which
the young squire had a very early relish for. At the age of
twenty his mother began to think she had not fulfilled the
duty of a parent; she therefore resolved to persuade her son, if
possible, to that which she imagined would well supply all that
he might have learned at a public school or university—this is
what they commonly call travelling; which, with the help of
the tutor, who was fixed on to attend him, she easily succeeded
in. He made in three years the tour of Europe, as they term it,
and returned home well furnished with French clothes, phrases,
and servants, with a hearty contempt for his own country;
especially what had any savour of the plain spirit and honesty
of our ancestors. His mother greatly applauded herself at his
return. And now, being master of his own fortune, he soon
procured himself a seat in Parliament, and was in the common
opinion one of the finest gentlemen of his age: but what distinguished him chiefly was a strange delight which he took in
everything which is ridiculous, odious, and absurd in his own
species; so that he never chose a companion without one or
more of these ingredients, and those who were marked by
nature in the most eminent degree with them were most his
favourites. If he ever found a man who either had not, or
endeavoured to conceal, these imperfections, he took great
pleasure in inventing methods of forcing him into absurdities
which were not natural to him, or in drawing forth and exposing
those that were; for which purpose he was always provided with
a set of fellows, whom we have before called curs, and who did,
indeed, no great honour to the canine kind; their business was
to hunt out and display everything that had any savour of the
above-mentioned qualities, and especially in the gravest and
best characters; but if they failed in their search, they were to
turn even virtue and wisdom themselves into ridicule, for the

diversion of their master and feeder. The gentlemen of curlike
disposition who were now at his house, and whom he had
brought with him from London, were, an old half-pay officer,
a player, a dull poet, a quack-doctor, a scraping fiddler, and a
lame German dancing-master.

As soon as dinner was served, while Mr. Adams was saying
grace, the captain conveyed his chair from behind him; so that
when he endeavoured to seat himself he fell down on the ground,
and this completed joke the first, to the great entertainment of
the whole company. The second joke was performed by the
poet, who sat next him on the other side, and took an opportunity, while poor Adams was respectfully drinking to the
master of the house, to overturn a plate of soup into his breeches;
which, with the many apologies he made, and the parson's gentle
answers, caused much mirth in the company. Joke the third
was served up by one of the waiting-men, who had been ordered
to convey a quantity of gin into Mr. Adams's ale, which he
declaring to be the best liquor he ever drank, but rather too rich
of the malt, contributed again to their laughter. Mr. Adams,
from whom we had most of this relation, could not recollect all
the jests of this kind practised on him, which the inoffensive
disposition of his own heart made him slow in discovering; and
indeed, had it not been for the information which we received
from a servant of the family, this part of our history, which we
take to be none of the least curious, must have been deplorably
imperfect; though we must own it probable that some more
jokes were (as they call it) cracked during their dinner; but we
have by no means been able to come at the knowledge of them.
When dinner was removed, the poet began to repeat some verses,
which, he said, were made extempore. The following is a copy
of them, procured with the greatest difficulty:

An extempore Poem on parson Adams

Did ever mortal such a parson view?
His cassock old, his wig not over-new,
Well might the hounds have him for fox mistaken.
In smell more like to that than rusty bacon;
But would it not make any mortal stare
To see this parson taken for a hare?
Could Phœbus err thus grossly, even he
For a good player might have taken thee.

At which words the bard whipt off the player's wig, and
received the approbation of the company, rather perhaps for

¹ All hounds that will hunt fox or other vermin will hunt a piece of rusty
bacon trailed on the ground.

the dexterity of his hand than his head. The player, instead of retorting the jest on the poet, began to display his talents on the same subject. He repeated many scraps of wit out of plays, reflecting on the whole body of the clergy, which were received with great acclamations by all present. It was now the dancing-master's turn to exhibit his talents; he therefore, addressing himself to Adams in broken English, told him, "He was a man ver well made for de dance, and he suppose by his walk dat he had learn of some great master." He said, "It was ver pretty quality in clergyman to dance;" and concluded with desiring him to dance a minuet, telling him, "his cassock would serve for petticoats; and that he would himself be his partner." At which words, without waiting for an answer, he pulled out his gloves, and the fiddler was preparing his fiddle. The company all offered the dancing-master wagers that the parson out-danced him, which he refused, saying "he believed so too, for he had never seen any man in his life who looked de dance so well as de gentleman:" he then stepped forwards to take Adams by the hand, which the latter hastily withdrew, and, at the same time clenching his fist, advised him not to carry the jest too far, for he would not endure being put upon. The dancing-master no sooner saw the fist than he prudently retired out of its reach, and stood aloof, mimicking Adams, whose eyes were fixed on him, not guessing what he was at, but to avoid his laying hold on him, which he had once attempted. In the meanwhile, the captain, perceiving an opportunity, pinned a cracker or devil to the cassock, and then lighted it with their little smoking-candle. Adams, being a stranger to this sport, and believing he had been blown up in reality, started from his chair, and jumped about the room, to the infinite joy of the beholders, who declared he was the best dancer in the universe. As soon as the devil had done tormenting him, and he had a little recovered his confusion, he returned to the table, standing up in the posture of one who intended to make a speech. They all cried out, "Hear him, hear him;" and he then spoke in the following manner: "Sir, I am sorry to see one to whom Providence hath been so bountiful in bestowing his favours make so ill and ungrateful a return for them; for, though you have not insulted me yourself, it is visible you have delighted in those that do it, nor have once discouraged the many rudenesses which have been shown towards me; indeed, towards yourself, if you rightly understood them; for I am your guest, and by the laws of hospitality entitled to your protection. One gentleman

had thought proper to produce some poetry upon me, of which
I shall only say, that I had rather be the subject than the
composer. He hath pleased to treat me with disrespect as a
parson. I apprehend my order is not the subject of scorn, nor
that I can become so, unless by being a disgrace to it, which
I hope poverty will never be called. Another gentleman,
indeed, hath repeated some sentences, where the order itself
is mentioned with contempt. He says they are taken from
plays. I am sure such plays are a scandal to the government
which permits them, and cursed will be the nation where they
are represented. How others have treated me I need not
observe; they themselves, when they reflect, must allow the
behaviour to be as improper to my years as to my cloth. You
found me, sir, travelling with two of my parishioners (I omit
your hounds falling on me; for I have quite forgiven it, whether
it proceeded from the wantonness or negligence of the huntsman): my appearance might very well persuade you that your
invitation was an act of charity, though in reality we were well
provided; yes, sir, if we had had an hundred miles to travel,
we had sufficient to bear our expenses in a noble manner."
(At which words he produced the half-guinea which was found
in the basket.) "I do not show you this out of ostentation
of riches, but to convince you I speak truth. Your seating me
at your table was an honour which I did not ambitiously affect.
When I was here, I endeavoured to behave towards you with
the utmost respect; if I have failed, it was not with design; nor
could I, certainly, so far be guilty as to deserve the insults I
have suffered. If they were meant, therefore, either to my
order or my poverty (and you see I am not very poor), the
shame doth not lie at my door, and I heartily pray that the
sin may be averted from yours." He thus finished, and received
a general clap from the whole company. Then the gentleman
of the house told him, "He was sorry for what had happened;
that he could not accuse him of any share in it; that the verses
were, as himself had well observed, so bad, that he might
easi'y answer them; and for the serpent, it was undoubtedly a
very great affront done him by the dancing-master, for which,
if he well thrashed him, as he deserved, he should be very
much pleased to see it" (in which, probably, he spoke truth).
Adams answered, "Whoever had done it, it was not his profession to punish him that way; but for the person whom he had
accused, I am a witness," says he, "of his innocence; for I had
my eye on him all the while. Whoever he was, God forgive

him, and bestow on him a little more sense as well as humanity."
The captain answered with a surly look and accent, "That he
hoped he did not mean to reflect upon him; d——n him, he had as
much imanity as another, and, if any man said he had not, he
would convince him of his mistake by cutting his throat."
Adams, smiling, said, "He believed he had spoke right by
accident." To which the captain returned, "What do you
mean by my speaking right? If you was not a parson, I would
not take these words; but your gown protects you. If any
man who wears a sword had said so much, I had pulled him by
the nose before this." Adams replied, "If he attempted any
rudeness to his person, he would not find any protection for
himself in his gown;" and, clenching his fist, declared "he had
thrashed many a stouter man." The gentleman did all he
could to encourage this warlike disposition in Adams, and was
in hopes to have produced a battle, but he was disappointed;
for the captain made no other answer than, "It is very well
you are a parson;" and so, drinking off a bumper to old mother
Church, ended the dispute.

Then the doctor, who had hitherto been silent, and who was
the gravest but most mischievous dog of all, in a very pompous
speech highly applauded what Adams had said, and as much
discommended the behaviour to him. He proceeded to encomiums on the Church and poverty; and, lastly, recommended
forgiveness of what had passed to Adams, who immediately
answered, "That everything was forgiven;" and in the warmth
of his goodness he filled a bumper of strong beer (a liquor he
preferred to wine), and drank a health to the whole company,
shaking the captain and the poet heartily by the hand, and
addressing himself with great respect to the doctor; who,
indeed, had not laughed outwardly at anything that past, as
he had a perfect command of his muscles, and could laugh
inwardly without betraying the least symptoms in his countenance. The doctor now began a second formal speech, in which
he declaimed against all levity of conversation, and what is
usually called mirth. He said, "There were amusements
fitted for persons of all ages and degrees, from the rattle to the
discussing a point of philosophy; and that men discovered
themselves in nothing more than in the choice of their amusements; for," says he, "as it must greatly raise our expectation
of the future conduct in life of boys whom in their tender years
we perceive, instead of taw or balls, or other childish play-
things, to chuse, at their leisure hours, to exercise their genius

in contentions of wit, learning, and such like; so must it inspire one with equal contempt of a man, if we should discover him playing at taw or other childish play." Adams highly commended the doctor's opinion, and said, "He had often wondered at some passages in ancient authors, where Scipio, Lælius, and other great men were represented to have passed many hours in amusements of the most trifling kind." The doctor replied, "He had by him an old Greek manuscript where a favourite diversion of Socrates was recorded." "Ay!" says the parson eagerly; "I should be most infinitely obliged to you for the favour of perusing it." The doctor promised to send it him, and farther said, "That he believed he could describe it. I think," says he, "as near as I can remember, it was this: there was a throne erected, on one side of which sat a king and on the other a queen, with their guards and attendants ranged on both sides; to them was introduced an ambassador, which part Socrates always used to perform himself; and when he was led up to the footsteps of the throne he addressed himself to the monarchs in some grave speech, full of virtue, and goodness, and morality, and such like. After which, he was seated between the king and queen, and royally entertained. This I think was the chief part. Perhaps I may have forgot some particulars; for it is long since I read it." Adams said, "It was, indeed, a diversion worthy the relaxation of so great a man; and thought something resembling it should be instituted among our great men, instead of cards and other idle pastime, in which, he was informed, they trifled away too much of their lives." He added, "The Christian religion was a nobler subject for these speeches than any Socrates could have invented." The gentleman of the house approved what Mr. Adams said, and declared "he was resolved to perform the ceremony this very evening." To which the doctor objected, as no one was prepared with a speech, "unless," said he (turning to Adams with a gravity of countenance which would have deceived a more knowing man), "you have a sermon about you, doctor." "Sir," said Adams, "I never travel without one, for fear of what may happen." He was easily prevailed on by his worthy friend, as he now called the doctor, to undertake the part of the ambassador; so that the gentleman sent immediate orders to have the throne erected, which was performed before they had drank two bottles; and, perhaps, the reader will hereafter have no great reason to admire the nimbleness of the servants. Indeed, to confess the truth, the throne was no more than this: there was a great tub of water provided, on each side of which were placed two stools raised higher than the surface of the tub, and over the whole was laid a blanket; on these stools were placed the king and queen, namely, the master of the house and the captain. And now the ambassador was introduced between the poet and the doctor; who, having read his sermon, to the great entertainment of all present, was led up to his place and seated between their majesties. They immediately rose up, when the blanket, wanting its supports at either end, gave way, and soused Adams over head and ears in the water. The captain made his escape, but, unluckily, the gentleman himself not being as nimble as he ought, Adams caught hold of him before he descended from his throne, and pulled him in with him, to the entire secret satisfaction of all the company. Adams, after ducking the squire twice or thrice, leapt out of the tub, and looked sharp for the doctor, whom he would certainly have conveyed to the same place of honour; but he had wisely withdrawn: he then searched for his crabstick, and having found that, as well as his fellow-travellers, he declared he would not stay a moment longer in such a house. He then departed, without taking leave of his host, whom he had exacted a more severe revenge on than he intended; for, as he did not use sufficient care to dry himself in time, he caught a cold by the accident which threw him into a fever that had like to have cost him his life.

CHAPTER VIII

WHICH SOME READERS WILL THINK TOO SHORT AND OTHERS TOO LONG

ADAMS, and Joseph, who was no less enraged than his friend at the treatment he met with, went out with their sticks in their hands, and carried off Fanny, notwithstanding the opposition of the servants, who did all, without proceeding to violence, in their power to detain them. They walked as fast as they could, not so much from any apprehension of being pursued as that Mr. Adams might, by exercise, prevent any harm from the water. The gentleman, who had given such orders to his servants concerning Fanny that he did not in the least fear her getting away, no sooner heard that she was gone, than he began to rave, and immediately despatched several with orders either to bring her back or never return. The poet, the player, and all but the dancing-master and doctor, went on this errand.

The night was very dark in which our friends began their journey; however, they made such expedition, that they soon arrived at an inn which was at seven miles' distance. Here they unanimously consented to pass the evening, Mr. Adams being now as dry as he was before he had set out on his embassy.

This inn, which indeed we might call an ale-house, had not the words, The New Inn, been writ on the sign, afforded them no better provision than bread and cheese and ale; on which, however, they made a very comfortable meal; for hunger is better than a French cook.

They had no sooner supped, than Adams, returning thanks to the Almighty for his food, declared he had eat his homely commons with much greater satisfaction than his splendid dinner; and expressed great contempt for the folly of mankind, who sacrificed their hopes of heaven to the acquisition of vast wealth, since so much comfort was to be found in the humblest state and the lowest provision. "Very true, sir," says a grave man who sat smoking his pipe by the fire, and who was a traveller as well as himself. "I have often been as much surprised as you are, when I consider the value which mankind in general set on riches, since every day's experience shows us how little is in their power; for what, indeed, truly desirable, can they bestow on us? Can they give beauty to the deformed, strength to the weak, or health to the infirm? Surely if they could we should not see so many ill-favoured faces haunting the assemblies of the great, nor would such numbers of feeble wretches languish in their coaches and palaces. No, not the wealth of a kingdom can purchase any paint to dress pale Ugliness in the bloom of that young maiden, nor any drugs to equip Disease with the vigour of that young man. Do not riches bring us to solicitude instead of rest, envy instead of affection, and danger instead of safety? Can they prolong their own possession, or lengthen his days who enjoys them? So far otherwise, that the sloth, the luxury, the care which attend them, shorten the lives of millions, and bring them with pain and misery to an untimely grave. Where, then, is their value if they can neither embellish nor strengthen our forms, sweeten nor prolong our lives?—Again: Can they adorn the mind more than the body? Do they not rather swell the heart with vanity, puff up the cheeks with pride, shut our ears to every call of virtue, and our bowels to every motive of compassion?"—"Give me your hand, brother," said Adams, in a rapture, "for I suppose you are a clergyman."—"No, truly," answered the other (indeed, he was a priest of the Church of Rome; but those who understand our laws will not wonder he was not over-ready to own it).—"Whatever you are," cries Adams, "you have spoken my sentiments: I believe I have preached every syllable of your speech twenty times over; for it hath always appeared to me easier for a cable-rope (which by the way is the true rendering of that word we have translated camel) to go through the eye of a needle than for a rich man to get into the kingdom of heaven."—"That, sir," said the other, "will be easily granted you by divines, and is deplorably true; but as the prospect of our good at a distance doth not so forcibly affect us, it might be of some service to mankind to be made thoroughly sensible—which I think they might be with very little serious attention—that even the blessings of this world are not to be purchased with riches; a doctrine, in my opinion, not only metaphysically, but, if I may so say, mathematically demonstrable; and which I have been always so perfectly convinced of that I have a contempt for nothing so much as for gold." Adams now began a long discourse: but as most which he said occurs among many authors who have treated this subject, I shall omit inserting it. During its continuance Joseph and Fanny retired to rest, and the host likewise left the room. When the English parson had concluded, the Romish resumed the discourse, which he continued with great bitterness and invective; and at last ended by desiring Adams to lend him eighteen-pence to pay his reckoning; promising, if he never paid him, he might be assured of his prayers. The good man answered that eighteen-pence would be too little to carry him any very long journey; that he had half a guinea in his pocket, which he would divide with him. He then fell to searching his pockets, but could find no money; for indeed the company with whom he dined had passed one jest upon him which we did not then enumerate, and had picked his pocket of all that treasure which he had so ostentatiously produced.

"Bless me!" cried Adams, "I have certainly lost it; I can never have spent it. Sir, as I am a Christian, I had a whole half-guinea in my pocket this morning, and have not now a single halfpenny of it left. Sure the devil must have taken it from me!"—"Sir," answered the priest, smiling, "you need make no excuses; if you are not willing to lend me the money,

I am contented."—"Sir," cries Adams, "if I had the greatest sum in the world—aye, if I had ten pounds about me—I would bestow it all to rescue any Christian from distress. I am more vexed at my loss on your account than my own. Was ever anything so unlucky? Because I have no money in my pocket I shall be suspected to be no Christian."—"I am more unlucky," quoth the other, "if you are as generous as you say; for really a crown would have made me happy, and conveyed me in plenty to the place I am going, which is not above twenty miles off, and where I can arrive by to-morrow night. I assure you I am not accustomed to travel pennyless. I am but just arrived in England; and we were forced by a storm in our passage to throw all we had overboard. I don't suspect but this fellow will take my word for the trifle I owe him; but I hate to appear so mean as to confess myself without a shilling to such people; for these, and indeed too many others, know little difference in their estimation between a beggar and a thief." However, he thought he should deal better with the host that evening than the next morning: he therefore resolved to set out immediately, notwithstanding the darkness; and accordingly, as soon as the host returned, he communicated to him the situation of his affairs; upon which the host, scratching his head, answered, "Why, I do not know, master; if it be so, and you have no money, I must trust, I think, though I had rather always have ready money if I could; but, marry, you look like so honest a gentleman that I don't fear your paying me if it was twenty times as much." The priest made no reply, but, taking leave of him and Adams as fast as he could, not without confusion, and perhaps with some distrust of Adams's sincerity, departed.

He was no sooner gone than the host fell a-shaking his head, and declared, if he had suspected the fellow had no money, he would not have drawn him a single drop of drink, saying he despaired of ever seeing his face again, for that he looked like a confounded rogue. "Rabbit the fellow," cries he, "I thought, by his talking so much about riches, that he had a hundred pounds at least in his pocket." Adams chid him for his suspicions, which, he said, were not becoming a Christian; and then, without reflecting on his loss, or considering how he himself should depart in the morning, he retired to a very homely bed, as his companions had before; however, health and fatigue gave them a sweeter repose than is often in the power of velvet and down to bestow.

CHAPTER IX

CONTAINING AS SURPRISING AND BLOODY ADVENTURES AS CAN BE
FOUND IN THIS OR PERHAPS ANY OTHER AUTHENTIC HISTORY

It was almost morning when Joseph Andrews, whose eyes the
thoughts of his dear Fanny had opened, as he lay fondly
meditating on that lovely creature, heard a violent knocking
at the door over which he lay. He presently jumped out of
bed, and, opening the window, was asked if there were no
travellers in the house? and presently, by another voice, if
two men and a woman had not taken up there their lodging
that night? Though he knew not the voices, he began to
entertain a suspicion of the truth—for indeed he had received
some information from one of the servants of the squire's house
of his design—and answered in the negative. One of the
servants, who knew the host well, called out to him by his
name just as he had opened another window, and asked him
the same question; to which he answered in the affirmative.
O ho! said another, have we found you? and ordered the host
to come down and open his door. Fanny, who was as wakeful
as Joseph, no sooner heard all this than she leaped from her
bed, and, hastily putting on her gown and petticoats, ran as
fast as possible to Joseph's room, who then was almost drest.
He immediately let her in, and, embracing her with the most
passionate tenderness, bid her fear nothing, for he would die
in her defence. "Is that a reason why I should not fear," says
she, "when I should lose what is dearer to me than the whole
world?" Joseph, then kissing her hand, said, "He could
almost thank the occasion which had extorted from her a
tenderness she would never indulge him with before." He
then ran and waked his bedfellow Adams, who was yet fast
asleep, notwithstanding many calls from Joseph; but was no
sooner made sensible of their danger than he leaped from his
bed, without considering the presence of Fanny, who hastily
turned her face from him, and enjoyed a double benefit from
the dark, which, as it would have prevented any offence, to
an innocence less pure, or a modesty less delicate, so it concealed
even those blushes which were raised in her.

Adams had soon put on all his clothes but his breeches, which,
in the hurry, he forgot; however, they were pretty well supplied
by the length of his other garments; and now, the house-door

being opened, the captain, the poet, the player, and three servants came in. The captain told the host that two fellows, who were in his house, had run away with a young woman, and desired to know in which room she lay. The host, who presently believed the story, directed them, and instantly the captain and poet, justling one another, ran up. The poet, who was the nimblest, entering the chamber first, searched the bed, and every other part, but to no purpose; the bird was flown, as the impatient reader, who might otherwise have been in pain for her, was before advertised. They then enquired where the men lay, and were approaching the chamber, when Joseph roared out, in a loud voice, that he would shoot the first man who offered to attack the door. The captain enquired what fire-arms they had; to which the host answered, he believed they had none; nay, he was almost convinced of it, for he had heard one ask the other in the evening what they should have done if they had been overtaken, when they had no arms; to which the other answered, they would have defended them-selves with their sticks as long as they were able, and God would assist a just cause. This satisfied the captain, but not the poet, who prudently retreated downstairs, saying, it was his business to record great actions, and not to do them. The captain was no sooner well satisfied that there were no fire-arms than, bidding defiance to gunpowder, and swearing he loved the smell of it, he ordered the servants to follow him, and, marching boldly up, immediately attempted to force the door, which the servants soon helped him to accomplish. When it was opened, they discovered the enemy drawn up three deep; Adams in the front, and Fanny in the rear. The captain told Adams that if they would go all back to the house again they should be civilly treated; but unless they consented he had orders to carry the young lady with him, whom there was great reason to believe they had stolen from her parents; for, notwithstanding her disguise, her air, which she could not conceal, sufficiently discovered her birth to be infinitely superior to theirs. Fanny, bursting into tears, solemnly assured him he was mistaken; that she was a poor helpless foundling, and had no relation in the world which she knew of; and, throwing herself on her knees, begged that he would not attempt to take her from her friends, who, she was convinced, would die before they would lose her; which Adams confirmed with words not far from amounting to an oath. The captain swore he had no leisure to talk, and, bidding them thank themselves for what happened, he ordered the servants to fall on, at the same time endeavouring to pass by Adams, in order to lay hold on Fanny; but the parson, interrupting him, received a blow from one of them, which, without considering whence it came, he returned to the captain, and gave him so dexterous a knock in that part of the stomach which is vulgarly called the pit, that he staggered some paces backwards. The captain, who was not accustomed to this kind of play, and who wisely apprehended the consequence of such another blow, two of them seeming to him equal to a thrust through the body, drew forth his hanger, as Adams approached him, and was levelling a blow at his head, which would probably have silenced the preacher for ever, had not Joseph in that instant lifted up a certain huge stone pot of the chamber with one hand, which six beaus could not have lifted with both, and discharged it, together with the contents, full in the captain's face. The uplifted hanger dropped from his hand, and he fell prostrated on the floor with a lumpish noise, and his halfpence rattled in his pocket; the red liquor which his veins contained, and the white liquor which the pot contained, ran in one stream down his face and his clothes. Nor had Adams quite escaped, some of the water having in its passage shed its honours on his head, and began to trickle down the wrinkles or rather furrows of his cheeks, when one of the servants, snatching a mop out of a pail of water, which had already done its duty in washing the house, pushed it in the parson's face; yet could not he bear him down, for the parson, wresting the mop from the fellow with one hand, with the other brought his enemy as low as the earth, having given him a stroke over that part of the face where, in some men of pleasure, the natural and artificial noses are conjoined.

Hitherto, Fortune seemed to incline the victory on the travellers' side, when, according to her custom, she began to show the fickleness of her disposition; for now the host, entering the field, or rather chamber of battle, flew directly at Joseph, and, darting his head into his stomach (for he was a stout fellow and an expert boxer), almost staggered him: but Joseph, stepping one leg back, did with his left hand so chuck him under the chin that he reeled. The youth was pursuing his blow with his right hand when he received from one of the servants such a stroke with a cudgel on his temples, that it instantly deprived him of sense, and he measured his length on the ground.

Fanny rent the air with her cries, and Adams was coming

to the assistance of Joseph; but the two serving-men and the host now fell on him, and soon subdued him, though he fought like a madman, and looked so black with the impressions he had received from the mop, that Don Quixote would certainly have taken him for an inchanted Moor. But now follows the most tragical part; for the captain was risen again, and, seeing Joseph on the floor, and Adams secured, he instantly laid hold on Fanny, and, with the assistance of the poet and player, who, hearing the battle was over, were now come up, dragged her, crying and tearing her hair, from the sight of her Joseph, and, with a perfect deafness to all her entreaties, carried her down-stairs by violence, and fastened her on the player's horse; and the captain, mounting his own, and leading that on which this poor miserable wretch was, departed, without any more con-sideration of her cries than a butcher hath of those of a lamb; for indeed his thoughts were entertained only with the degree of favour which he promised himself from the squire on the success of this adventure.

The servants, who were ordered to secure Adams and Joseph as safe as possible, that the squire might receive no interruption to his design on poor Fanny, immediately, by the poet's advice, tied Adams to one of the bed-posts, as they did Joseph on the other side, as soon as they could bring him to himself; and then, leaving them together, back to back, and desiring the host not to set them at liberty, nor to go near them, till he had further orders, they departed towards their master; but happened to take a different road from that which the captain had fallen into.

CHAPTER X

A DISCOURSE BETWEEN THE POET AND THE PLAYER; OF NO OTHER USE IN THIS HISTORY BUT TO DIVERT THE READER

BEFORE we proceed any farther in this tragedy we shall leave Mr. Joseph and Mr. Adams to themselves, and imitate the wise conductors of the stage, who in the midst of a grave action entertain you with some excellent piece of satire or humour called a dance. Which piece, indeed, is therefore danced, and not spoke, as it is delivered to the audience by persons whose thinking faculty is by most people held to lie in their heels; and to whom, as well as heroes, who think with their hands, Nature hath only given heads for the sake of conformity, and as they are of use in dancing, to hang their hats on.

The poet, addressing the player, proceeded thus, "As I was saying" (for they had been at this discourse all the time of the engagement above-stairs), "the reason you have no good new plays is evident; it is from your discouragement of authors. Gentlemen will not write, sir, they will not write, without the expectation of fame or profit, or perhaps both. Plays are like trees, which will not grow without nourishment; but like mush-rooms, they shoot up spontaneously, as it were, in a rich soil. The muses, like vines, may be pruned, but not with a hatchet. The town, like a peevish child, knows not what it desires, and is always best pleased with a rattle. A farce-writer hath indeed some chance for success: but they have lost all taste for the sublime. Though I believe one reason of their depravity is the badness of the actors. If a man writes like an angel, sir, those fellows know not how to give a sentiment utterance."—"Not so fast," says the player: "the modern actors are as good at least as their authors, nay, they come nearer their illustrious predecessors; and I expect a Booth on the stage again, sooner than a Shakespear or an Otway; and indeed I may turn your observation against you, and with truth say, that the reason no authors are encouraged is because we have no good new plays."—"I have not affirmed the contrary," said the poet; "but I am surprised you grow so warm; you cannot imagine yourself interested in this dispute; I hope you have a better opinion of my taste than to apprehend I squinted at yourself. No, sir, if we had six such actors as you, we should soon rival the Bettertons and Sandfords of former times; for, without a compliment to you, I think it impossible for any one to have excelled you in most of your parts. Nay, it is solemn truth, and I have heard many, and all great judges, express as much; and, you will pardon me if I tell you, I think every time I have seen you lately you have constantly acquired some new excellence, like a snowball. You have deceived me in my estimation of perfection, and have outdone what I thought inimitable."—"You are as little interested," answered the player, "in what I have said of other poets; for d—n me if there are not many strokes, ay, whole scenes, in your last tragedy, which at least equal Shakespear. There is a delicacy of sentiment, a dignity of expression in it, which I will own many of our gentlemen did not do adequate justice to. To confess the truth, they are bad enough, and I pity an author who is present at the murder of his works."—"Nay, it is but seldom that it can happen," returned the poet; "the works of

most modern authors, like dead-born children, cannot be
murdered. It is such wretched half-begotten, half-writ, lifeless, spiritless, low, grovelling stuff, that I almost pity the actor
who is obliged to get it by heart, which must be almost as
difficult to remember as words in a language you don't understand."—"I am sure," said the player, "if the sentences have
little meaning when they are writ, when they are spoken they
have less. I know scarce one who ever lays an emphasis right,
and much less adapts his action to his character. I have seen
a tender lover in an attitude of fighting with his mistress, and
a brave hero suing to his enemy with his sword in his hand.
I don't care to abuse my profession, but rot me if in my heart
I am not inclined to the poet's side."—"It is rather generous
in you than just," said the poet; "and, though I hate to speak
ill of any person's production—nay, I never do it, nor will—
but yet, to do justice to the actors, what could Booth or Better-
ton have made of such horrible stuff as Fenton's Mariamne,
Frowd's Philotas, or Mallet's Eurydice; or those low, dirty,
last-dying-speeches, which a fellow in the city of Wapping,
your Dillo or Lillo, what was his name, called tragedies?"—
"Very well," says the player; "and pray what do you think
of such fellows as Quin and Delane, or that face-making puppy
young Cibber, that ill-looked dog Macklin, or that saucy slut
Mrs. Clive? What work would they make with your Shake-
spears, Otways, and Lees? How would those harmonious lines
of the last come from their tongues?—

> ——No more; for I disdain
> All pomp when thou art by: far be the noise
> Of kings and crowns from us, whose gentle souls
> Our kinder fates have steer'd another way.
> Free as the forest birds we'll pair together,
> Without rememb'ring who our fathers were:
> Fly to the arbors, grots, and flow'ry meads;
> There in soft murmurs interchange our souls;
> Together drink the crystal of the stream,
> Or taste the yellow fruit which autumn yields,
> And, when the golden evening calls us home,
> Wing to our downy nests, and sleep till morn.

Or how would this disdain of Otway—

> 'Who'd be that foolish sordid thing call'd man?

"Hold! hold! hold!" said the poet: "Do repeat that tender
speech in the third act of my play which you made such a
figure in."—"I would willingly," said the player, "but I have
forgot it."—"Ay, you was not quite perfect in it when you

played it," cries the poet, "or you would have had such an applause as was never given on the stage; an applause I was extremely concerned for your losing."—"Sure," says the player, "if I remember, that was hissed more than any passage in the whole play."—"Ay, your speaking it was hissed," said the poet.—"My speaking it!" said the player.—"I mean your not speaking it," said the poet. "You was out, and then they hissed."—"They hissed, and then I was out, if I remember," answered the player; "and I must say this for myself, that the whole audience allowed I did your part justice; so don't lay the damnation of your play to my account."—"I don't know what you mean by damnation," replied the poet.—"Why, you know it was acted but one night," cried the player.— "No," said the poet, "you and the whole town were enemies; the pit were all my enemies, fellows that would cut my throat, if the fear of hanging did not restrain them. All taylors, sir, all taylors."—"Why should the taylors be so angry with you?" cries the player. "I suppose you don't employ so many in making your clothes."—"I admit your jest," answered the poet; "but you remember the affair as well as myself; you know there was a party in the pit and upper gallery that would not suffer it to be given out again; though much, ay infinitely, the majority, all the boxes in particular, were desirous of it; nay, most of the ladies swore they never would come to the house till it was acted again. Indeed, I must own their policy was good in not letting it be given out a second time: for the rascals knew if it had gone a second night it would have run fifty; for if ever there was distress in a tragedy—I am not fond of my own performance; but if I should tell you what the best judges said of it——Nor was it entirely owing to my enemies neither that it did not succeed on the stage as well as it hath since among the polite readers; for you can't say it had justice done it by the performers."—"I think," answered the player, "the performers did the distress of it justice; for I am sure we were in distress enough, who were pelted with oranges all the last act: we all imagined it would have been the last act of our lives."

The poet, whose fury was now raised, had just attempted to answer when they were interrupted, and an end put to their discourse, by an accident, which if the reader is impatient to know, he must skip over the next chapter, which is a sort of counterpart to this, and contains some of the best and gravest matters in the whole book, being a discourse between parson Abraham Adams and Mr. Joseph Andrews.

CHAPTER XI

CONTAINING THE EXHORTATIONS OF PARSON ADAMS TO HIS
FRIEND IN AFFLICTION; CALCULATED FOR THE INSTRUCTION
AND IMPROVEMENT OF THE READER

JOSEPH no sooner came perfectly to himself than, perceiving
his mistress gone, he bewailed her loss with groans which would
have pierced any heart but those which are possessed by some
people, and are made of a certain composition not unlike flint
in its hardness and other properties; for you may strike fire
from them, which will dart through the eyes, but they can never
distil one drop of water the same way. His own, poor youth!
was of a softer composition; and at those words, "O my dear
Fanny! O my love! shall I never, never see thee more?" his
eyes overflowed with tears, which would have become any but
a hero. In a word, his despair was more easy to be conceived
than related.

Mr. Adams, after many groans, sitting with his back to
Joseph, began thus in a sorrowful tone: "You cannot imagine,
my good child, that I entirely blame these first agonies of your
grief; for, when misfortunes attack us by surprise, it must
require infinitely more learning than you are master of to resist
them; but it is the business of a man and a Christian to summon
Reason as quickly as he can to his aid; and she will presently
teach him patience and submission. Be comforted, therefore,
child; I say be comforted. It is true, you have lost the prettiest,
kindest, loveliest, sweetest young woman, one with whom you
might have expected to have lived in happiness, virtue, and
innocence; by whom you might have promised yourself many
little darlings, who would have been the delight of your youth
and the comfort of your age. You have not only lost her, but
have reason to fear the utmost violence which lust and power
can inflict upon her. Now, indeed, you may easily raise ideas
of horror, which might drive you to despair."—"O I shall run
mad!" cries Joseph. "O that I could but command my hands
to tear my eyes out and my flesh off!"—"If you would use them
to such purposes, I am glad you can't," answered Adams. "I
have stated your misfortune as strong as I possibly can; but,
on the other side, you are to consider you are a Christian, that
no accident happens to us without the Divine permission, and
that it is the duty of a man, and a Christian, to submit. We

did not make ourselves; but the same power which made us rules over us, and we are absolutely at his disposal; he may do with us what he pleases, nor have we any right to complain. A second reason against our complaint is our ignorance; for, as we know not future events, so neither can we tell to what purpose any accident tends; and that which at first threatens us with evil may in the end produce our good. I should indeed have said our ignorance is twofold (but I have not at present time to divide properly), for, as we know not to what purpose any event is ultimately directed, so neither can we affirm from what cause it originally sprung. You are a man, and consequently a sinner; and this may be a punishment to you for your sins: indeed in this sense it may be esteemed as a good, yea, as the greatest good, which satisfies the anger of Heaven, and averts that wrath which cannot continue without our destruction. Thirdly, our impotency of relieving ourselves demonstrates the folly and absurdity of our complaints: for whom do we resist, or against whom do we complain, but a power from whose shafts no armour can guard us, no speed can fly?—a power which leaves us no hope but in submission." "O sir!" cried Joseph, "all this is very true, and very fine, and I could hear you all day if I was not so grieved at heart as now I am."—"Would you take physic," says Adams, "when you are well, and refuse it when you are sick? Is not comfort to be administered to the afflicted, and not to those who rejoice or those who are at ease?" "O! you have not spoken one word of comfort to me yet!" returned Joseph. "No!" cried Adams; "what am I then doing? what can I say to comfort you?" "O tell me," cried Joseph, "that Fanny will escape back to my arms, that they shall again enclose that lovely creature, with all her sweetness, all her untainted innocence about her!" "Why, perhaps you may," cries Adams, "but I can't promise you what's to come. You must, with perfect resignation, wait the event: if she be restored to you again, it is your duty to be thankful, and so it is if she be not. Joseph, if you are wise and truly know your own interest, you will peaceably and quietly submit to all the dispensations of Providence, being thoroughly assured that all the misfortunes, how great soever, which happen to the righteous, happen to them for their own good. Nay, it is not your interest only, but your duty, to abstain from immoderate grief; which if you indulge, you are not worthy the name of a Christian." He spoke these last words with an accent a little severer than usual; upon which

Joseph begged him not to be angry, saying, he mistook him if he thought he denied it was his duty, for he had known that long ago. "What signifies knowing your duty, if you do not perform it?" answered Adams. "Your knowledge increases your guilt. O Joseph! I never thought you had this stubbornness in your mind." Joseph replied, "He fancied he misunderstood him; which I assure you," says he, "you do, if you imagine I endeavour to grieve; upon my soul I don't." Adams rebuked him for swearing, and then proceeded to enlarge on the folly of grief, telling him, all the wise men and philosophers, even among the heathens, had written against it, quoting several passages from Seneca, and the Consolation, which, though it was not Cicero's, was, he said, as good almost as any of his works; and concluded all by hinting that immoderate grief in this case might incense that power which alone could restore him his Fanny. This reason, or indeed rather the idea which it raised of the restoration of his mistress, had more effect than all which the parson had said before, and for a moment abated his agonies; but, when his fears sufficiently set before his eyes the danger that poor creature was in, his grief returned again with repeated violence, nor could Adams in the least asswage it; though it may be doubted in his behalf whether Socrates himself could have prevailed any better.

They remained some time in silence, and groans and sighs issued from them both; at length Joseph burst out into the following soliloquy:

> "Yes, I will bear my sorrows like a man,
> But I must also feel them as a man.
> I cannot but remember such things were,
> And were most dear to me."

Adams asked him what stuff that was he repeated? To which he answered, they were some lines he had gotten by heart out of a play. "Ay, there is nothing but heathenism to be learned from plays," replied he. "I never heard of any plays fit for a Christian to read, but Cato and the Conscious Lovers; and, I must own, in the latter there are some things almost solemn enough for a sermon." But we shall now leave them a little, and enquire after the subject of their conversation.

*H 467

CHAPTER XII

MORE ADVENTURES, WHICH WE HOPE WILL AS MUCH PLEASE AS
SURPRISE THE READER

NEITHER the facetious dialogue which passed between the poet
and the player, nor the grave and truly solemn discourse of
Mr. Adams, will, we conceive, make the reader sufficient amends
for the anxiety which he must have felt on the account of poor
Fanny, whom we left in so deplorable a condition. We shall
therefore now proceed to the relation of what happened to that
beautiful and innocent virgin, after she fell into the wicked
hands of the captain.

The man of war, having conveyed his charming prize out of
the inn a little before day, made the utmost expedition in his
power towards the squire's house, where this delicate creature
was to be offered up a sacrifice to the lust of a ravisher. He
was not only deaf to all her bewailings and entreaties on the
road, but accosted her ears with impurities which, having been
never before accustomed to them, she happily for herself very
little understood. At last he changed his note, and attempted
to soothe and mollify her, by setting forth the splendor and
luxury which would be her fortune with a man who would
have the inclination, and power too, to give her whatever
her utmost wishes could desire; and told her he doubted not but
she would soon look kinder on him, as the instrument of her
happiness, and despise that pitiful fellow whom her ignorance
only could make her fond of. She answered, she knew not
whom he meant; she never was fond of any pitiful fellow.
"Are you affronted, madam," says he, "at my calling him so?
But what better can be said of one in a livery, notwithstanding
your fondness for him?" She returned, that she did not understand him, that the man had been her fellow-servant, and she
believed was as honest a creature as any alive; but as for
fondness for men—"I warrant ye," cried the captain, "we
shall find means to persuade you to be fond; and I advise you
to yield to gentle ones, for you may be assured that it is not
in your power, by any struggles whatever, to preserve your
virginity two hours longer. It will be your interest to consent;
for the squire will be much kinder to you if he enjoys you
willingly than by force." At which words she began to call
aloud for assistance (for it was now open day), but, finding

none, she lifted her eyes to heaven, and supplicated the Divine assistance to preserve her innocence. The captain told her, if she persisted in her vociferation, he would find a means of stopping her mouth. And now the poor wretch, perceiving no hopes of succour, abandoned herself to despair, and, sighing out the name of Joseph! Joseph! a river of tears ran down her lovely cheeks, and wet the handkerchief which covered her bosom. A horseman now appeared in the road, upon which the captain threatened her violently if she complained; however, the moment they approached each other she begged him with the utmost earnestness to relieve a distressed creature who was in the hands of a ravisher. The fellow stopt at those words, but the captain assured him it was his wife, and that he was carrying her home from her adulterer, which so satisfied the fellow, who was an old one (and perhaps a married one too), that he wished him a good journey, and rode on. He was no sooner past than the captain abused her violently for breaking his commands, and threatened to gagg her, when two more horsemen, armed with pistols, came into the road just before them. She again solicited their assistance, and the captain told the same story as before. Upon which one said to the other, "That's a charming wench, Jack; I wish I had been in the fellow's place, whoever he is." But the other, instead of answering him, cried out, "Zounds, I know her;" and then, turning to her, said, "Sure, you are not Fanny Goodwill?"— "Indeed, indeed, I am," she cried—"O John, I know you now —Heaven hath sent you to my assistance, to deliver me from this wicked man, who is carrying me away for his vile purposes —O for God's sake rescue me from him!" A fierce dialogue immediately ensued between the captain and these two men, who, being both armed with pistols, and the chariot which they attended being now arrived, the captain saw both force and stratagem were vain, and endeavoured to make his escape, in which however he could not succeed. The gentleman who rode in the chariot ordered it to stop, and with an air of authority examined into the merits of the cause; of which being advertised by Fanny, whose credit was confirmed by the fellow who knew her, he ordered the captain, who was all bloody from his encounter at the inn, to be conveyed as a prisoner behind the chariot, and very gallantly took Fanny into it; for, to say the truth, this gentleman (who was no other than the celebrated Mr. Peter Pounce, and who preceded the Lady Booby only a few miles, by setting out earlier in the morning) was a very gallant person, and loved a pretty girl better than anything besides his own money or the money of other people.

The chariot now proceeded towards the inn, which, as Fanny was informed, lay in their way, and where it arrived at that very time while the poet and player were disputing below-stairs, and Adams and Joseph were discoursing back to back above; just at that period to which we brought them both in the two preceding chapters the chariot stopt at the door, and in an instant Fanny, leaping from it, ran up to her Joseph.—O reader! conceive if thou canst the joy which fired the breasts of these lovers on this meeting; and if thy own heart doth not sympathetically assist thee in this conception, I pity thee sincerely from my own; for let the hard-hearted villain know this, that there is a pleasure in a tender sensation beyond any which he is capable of tasting.

Peter, being informed by Fanny of the presence of Adams, stopt to see him, and receive his homage; for, as Peter was an hypocrite, a sort of people whom Mr. Adams never saw through, the one paid that respect to his seeming goodness which the other believed to be paid to his riches; hence Mr. Adams was so much his favourite, that he once lent him four pounds thirteen shillings and sixpence to prevent his going to gaol, on no greater security than a bond and judgment, which probably he would have made no use of, though the money had not been (as it was) paid exactly at the time.

It is not perhaps easy to describe the figure of Adams; he had risen in such a hurry, that he had on neither breeches, garters, nor stockings; nor had he taken from his head a red spotted handkerchief, which by night bound his wig, turned inside out, around his head. He had on his torn cassock and his greatcoat; but, as the remainder of his cassock hung down below his greatcoat, so did a small stripe of white, or rather whitish, linen appear below that; to which we may add the several colours which appeared on his face, where a long piss-burnt beard served to retain the liquor of the stone-pot, and that of a blacker hue which distilled from the mop.—This figure, which Fanny had delivered from his captivity, was no sooner espied by Peter than it disordered the composed gravity of his muscles; however, he advised him immediately to make himself clean, nor would accept his homage in that pickle.

The poet and player no sooner saw the captain in captivity than they began to consider of their own safety, of which flight presented itself as the only means; they therefore both of them mounted the poet's horse, and made the most expeditious retreat in their power.

The host, who well knew Mr. Pounce and Lady Booby's livery, was not a little surprised at this change of the scene; nor was his confusion much helped by his wife, who was now just risen, and, having heard from him the account of what had passed, comforted him with a decent number of fools and blockheads; asked him why he did not consult her, and told him he would never leave following the nonsensical dictates of his own numskull till she and her family were ruined.

Joseph, being informed of the captain's arrival, and seeing his Fanny now in safety, quitted her a moment, and, running downstairs, went directly to him, and stripping off his coat, challenged him to fight; but the captain refused, saying he did not understand boxing. He then grasped a cudgel in one hand, and, catching the captain by the collar with the other, gave him a most severe drubbing, and ended with telling him he had now had some revenge for what his dear Fanny had suffered.

When Mr. Pounce had a little regaled himself with some provision which he had in his chariot, and Mr. Adams had put on the best appearance his clothes would allow him, Pounce ordered the captain into his presence, for he said he was guilty of felony, and the next justice of peace should commit him; but the servants (whose appetite for revenge is soon satisfied), being sufficiently contented with the drubbing which Joseph had inflicted on him, and which was indeed of no very moderate kind, had suffered him to go off, which he did, threatening a severe revenge against Joseph, which I have never heard he thought proper to take.

The mistress of the house made her voluntary appearance before Mr. Pounce, and with a thousand curtsies told him, "She hoped his honour would pardon her husband, who was a very nonsense man, for the sake of his poor family; that indeed if he could be ruined alone, she should be very willing of it; for because as why, his worship very well knew he deserved it; but she had three poor small children, who were not capable to get their own living; and if her husband was sent to gaol, they must all come to the parish; for she was a poor weak woman, continually a-breeding, and had no time to work for them. She therefore hoped his honour would take it into his worship's consideration, and forgive her husband this time; for she was sure he never intended any harm to man, woman, or child; and if it was not for that block-head of his own, the man in some things was well enough; for she had had three children by him in less than three years, and was almost ready to cry out the fourth time." She would have proceeded in this manner much longer, had not Peter stopt her tongue, by telling her he had nothing to say to her husband nor her neither. So, as Adams and the rest had assured her of forgiveness, she cried and curtsied out of the room.

Mr. Pounce was desirous that Fanny should continue her journey with him in the chariot; but she absolutely refused, saying she would ride behind Joseph on a horse which one of Lady Booby's servants had equipped him with. But, alas! when the horse appeared, it was found to be no other than that identical beast which Mr. Adams had left behind him at the inn, and which these honest fellows, who knew him, had redeemed. Indeed, whatever horse they had provided for Joseph, they would have prevailed with him to mount none, no, not even to ride before his beloved Fanny, till the parson was supplied; much less would he deprive his friend of the beast which belonged to him, and which he knew the moment he saw, though Adams did not; however, when he was reminded of the affair, and told that they had brought the horse with them which he left behind, he answered—Bless me! and so I did.

Adams was very desirous that Joseph and Fanny should mount this horse, and declared he could very easily walk home. "If I walked alone," says he, "I would wage a shilling that the pedestrian outstripped the equestrian travellers; but, as I intend to take the company of a pipe, peradventure I may be an hour later." One of the servants whispered Joseph to take him at his word, and suffer the old put to walk if he would: this proposal was answered with an angry look and a peremptory refusal by Joseph, who, catching Fanny up in his arms, averred he would rather carry her home in that manner, than take away Mr. Adams's horse and permit him to walk on foot.

Perhaps, reader, thou hast seen a contest between two gentlemen, or two ladies, quickly decided, though they have both asserted they would not eat such a nice morsel, and each insisted on the other's accepting; but in reality both were very desirous to swallow it themselves. Do not therefore conclude hence that this dispute would have come to a speedy decision: for here both parties were heartily in earnest, and it is very probable they would have remained in the inn-yard to this day, had not the good Peter Pounce put a stop to it; for, finding he had no longer hopes of satisfying his old appetite with Fanny, and

being desirous of having some one to whom he might communicate his grandeur, he told the parson he would convey
him home in his chariot. This favour was by Adams, with
many bows and acknowledgments, accepted, though he afterwards said, "he ascended the chariot rather that he might not
offend than from any desire of riding in it, for that in his heart
he preferred the pedestrian even to the vehicular expedition."
All matters being now settled, the chariot, in which rode Adams
and Pounce, moved forwards; and Joseph having borrowed a
pillion from the host, Fanny had just seated herself thereon,
and had laid hold of the girdle which her lover wore for that
purpose, when the wise beast, who concluded that one at a
time was sufficient, that two to one were odds, etc., discovered
much uneasiness at his double load, and began to consider his
hinder as his fore legs, moving the direct contrary way to that
which is called forwards. Nor could Joseph, with all his horsemanship, persuade him to advance; but, without having any
regard to the lovely part of the lovely girl which was on his
back, he used such agitations, that, had not one of the men
come immediately to her assistance, she had, in plain English,
tumbled backwards on the ground. This inconvenience was
presently remedied by an exchange of horses; and then Fanny
being again placed on her pillion, on a better-natured and somewhat a better-fed beast, the parson's horse, finding he had no
longer odds to contend with, agreed to march; and the whole
procession set forwards for Booby-hall, where they arrived in
a few hours without anything remarkable happening on the
road, unless it was a curious dialogue between the parson and
the steward: which, to use the language of a late Apologist,
a pattern to all biographers, "waits for the reader in the next
chapter."

CHAPTER XIII

A CURIOUS DIALOGUE WHICH PASSED BETWEEN MR. ABRAHAM
ADAMS AND MR. PETER POUNCE, BETTER WORTH READING
THAN ALL THE WORKS OF COLLEY CIBBER AND MANY OTHERS

THE chariot had not proceeded far before Mr. Adams observed
it was a very fine day. "Ay, and a very fine country too,"
answered Pounce.—"I should think so more," returned Adams,
"if I had not lately travelled over the Downs, which I take to

exceed this and all other prospects in the universe."—"A fig for prospects!" answered Pounce; "one acre here is worth ten there; and for my own part, I have no delight in the prospect of any land but my own."—"Sir," said Adams, "you can indulge yourself with many fine prospects of that kind."—"I thank God I have a little," replied the other, "with which I am content, and envy no man: I have a little, Mr. Adams, with which I do as much good as I can."   Adams answered, "That riches without charity were nothing worth; for that they were a blessing only to him who made them a blessing to others."—"You and I," said Peter, "have different notions of charity. I own, as it is generally used, I do not like the word, nor do I think it becomes one of us gentlemen; it is a mean parson-like quality; though I would not infer many parsons have it neither."— "Sir," said Adams, "my definition of charity is, a generous disposition to relieve the distressed."—"There is something in that definition," answered Peter, "which I like well enough; it is, as you say, a disposition, and does not so much consist in the act as in the disposition to do it. But, alas! Mr. Adams, who are meant by the distressed? Believe me, the distresses of mankind are mostly imaginary, and it would be rather folly than goodness to relieve them."—"Sure, sir," replied Adams, "hunger and thirst, cold and nakedness, and other distresses which attend the poor, can never be said to be imaginary evils."—"How can any man complain of hunger," said Peter, "in a country where such excellent salads are to be gathered in almost every field? or of thirst, where every river and stream produces such delicious potations? And as for cold and nakedness, they are evils introduced by luxury and custom. A man naturally wants clothes no more than a horse or any other animal; and there are whole nations who go without them; but these are things perhaps which you, who do not know the world"—— "You will pardon me, sir," returned Adams; "I have read of the Gymnosophists."—"A plague of your Jehosaphats!" cried Peter; "the greatest fault in our constitution is the provision made for the poor, except that perhaps made for some others. Sir, I have not an estate which doth not contribute almost as much again to the poor as to the land-tax; and I do assure you I expect to come myself to the parish in the end."   To which Adams giving a dissenting smile, Peter thus proceeded: "I fancy, Mr. Adams, you are one of those who imagine I am a lump of money; for there are many who, I fancy, believe that not only my pockets, but my whole clothes, are lined with bank-bills; but I assure you, you are all mistaken; I am not the man the world esteems me. If I can hold my head above water it is all I can. I have injured myself by purchasing. I have been too liberal of my money. Indeed, I fear my heir will find my affairs in a worse situation than they are reputed to be. Ah! he will have reason to wish I had loved money more and land less. Pray, my good neighbour, where should I have that quantity of riches the world is so liberal to bestow on me? Where could I possibly, without I had stole it, acquire such a treasure?" "Why, truly," says Adams, "I have been always of your opinion; I have wondered as well as yourself with what confidence they could report such things of you, which have to me appeared as mere impossibilities; for you know, sir, and I have often heard you say it, that your wealth is of your own acquisition; and can it be credible that in your short time you should have amassed such a heap of treasure as these people will have you worth? Indeed, had you inherited an estate like Sir Thomas Booby, which had descended in your family for many generations, they might have had a colour for their assertions." "Why, what do they say I am worth?" cries Peter, with a malicious sneer. "Sir," answered Adams, "I have heard some aver you are not worth less than twenty thousand pounds." At which Peter frowned. "Nay, sir," said Adams, "you ask me only the opinion of others; for my own part, I have always denied it, nor did I ever believe you could possibly be worth half that sum." "However, Mr. Adams," said he, squeezing him by the hand, "I would not sell them all I am worth for double that sum; and as to what you believe, or they believe, I care not a fig, no not a fart. I am not poor because you think me so, nor because you attempt to under-value me in the country. I know the envy of mankind very well; but I thank Heaven I am above them. It is true, my wealth is of my own acquisition. I have not an estate, like Sir Thomas Booby, that has descended in my family through many generations; but I know heirs of such estates who are forced to travel about the country like some people in torn cassocks, and might be glad to accept of a pitiful curacy for what I know. Yes, sir, as shabby fellows as yourself, whom no man of my figure, without that vice of good-nature about him, would suffer to ride in a chariot with him." "Sir," said Adams, "I value not your chariot of a rush; and if I had known you had intended to affront me, I would have walked to the world's end on foot ere I would have accepted a place in it.

However, sir, I will soon rid you of that inconvenience;" and, so saying, he opened the chariot door, without calling to the coachman, and leapt out into the highway, forgetting to take his hat along with him; which, however, Mr. Pounce threw after him with great violence. Joseph and Fanny stopt to bear him company the rest of the way, which was not above a mile.

BOOK IV

CHAPTER I

THE coach and six, in which Lady Booby rode, overtook the other travellers as they entered the parish. She no sooner saw Joseph than her cheeks glowed with red, and immediately after became as totally pale. She had in her surprise almost stopt her coach; but recollected herself timely enough to prevent it. She entered the parish amidst the ringing of bells and the acclamations of the poor, who were rejoiced to see their patroness returned after so long an absence, during which time all her rents had been drafted to London, without a shilling being spent among them, which tended not a little to their utter impoverishing; for, if the court would be severely missed in such a city as London, how much more must the absence of a person of great fortune be felt in a little country village, for whose inhabitants such a family finds a constant employment and supply; and with the offals of whose table the infirm, aged, and infant poor are abundantly fed, with a generosity which hath scarce a visible effect on their benefactors' pockets!

But, if their interest inspired so public a joy into every countenance, how much more forcibly did the affection which they bore parson Adams operate upon all who beheld his return! They flocked about him like dutiful children round an indulgent parent, and vyed with each other in demonstrations of duty and love. The parson on his side shook every one by the hand, enquired heartily after the healths of all that were absent, of their children, and relations; and exprest a satisfaction in his face which nothing but benevolence made happy by its objects could infuse.

Nor did Joseph and Fanny want a hearty welcome from all who saw them. In short, no three persons could be more kindly received, as, indeed, none ever more deserved to be universally beloved.

Adams carried his fellow-travellers home to his house, where he insisted on their partaking whatever his wife, whom, with

219

his children, he found in health and joy, could provide: where we shall leave them enjoying perfect happiness over a homely meal, to view scenes of greater splendour, but infinitely less bliss.

Our more intelligent readers will doubtless suspect, by this second appearance of Lady Booby on the stage, that all was not ended by the dismission of Joseph; and, to be honest with them, they are in the right: the arrow had pierced deeper than she imagined; nor was the wound so easily to be cured. The removal of the object soon cooled her rage, but it had a different effect on her love; that departed with his person, but this remained lurking in her mind with his image. Restless, interrupted slumbers, and confused horrible dreams were her portion the first night. In the morning, fancy painted her a more delicious scene; but to delude, not to delight her; for, before she could reach the promised happiness, it vanished, and left her to curse, not bless, the vision.

She started from her sleep, her imagination being all on fire with the phantom, when, her eyes accidentally glancing towards the spot where yesterday the real Joseph had stood, that little circumstance raised his idea in the liveliest colours in her memory. Each look, each word, each gesture rushed back on her mind with charms which all his coldness could not abate. Nay, she imputed that to his youth, his folly, his awe, his religion, to everything but what would instantly have produced contempt, want of passion for the sex, or that which would have roused her hatred, want of liking to her.

Reflection then hurried her farther, and told her she must see this beautiful youth no more; nay, suggested to her that she herself had dismissed him for no other fault than probably that of too violent an awe and respect for herself; and which she ought rather to have esteemed a merit, the effects of which were besides so easily and surely to have been removed; she then blamed, she cursed the hasty rashness of her temper; her fury was vented all on herself, and Joseph appeared innocent in her eyes. Her passion at length grew so violent, that it forced her on seeking relief, and now she thought of recalling him: but pride forbad that; pride, which soon drove all softer passions from her soul, and represented to her the meanness of him she was fond of. That thought soon began to obscure his beauties; contempt succeeded next, and then disdain, which presently introduced her hatred of the creature who had given her so much uneasiness. These enemies of Joseph had no sooner taken possession of her mind than they insinuated to

her a thousand things in his disfavour; everything but dislike
of her person; a thought which, as it would have been intolerable
to bear, she checked the moment it endeavoured to arise.
Revenge came now to her assistance; and she considered her
dismission of him, stript, and without a character, with the
utmost pleasure. She rioted in the several kinds of misery
which her imagination suggested to her might be his fate; and,
with a smile composed of anger, mirth, and scorn, viewed him
in the rags in which her fancy had drest him.

Mrs. Slipslop, being summoned, attended her mistress, who
had now in her own opinion totally subdued this passion.
Whilst she was dressing she asked if that fellow had been
turned away according to her orders. Slipslop answered, she
had told her ladyship so (as indeed she had).—"And how did
he behave?" replied the lady. "Truly, madam," cries Slipslop,
"in such a manner that infected everybody who saw him. The
poor lad had but little wages to receive; for he constantly
allowed his father and mother half his income; so that, when
your ladyship's livery was stript off, he had not wherewithal
to buy a coat, and must have gone naked if one of the footmen
had not incommodated him with one; and whilst he was standing
in his shirt (and, to say truth, he was an amorous figure), being
told your ladyship would not give him a character, he sighed,
and said he had done nothing willingly to offend; that for his
part, he should always give your ladyship a good character
wherever he went; and he prayed God to bless you; for you
was the best of ladies, though his enemies had set you against
him. I wish you had not turned him away; for I believe you
have not a faithfuller servant in the house."—"How came you
then," replied the lady, "to advise me to turn him away?"—
"I, madam!" said Slipslop; "I am sure you will do me the justice
to say, I did all in my power to prevent it; but I saw your
ladyship was angry; and it is not the business of us upper
servants to hinterfear on these occasions." "And was it not
you, audacious wretch!" cried the lady, "who made me angry?
Was it not your tittle-tattle, in which I believe you belyed the
poor fellow, which incensed me against him? He may thank
you for all that hath happened; and so may I for the loss of a
good servant, and one who probably had more merit than all of
you. Poor fellow! I am charmed with his goodness to his
parents. Why did not you tell me of that, but suffer me to
dismiss so good a creature without a character? I see the
reason of your whole behaviour now as well as your complaint;

you was jealous of the wenches." "I jealous!" said Slipslop; "I assure you, I look upon myself as his betters; I am not meat for a footman, I hope." These words threw the lady into a violent passion, and she sent Slipslop from her presence, who departed, tossing her nose, and crying, "Marry, come up! there are some people more jealous than I, I believe." Her lady affected not to hear the words, though in reality she did, and understood them too. Now ensued a second conflict, so like the former, that it might savour of repetition to relate it minutely. It may suffice to say that Lady Booby found good reason to doubt whether she had so absolutely conquered her passion as she had flattered herself; and, in order to accomplish it quite, took a resolution, more common than wise, to retire immediately into the country. The reader hath long ago seen the arrival of Mrs. Slipslop, whom no pertness could make her mistress resolve to part with; lately, that of Mr. Pounce, her forerunners; and, lastly, that of the lady herself.

The morning after her arrival being Sunday, she went to church, to the great surprise of everybody, who wondered to see her ladyship, being no very constant churchwoman, there so suddenly upon her journey. Joseph was likewise there; and I have heard it was remarked that she fixed her eyes on him much more than on the parson; but this I believe to be only a malicious rumour. When the prayers were ended Mr. Adams stood up, and with a loud voice pronounced, "I publish the banns of marriage between Joseph Andrews and Frances Goodwill, both of this parish," &c. Whether this had any effect on Lady Booby or no, who was then in her pew, which the congregation could not see into, I could never discover: but certain it is that in about a quarter of an hour she stood up, and directed her eyes to that part of the church where the women sat, and persisted in looking that way during the remainder of the sermon in so scrutinising a manner, and with so angry a countenance, that most of the women were afraid she was offended at them. The moment she returned home she sent for Slipslop into her chamber, and told her she wondered what that impudent fellow Joseph did in that parish? Upon which Slipslop gave her an account of her meeting Adams with him on the road, and likewise the adventure with Fanny. At the relation of which the lady often changed her countenance; and when she had heard all, she ordered Mr. Adams into her presence, to whom she behaved as the reader will see in the next chapter.

CHAPTER II

A DIALOGUE BETWEEN MR. ABRAHAM ADAMS AND THE LADY BOOBY

MR. ADAMS was not far off, for he was drinking her ladyship's health below in a cup of her ale. He no sooner came before her than she began in the following manner: "I wonder, sir, after the many great obligations you have had to this family" (with all which the reader hath in the course of this history been minutely acquainted), "that you will ungratefully show any respect to a fellow who hath been turned out of it for his misdeeds. Nor doth it, I can tell you, sir, become a man of your character, to run about the country with an idle fellow and wench. Indeed, as for the girl, I know no harm of her. Slip-slop tells me she was formerly bred up in my house, and behaved as she ought, till she hankered after this fellow, and he spoiled her. Nay, she may still, perhaps, do very well, if he will let her alone. You are, therefore, doing a monstrous thing in endeavouring to procure a match between these two people, which will be to the ruin of them both."—"Madam," said Adams, "if your ladyship will but hear me speak, I protest I never heard any harm of Mr. Joseph Andrews; if I had, I should have corrected him for it; for I never have, nor will, encourage the faults of those under my care. As for the young woman, I assure your ladyship I have as good an opinion of her as your ladyship yourself or any other can have. She is the sweetest-tempered, honestest, worthiest young creature; indeed, as to her beauty, I do not commend her on that account, though all men allow she is the handsomest woman, gentle or simple, that ever appeared in the parish."—"You are very impertinent," says she, "to talk such fulsome stuff to me. It is mighty becoming truly in a clergyman to trouble himself about hand-some women, and you are a delicate judge of beauty, no doubt. A man who hath lived all his life in such a parish as this is a rare judge of beauty! Ridiculous! beauty indeed! a country wench a beauty! I shall be sick whenever I hear beauty men-tioned again. And so this wench is to stock the parish with beauties, I hope. But, sir, our poor is numerous enough already; I will have no more vagabonds settled here."—"Madam," says Adams, "your ladyship is offended with me, I protest, without any reason. This couple were desirous to consummate long ago, and I dissuaded them from it; nay, I may venture to say, I believe I was the sole cause of their delaying it."—"Well," says she, "and you did very wisely and honestly too, notwithstanding she is the greatest beauty in the parish."—"And now, madam," continued he, "I only perform my office to Mr. Joseph."—"Pray, don't mister such fellows to me," cries the lady. "He," said the parson, "with the consent of Fanny, before my face, put in the banns."—"Yes," answered the lady, "I suppose the slut is forward enough; Slipslop tells me how her head runs upon fellows; that is one of her beauties, I suppose. But if they have put in the banns, I desire you will publish them no more without my orders."—"Madam," cries Adams, "if any one puts in a sufficient caution, and assigns a proper reason against them, I am willing to surcease."—"I tell you a reason," says she: "he is a vagabond, and he shall not settle here, and bring a nest of beggars into the parish; it will make us but little amends that they will be beauties."— "Madam," answered Adams, "with the utmost submission to your ladyship, I have been informed by lawyer Scout that any person who serves a year gains a settlement in the parish where he serves."—"Lawyer Scout," replied the lady, "is an impudent coxcomb; I will have no lawyer Scout interfere with me. I repeat to you again, I will have no more incumbrances brought on us: so I desire you will proceed no farther."—"Madam," returned Adams, "I would obey your ladyship in everything that is lawful; but surely the parties being poor is no reason against their marrying. God forbid there should be any such law! The poor have little share enough of this world already; it would be barbarous indeed to deny them the common privileges and innocent enjoyments which nature indulges to the animal creation."—"Since you understand yourself no better," cries the lady, "nor the respect due from such as you to a woman of my distinction, than to affront my ears by such loose discourse, I shall mention but one short word; it is my orders to you that you publish these banns no more; and if you dare, I will recommend it to your master, the doctor, to discard you from his service. I will, sir, notwithstanding your poor family; and then you and the greatest beauty in the parish may go and beg together."—"Madam," answered Adams, "I know not what your ladyship means by the terms master and service. I am in the service of a Master who will never discard me for doing my duty; and if the doctor (for indeed I have never been able to pay for a licence) thinks proper to turn me from my cure,

God will provide me, I hope, another. At least, my family, as well as myself, have hands; and he will prosper, I doubt not, our endeavours to get our bread honestly with them. Whilst my conscience is pure, I shall never fear what man can do unto me."—"I condemn my humility," said the lady, "for demeaning myself to converse with you so long. I shall take other measures; for I see you are a confederate with them. But the sooner you leave me the better; and I shall give orders that my doors may no longer be open to you. I will suffer no parsons who run about the country with beauties to be entertained here."—"Madam," said Adams, "I shall enter into no persons' doors against their will; but I am assured, when you have enquired farther into this matter, you will applaud, not blame, my proceeding; and so I humbly take my leave:" which he did with many bows, or at least many attempts at a bow.

CHAPTER III

WHAT PASSED BETWEEN THE LADY AND LAWYER SCOUT

IN the afternoon the lady sent for Mr. Scout, whom she attacked most violently for intermeddling with her servants, which he denied, and indeed with truth, for he had only asserted accidentally, and perhaps rightly, that a year's service gained a settlement; and so far he owned he might have formerly informed the parson and believed it was law. "I am resolved," said the lady, "to have no discarded servants of mine settled here; and so, if this be your law, I shall send to another lawyer." Scout said, "If she sent to a hundred lawyers, not one or all of them could alter the law. The utmost that was in the power of a lawyer was to prevent the law's taking effect; and that he himself could do for her ladyship as well as any other; and I believe," says he, "madam, your ladyship, not being conversant in these matters, hath mistaken a difference; for I asserted only that a man who served a year was settled. Now there is a material difference between being settled in law and settled in fact; and as I affirmed generally he was settled, and law is preferable to fact, my settlement must be understood in law and not in fact. And suppose, madam, we admit he was settled in law, what use will they make of it? how doth that relate to fact? He is not settled in fact; and if he be not settled in fact, he is not an inhabitant; and if he is not an inhabitant, he is not of this parish; and then undoubtedly he ought not to be published here; for Mr. Adams hath told me your ladyship's pleasure, and the reason, which is a very good one, to prevent burdening us with the poor; we have too many already, and I think we ought to have an act to hang or transport half of them. If we can prove in evidence that he is not settled in fact, it is another matter. What I said to Mr. Adams was on a supposition that he was settled in fact; and indeed, if that was the case, I should doubt."—"Don't tell me your facts and your ifs," said the lady; "I don't understand your gibberish; you take too much upon you, and are very impertinent, in pretending to direct in this parish; and you shall be taught better, I assure you, you shall. But as to the wench, I am resolved she shall not settle here; I will not suffer such beauties as these to produce children for us to keep."—"Beauties, indeed! your ladyship is pleased to be merry," answered Scout. —"Mr. Adams described her so to me," said the lady. "Pray, what sort of dowdy is it, Mr. Scout?"—"The ugliest creature almost I ever beheld; a poor dirty drab, your ladyship never saw such a wretch."—"Well, but, dear Mr. Scout, let her be what she will, these ugly women will bring children, you know; so that we must prevent the marriage."—"True, madam," replied Scout, "for the subsequent marriage co-operating with the law will carry law into fact. When a man is married he is settled in fact, and then he is not removable. I will see Mr. Adams, and I make no doubt of prevailing with him. His only objection is, doubtless, that he shall lose his fee; but that being once made easy, as it shall be, I am confident no farther objection will remain. No, no, it is impossible; but your ladyship can't discommend his unwillingness to depart from his fee. Every man ought to have a proper value for his fee. As to the matter in question, if your ladyship pleases to employ me in it, I will venture to promise you success. The laws of this land are not so vulgar to permit a mean fellow to contend with one of your ladyship's fortune. We have one sure card, which is, to carry him before Justice Frolick, who, upon hearing your ladyship's name, will commit him without any farther questions. As for the dirty slut, we shall have nothing to do with her; for, if we get rid of the fellow, the ugly jade will——"—"Take what measures you please, good Mr. Scout," answered the lady: "but I wish you could rid the parish of both; for Slipslop tells me such stories of this wench, that I abhor the thoughts of her; and, though you say she is such an ugly slut, yet you know, dear Mr. Scout, these forward creatures, who run after men, will always find some as forward as themselves; so that, to prevent the increase of beggars, we must get rid of her."—"Your lady-ship is very much in the right," answered Scout; "but I am afraid the law is a little deficient in giving us any such power of prevention; however, the justice will stretch it as far as he is able, to oblige your ladyship. To say truth, it is a great blessing to the country that he is in the commission, for he hath taken several poor off our hands that the law would never lay hold on. I know some justices who think as much of com-mitting a man to Bridewell as his lordship at 'size would of hanging him; but it would do a man good to see his worship, our justice, commit a fellow to Bridewell, he takes so much pleasure in it; and when once we ha'um there, we seldom hear any more o'um. He's either starved or eat up by vermin in a month's time."—Here the arrival of a visitor put an end to the conversation, and Mr. Scout, having undertaken the cause and promised it success, departed.

This Scout was one of those fellows who, without any know-ledge of the law, or being bred to it, take upon them, in defiance of an act of Parliament, to act as lawyers in the country, and are called so. They are the pests of society, and a scandal to a profession, to which indeed they do not belong, and which owes to such kind of rascallions the ill-will which weak persons bear towards it. With this fellow, to whom a little before she would not have condescended to have spoken, did a certain passion for Joseph, and the jealousy and the disdain of poor innocent Fanny, betray the Lady Booby into a familiar dis-course, in which she inadvertently confirmed many hints with which Slipslop, whose gallant he was, had preacquainted him; and whence he had taken an opportunity to assert those severe falsehoods of little Fanny which possibly the reader might not have been well able to account for if we had not thought proper to give him this information.

CHAPTER IV

A SHORT CHAPTER, BUT VERY FULL OF MATTER; PARTICULARLY
THE ARRIVAL OF MR. BOOBY AND HIS LADY

ALL that night, and the next day, the Lady Booby past with
the utmost anxiety; her mind was distracted and her soul
tossed up and down by many turbulent and opposite passions.
She loved, hated, pitied, scorned, admired, despised the same
person by fits, which changed in a very short interval. On
Tuesday morning, which happened to be a holiday, she went
to church, where, to her surprise, Mr. Adams published the
banns again with as audible a voice as before. It was lucky
for her that, as there was no sermon, she had an immediate
opportunity of returning home to vent her rage, which she
could not have concealed from the congregation five minutes;
indeed, it was not then very numerous, the assembly consisting
of no more than Adams, his clerk, his wife, the lady, and one of
her servants. At her return she met Slipslop, who accosted her
in these words:—"O meam, what doth your ladyship think?
To be sure, lawyer Scout hath carried Joseph and Fanny both
before the justice. All the parish are in tears, and say they
will certainly be hanged; for nobody knows what it is for."—
"I suppose they deserve it," says the lady. "What! dost thou
mention such wretches to me?"—"O dear madam," answered
Slipslop, "is it not a pity such a graceless young man should
die a virulent death? I hope the judge will take commensuration on his youth. As for Fanny, I don't think it signifies
much what becomes of her; and if poor Joseph hath done anything, I could venture to swear she traduced him to it: few
men ever come to a fragrant punishment, but by those nasty
creatures, who are a scandal to our sect." The lady was no
more pleased at this news, after a moment's reflection, than
Slipslop herself; for, though she wished Fanny far enough, she
did not desire the removal of Joseph, especially with her. She
was puzzled how to act or what to say on this occasion, when a
coach and six drove into the court, and a servant acquainted
her with the arrival of her nephew Booby and his lady. She
ordered them to be conducted into a drawing-room, whither she
presently repaired, having composed her countenance as well
as she could, and being a little satisfied that the wedding would
by these means be at least interrupted, and that she should

have an opportunity to execute any resolution she might take, for which she saw herself provided with an excellent instrument in Scout.

The Lady Booby apprehended her servant had made a mistake when he mentioned Mr. Booby's lady; for she had never heard of his marriage: but how great was her surprise when, at her entering the room, her nephew presented his wife to her; saying, "Madam, this is that charming Pamela, of whom I am convinced you have heard so much." The lady received her with more civility than he expected; indeed with the utmost; for she was perfectly polite, nor had any vice inconsistent with good-breeding. They past some little time in ordinary discourse, when a servant came and whispered Mr. Booby, who presently told the ladies he must desert them a little on some business of consequence; and, as their discourse during his absence would afford little improvement or entertainment to the reader, we will leave them for a while to attend Mr. Booby.

CHAPTER V

CONTAINING JUSTICE BUSINESS; CURIOUS PRECEDENTS OF DEPOSITIONS, AND OTHER MATTERS NECESSARY TO BE PERUSED BY ALL JUSTICES OF THE PEACE AND THEIR CLERKS

THE young squire and his lady were no sooner alighted from their coach than the servants began to inquire after Mr. Joseph, from whom they said their lady had not heard a word, to her great surprise, since he had left Lady Booby's. Upon this they were instantly informed of what had lately happened, with which they hastily acquainted their master, who took an immediate resolution to go himself, and endeavour to restore his Pamela her brother, before she even knew she had lost him.

The justice before whom the criminals were carried, and who lived within a short mile of the lady's house, was luckily Mr. Booby's acquaintance, by his having an estate in his neighbourhood. Ordering therefore his horses to his coach, he set out for the judgment-seat, and arrived when the justice had almost finished his business. He was conducted into a hall, where he was acquainted that his worship would wait on him in a moment; for he had only a man and a woman to commit to Bridewell first. As he was now convinced he had not a minute to lose, he insisted on the servant's introducing him directly into the room where the justice was then executing his office, as he called it. Being brought thither, and the first compliments being passed between the squire and his worship, the former asked the latter what crime those two young people had been guilty of? "No great crime," answered the justice; "I have only ordered them to Bridewell for a month." "But what is their crime?" repeated the squire. "Larceny, an't please your honour," said Scout. "Ay," says the justice, "a kind of felonious larcenous thing. I believe I must order them a little correction too, a little stripping and whipping." (Poor Fanny, who had hitherto supported all with the thoughts of Joseph's company, trembled at that sound; but, indeed, without reason, for none but the devil himself would have executed such a sentence on her.) "Still," said the squire, "I am ignorant of the crime—the fact I mean." "Why, there it is in peaper," answered the justice, showing him a deposition which, in the absence of his clerk, he had writ himself, of which we have with great difficulty procured an authentic copy; and here it follows *verbatim et literatim*:—

The depusition of James Scout, layer, and Thomas Trotter, yeoman, taken before mee, one of his magesty's justasses of the piece for Zumersetshire.

THESE deponants saith, and first Thomas Trotter for himself saith, that on the   of this instant October, being Sabbath-day, betwin the ours of 2 and 4 in the afternoon, he zeed Joseph Andrews and Francis Goodwill walk akross a certane felde belunging to layer Scout, and out of the path which ledes thru the said felde, and there he zede Joseph Andrews with a nife cut one hassel twig, of the value, as he believes, of three half-pence, or thereabouts; and he saith that the said Francis Goodwill was likewise walking on the grass out of the said path in the said felde, and did receive and karry in her hand the said twig, and so was cumfarting, eading, and abatting to the said Joseph therein. And the said James Scout for himself says that he verily believes the said twig to be his own proper twig, etc.

"Jesu!" said the squire, "would you commit two persons to Bridewell for a twig?" "Yes," said the lawyer, "and with great lenity too; for if we had called it a young tree, they would have been both hanged." "Harkee," says the justice, taking aside the squire; "I should not have been so severe on this occasion, but Lady Booby desires to get them out of the parish; so lawyer Scout will give the constable orders to let them run away, if they please, but it seems they intend to marry together, and the lady hath no other means, as they are legally settled there, to prevent their bringing an incumbrance on her own parish." "Well," said the squire, "I will take care my aunt shall be satisfied in this point; and likewise I promise you, Joseph here shall never be any incumbrance on her. I shall be obliged to you, therefore, if, instead of Bridewell, you will commit them to my custody." "O! to be sure, sir, if you desire it," answered the justice; and without more ado Joseph and Fanny were delivered over to Squire Booby, whom Joseph very well knew, but little guessed how nearly he was related to him. The justice burnt his mittimus, the constable was sent about his business; the lawyer made no complaint for want of justice; and the prisoners, with exulting hearts, gave a thousand thanks to his honour Mr. Booby; who did not intend their obligations to him should cease here; for, ordering his man to produce a cloak-bag, which he had caused to be brought from Lady Booby's on purpose, he desired the justice that he might have Joseph with him into a room; where, ordering his servant to take out a suit of his own clothes, with linnen and other necessaries, he left Joseph to dress himself, who, not yet knowing the cause of all this civility, excused his accepting such a favour as long as decently he could. Whilst Joseph was dressing, the squire repaired to the justice, whom he found talking with Fanny; for, during the examination, she had flopped her hat over her eyes, which were also bathed in tears, and had by that means concealed from his worship what might perhaps have rendered the arrival of Mr. Booby unnecessary, at least for herself. The justice no sooner saw her countenance cleared up, and her bright eyes shining through her tears, than he secretly cursed himself for having once thought of Bridewell for her. He would willingly have sent his own wife thither, to have had Fanny in her place. And, conceiving almost at the same instant desires and schemes to accomplish them, he employed the minutes whilst the squire was absent with Joseph in assuring her how sorry he was for having treated her so roughly before he knew her merit; and told her, that since Lady Booby was unwilling that she should settle in her parish, she was heartily welcome to his, where he promised her his pro- tection, adding that he would take Joseph and her into his own family, if she liked it; which assurance he confirmed with a squeeze by the hand. She thanked him very kindly, and said, "She would acquaint Joseph with the offer, which he would certainly be glad to accept; for that Lady Booby was angry with them both; though she did not know either had done anything to offend her, but imputed it to Madam Slipslop, who had always been her enemy."

The squire now returned, and prevented any farther continuance of this conversation; and the justice, out of a pretended respect to his guest, but in reality from an apprehension of a rival (for he knew nothing of his marriage), ordered Fanny into the kitchen, whither she gladly retired; nor did the squire, who declined the trouble of explaining the whole matter, oppose it.

It would be unnecessary, if I was able, which indeed I am not, to relate the conversation between these two gentlemen, which rolled, as I have been informed, entirely on the subject of horse-racing. Joseph was soon drest in the plainest dress he could find, which was a blue coat and breeches, with a gold edging, and a red waistcoat with the same: and as this suit, which was rather too large for the squire, exactly fitted him, so he became it so well, and looked so genteel, that no person would have doubted its being as well adapted to his quality as his shape; nor have suspected, as one might, when my Lord ——, or Sir ——, or Mr. ——, appear in lace or embroidery, that the taylor's man wore those clothes home on his back which he should have carried under his arm.

The squire now took leave of the justice; and, calling for Fanny, made her and Joseph, against their wills, get into the coach with him, which he then ordered to drive to Lady Booby's. It had moved a few yards only, when the squire asked Joseph if he knew who that man was crossing the field; for, added he, I never saw one take such strides before. Joseph answered eagerly, "O, sir, it is parson Adams!" "O la, indeed, and so it is," said Fanny; "poor man, he is coming to do what he could for us. Well, he is the worthiest, best-natured creature." —"Ay," said Joseph; "God bless him! for there is not such another in the universe." "The best creature living sure," cries Fanny. "Is he?" says the squire; "then I am resolved to have the best creature living in my coach;" and so saying, he ordered it to stop, whilst Joseph, at his request, hallowed to the parson, who, well knowing his voice, made all the haste imaginable, and soon came up with them. He was desired by the master, who could scarce refrain from laughter at his figure, to mount into the coach, which he with many thanks refused, saying he could walk by its side, and he'd warrant he kept up with it; but he was at length over-prevailed on. The squire now acquainted Joseph with his marriage; but he might have spared himself that labour; for his servant, whilst Joseph was dressing, had performed that office before. He continued to express the vast happiness he enjoyed in his sister, and the value he had for all who belonged to her. Joseph made many bows, and exprest as many acknowledgments: and parson Adams, who now first perceived Joseph's new apparel, burst into tears with joy, and fell to rubbing his hands and snapping his fingers as if he had been mad.

They were now arrived at the Lady Booby's, and the squire, desiring them to wait a moment in the court, walked in to his aunt, and calling her out from his wife, acquainted her with Joseph's arrival; saying, "Madam, as I have married a virtuous and worthy woman, I am resolved to own her relations, and show them all a proper respect; I shall think myself therefore infinitely obliged to all mine who will do the same. It is true, her brother hath been your servant, but he is now become my brother; and I have one happiness, that neither his character, his behaviour, nor appearance, give me any reason to be ashamed of calling him so. In short, he is now below, dressed like a gentleman, in which light I intend he shall hereafter be seen; and you will oblige me beyond expression if you will admit him to be of our party; for I know it will give great pleasure to my wife, though she will not mention it."

This was a stroke of fortune beyond the Lady Booby's hopes or expectation; she answered him eagerly, "Nephew, you know how easily I am prevailed on to do anything which Joseph Andrews desires—Phoo, I mean which you desire me; and, as he is now your relation, I cannot refuse to entertain him as such." The squire told her he knew his obligation to her for her compliance; and going three steps, returned and told her —he had one more favour, which he believed she would easily grant, as she had accorded him the former. "There is a young woman——"—"Nephew," says she, "don't let my good-nature make you desire, as is too commonly the case, to impose on me. Nor think, because I have with so much condescension agreed to suffer your brother-in-law to come to my table, that I will submit to the company of all my own servants, and all the dirty trollops in the country." "Madam," answered the squire, "I believe you never saw this young creature. I never beheld such sweetness and innocence joined with such beauty, and withal so genteel." "Upon my soul I won't admit her," replied the lady in a passion; "the whole world shan't prevail on me; I resent even the desire as an affront, and——" The squire, who knew her inflexibility, interrupted her, by asking pardon, and promising not to mention it more. He then returned to Joseph, and she to Pamela. He took Joseph aside, and told him he would carry him to his sister, but could not prevail as yet for Fanny. Joseph begged that he might see his sister alone, and then be with his Fanny; but the squire, knowing the pleasure his wife would have in her brother's company, would not admit it, telling Joseph there would be nothing in so short an absence from Fanny, whilst he was assured of her safety; adding, he hoped he could not so easily quit a sister whom he had not seen so long, and who so tenderly loved him. Joseph immediately complied; for indeed no brother could love a sister more; and, recommending Fanny, who rejoiced that she was not to go before Lady Booby, to the care of Mr. Adams, he attended the squire upstairs, whilst Fanny repaired with the parson to his house, where she thought herself secure of a kind reception.

CHAPTER VI

OF WHICH YOU ARE DESIRED TO READ NO MORE THAN YOU LIKE

THE meeting between Joseph and Pamela was not without tears of joy on both sides; and their embraces were full of tenderness and affection. They were, however, regarded with much more pleasure by the nephew than by the aunt, to whose flame they were fuel only; and this was increased by the addition of dress, which was indeed not wanted to set off the lively colours in which Nature had drawn health, strength, comeliness, and youth. In the afternoon Joseph, at their request, entertained them with an account of his adventures: nor could Lady Booby conceal her dissatisfaction at those parts in which Fanny was concerned, especially when Mr. Booby launched forth into such rapturous praises of her beauty. She said, applying to her niece, that she wondered her nephew, who had pretended to marry for love, should think such a subject proper to amuse his wife with; adding, that, for her part, she should be jealous of a husband who spoke so warmly in praise of another woman. Pamela answered, indeed, she thought she had cause; but it was an instance of Mr. Booby's aptness to see more beauty in women than they were mistresses of. At which words both the women fixed their eyes on two looking-glasses; and Lady Booby replied, that men were, in the general, very ill judges of beauty; and then, whilst both contemplated only their own faces, they paid a cross compliment to each other's charms. When the hour of rest approached, which the lady of the house deferred as long as decently she could, she informed Joseph (whom for the future we shall call Mr. Joseph, he having as good a title to that appellation as many others—I mean that incontested one of good clothes) that she had ordered a bed to be provided for him. He declined this favour to his utmost; for his heart had long been with his Fanny; but she insisted on his accepting it, alledging that the parish had no proper accommodation for such a person as he was now to esteem himself. The squire and his lady both joining with her, Mr. Joseph was at last forced to give over his design of visiting Fanny that evening; who, on her side, as impatiently expected him till midnight, when, in complacence to Mr. Adams's family, who had sat up two hours out of respect to her, she retired to bed, but not to sleep; the thoughts of her love kept her waking, and his not returning according to his promise filled her with uneasiness; of which, however, she could not assign any other cause than merely that of being absent from him.

Mr. Joseph rose early in the morning, and visited her in whom his soul delighted. She no sooner heard his voice in the parson's parlour than she leapt from her bed, and, dressing herself in a few minutes, went down to him. They passed two hours with inexpressible happiness together; and then, having appointed Monday, by Mr. Adams's permission, for their marriage, Mr. Joseph returned, according to his promise, to breakfast at the Lady Booby's, with whose behaviour, since the evening, we shall now acquaint the reader.

She was no sooner retired to her chamber than she asked Slipslop "What she thought of this wonderful creature her nephew had married?"—"Madam?" said Slipslop, not yet sufficiently understanding what answer she was to make. "I ask you," answered the lady, "what you think of the dowdy, my niece, I think I am to call her?" Slipslop, wanting no further hint, began to pull her to pieces, and so miserably defaced her, that it would have been impossible for any one to have known the person. The lady gave her all the assistance she could, and ended with saying, "I think, Slipslop, you have done her justice; but yet, bad as she is, she is an angel compared to this Fanny." Slipslop then fell on Fanny, whom she hacked and hewed in the like barbarous manner, concluding with an observation that there was always something in those low-life creatures which must eternally extinguish them from their betters. "Really," said the lady, "I think there is one exception to your rule; I am certain you may guess who I mean."—"Not I, upon my word, madam," said Slipslop. "I mean a young fellow; sure you are the dullest wretch," said the lady. "O la! I am indeed. Yes, truly, madam, he is an accession," answered Slipslop. "Ay, is he not, Slipslop?" returned the lady. "Is he not so genteel that a prince might, without a blush, acknowledge him for his son? His behaviour is such that would not shame the best education. He borrows from his station a condescension in everything to his superiors, yet unattended by that mean servility which is called good behaviour in such persons. Everything he doth hath no mark of the base motive of fear, but visibly shows some respect and gratitude, and carries with it the persuasion of love. And then for his virtues: such piety to his parents, such tender affection to his sister, such integrity in his friendship, such bravery, such goodness, that, if he had been born a gentleman, his wife would have possessed the most invaluable blessing."—"To be sure, ma'am," says Slipslop. "But as he is," answered the lady, "if he had a thousand more good qualities, it must render a woman of fashion contemptible even to be suspected of thinking of him; yes, I should despise myself for such a thought."—"To be sure, ma'am," said Slipslop. "And why to be sure?" replied the lady; "thou art always one's echo. Is he not more worthy of affection than a dirty country clown, though born of a family as old as the flood? or an idle worthless rake, or little puisny beau of quality? And yet these we must condemn ourselves to, in order to avoid the censure of the world; to shun the contempt of others, we must ally ourselves to those we despise; we must prefer birth, title, and fortune, to real merit. It is a tyranny of custom, a tyranny we must comply with; for we people of fashion are the slaves of custom."—"Marry come up!" said Slipslop, who now knew well which party to take. "If I was a woman of your ladyship's fortune and quality, I would be a slave to nobody."—"Me," said the lady; "I am speaking if a young woman of fashion, who had seen nothing of the world, should happen to like such a fellow.—Me, indeed! I hope thou dost not imagine——"—"No, ma'am, to be sure," cries Slipslop. "No! what no?" cried the lady. "Thou art always ready to answer before thou hast heard one. So far I must allow he is a charming fellow. Me, indeed! No, Slipslop, all thoughts of men are over with me. I have lost a husband who—but if I should reflect I should run mad. My future ease must depend upon forgetfulness. Slipslop, let me hear some of thy nonsense, to turn my thoughts another way. What dost thou think of Mr. Andrews?"—"Why, I think," says Slipslop, "he is the handsomest, most properest man I ever saw; and if I was a lady of the greatest degree it would be well for some folks. Your ladyship may talk of custom, if you please: but I am confidous there is no more comparison between young Mr. Andrews and most of the young gentlemen who come to your ladyship's house in London; a parcel of whipper-snapper sparks: I would sooner marry our old parson Adams. Never tell me what people say, whilst I am happy in the arms of him I love. Some folks rail against other folks because other folks have what some folks would be glad of."—"And so," answered the lady, "if you was a woman of condition, you would really marry Mr. Andrews?"—"Yes, I assure your ladyship," replied Slipslop, "if he would have me."—"Fool, idiot!" cries the lady; "if he would have a woman of fashion! is that a question?"—"No, truly, madam," said Slipslop, "I believe it would be none if Fanny was out of the way; and I am confidous, if I was in your ladyship's place, and liked Mr. Joseph Andrews, she should not stay in the parish a moment. I am sure lawyer Scout would send her packing if your ladyship would but say the word." This last speech of Slipslop raised a tempest in the mind of her mistress. She feared Scout had betrayed her, or rather that she had betrayed herself. After some silence, and a double change of her complexion, first to pale and then to red, she thus spoke: "I am astonished at the liberty you give your tongue. Would you insinuate that I employed Scout against this wench on account of the fellow?"—"La, ma'am," said Slipslop, frighted out of her wits, "I assassinate such a thing!"—"I think you dare not," answered the lady; "I believe my conduct may defy malice itself to assert so cursed a slander. If I had ever discovered any wantonness, any lightness in my behaviour; if I had followed the example of some whom thou hast, I believe, seen, in allowing myself indecent liberties, even with a husband; but the dear man who is gone" (here she began to sob), "was he alive again" (then she produced tears), "could not upbraid me with any one act of tenderness or passion. No, Slipslop, all the time I cohabited with him he never obtained even a kiss from me without my expressing reluctance in the granting it. I am sure he himself never suspected how much I loved him. Since his death, thou knowest, though it is almost six weeks (it wants but a day) ago, I have not admitted one visitor till this fool my nephew arrived. I have confined myself quite to one party of friends. And can such a conduct as this fear to be arraigned? To be accused, not only of a passion which I have always despised, but of fixing it on such an object, a creature so much beneath my notice!"—"Upon my word, ma'am," says Slipslop, "I do not understand your ladyship; nor know I anything of the matter."—"I believe indeed thou dost not understand me. Those are delicacies which exist only in superior minds; thy coarse ideas cannot comprehend them. Thou art a low creature, of the Andrews breed, a reptile of a lower order, a weed that grows in the common garden of the creation."—"I assure your ladyship," says Slipslop, whose passions were almost of as high an order as her lady's, "I have no more to do with Common Garden than other folks. Really, your ladyship talks of servants as if they were not born of the Christian specious. Servants have flesh and blood as well as quality; and Mr. Andrews himself is a proof that they have as good, if not better. And for my own part, I can't perceive my dears[1] are coarser than other people's; and I am sure, if Mr. Andrews was a dear of mine, I should not be ashamed of him in company with gentlemen; for whoever hath seen him in his new clothes must confess he looks as much like a gentleman as anybody. Coarse, quotha! I can't bear to hear the poor young fellow run down neither; for I will say this, I never heard him say an ill word of anybody in his life. I am sure his coarseness doth not lie in his heart, for he is the best-natured man in the world; and as for his skin, it is no coarser than other people's, I am sure. His bosom, when a boy, was as white as driven snow; and, where it is not covered with hairs, is so still. Ifakins! if I was Mrs. Andrews, with a hundred a year, I should not envy the best she who wears a head. A woman that could not be happy with such a man ought never to be so; for if he can't make a woman happy, I never yet beheld the man who could. I say again, I wish I was a great lady for his sake. I believe, when I had made a gentleman of him, he'd behave so that nobody should deprecate what I had done; and I fancy few would venture to tell him he was no gentleman to his face, nor to mine neither." At which words, taking up the candles, she asked her mistress, who had been some time in her bed, if she

---

[1] Meaning perhaps ideas.

had any farther commands? who mildly answered, she had none; and, telling her she was a comical creature, bid her good-night.

CHAPTER VII

PHILOSOPHICAL REFLECTIONS, THE LIKE NOT TO BE FOUND IN
ANY LIGHT FRENCH ROMANCE.   MR. BOOBY'S GRAVE ADVICE
TO JOSEPH, AND FANNY'S ENCOUNTER WITH A BEAU

HABIT, my good reader, hath so vast a prevalence over the human mind, that there is scarce anything too strange or too strong to be asserted of it. The story of the miser, who, from long accustoming to cheat others, came at last to cheat himself, and with great delight and triumph picked his own pocket of a guinea to convey to his hoard, is not impossible or improbable. In like manner it fares with the practisers of deceit, who, from having long deceived their acquaintance, gain at last a power of deceiving themselves, and acquire that very opinion (however false) of their own abilities, excellencies, and virtues, into which they have for years perhaps endeavoured to betray their neighbours. Now, reader, to apply this observation to my present purpose, thou must know, that as the passion generally called love exercises most of the talents of the female or fair world, so in this they now and then discover a small inclination to deceit; for which thou wilt not be angry with the beautiful creatures when thou hast considered that at the age of seven, or something earlier, miss is instructed by her mother that master is a very monstrous kind of animal, who will, if she suffers him to come too near her, infallibly eat her up and grind her to pieces: that, so far from kissing or toying with him of her own accord, she must not admit him to kiss or toy with her: and, lastly, that she must never have any affection towards him; for if she should, all her friends in petticoats would esteem her a traitress, point at her, and hunt her out of their society. These impressions, being first received, are farther and deeper inculcated by their school-mistresses and companions; so that by the age of ten they have contracted such a dread and abhorrence of the above-named monster, that whenever they see him they fly from him as the innocent hare doth from the greyhound. Hence, to the age of fourteen or fifteen, they entertain a mighty antipathy to master; they resolve, and frequently profess, that they will never have any commerce with him, and entertain fond hopes of passing their lives out of his reach, of the possibility of which they have so visible an example in their good maiden aunt. But when they arrive at this period, and have now passed their second climacteric, when their wisdom, grown riper, begins to see a little farther, and, from almost daily falling in master's way, to apprehend the great difficulty of keeping out of it; and when they observe him look often at them, and sometimes very eagerly and earnestly too (for the monster seldom takes any notice of them till at this age), they then begin to think of their danger; and, as they perceive they cannot easily avoid him, the wiser part bethink themselves of providing by other means for their security. They endeavour, by all methods they can invent, to render themselves so amiable in his eyes, that he may have no inclination to hurt them; in which they generally succeed so well, that his eyes, by frequent languishing, soon lessen their ideas of his fierceness, and so far abate their fears, that they venture to parley with him; and when they perceive him so different from what he hath been described, all gentleness, softness, kindness, tenderness, fondness, their dreadful apprehensions vanish in a moment; and now (it being usual with the human mind to skip from one extreme to its opposite, as easily, and almost as suddenly, as a bird from one bough to another) love instantly succeeds to fear: but, as it happens to persons who have in their infancy been thoroughly frightened with certain no-persons called ghosts, that they retain their dread of those beings after they are convinced that there are no such things, so these young ladies, though they no longer apprehend devouring, cannot so entirely shake off all that hath been instilled into them; they still entertain the idea of that censure which was so strongly imprinted on their tender minds, to which the declarations of abhorrence they every day hear from their companions greatly contribute. To avoid this censure, therefore, is now their only care; for which purpose they still pretend the same aversion to the monster: and the more they love him, the more ardently they counterfeit the antipathy. By the continual and constant practice of which deceit on others, they at length impose on themselves, and really believe they hate what they love. Thus, indeed, it happened to Lady Booby, who loved Joseph long before she knew it; and now loved him much more than she suspected. She had indeed, from the time of his sister's arrival in the quality of her niece, and from the instant she viewed him in the dress and character of a gentleman, began to conceive secretly a design which love had concealed from herself till a dream betrayed it to her.

She had no sooner risen than she sent for her nephew. When he came to her, after many compliments on his choice, she told him, "He might perceive, in her condescension to admit her own servant to her table, that she looked on the family of Andrews as his relations, and indeed hers; that, as he had married into such a family, it became him to endeavour by all methods to raise it as much as possible. At length she advised him to use all his heart to dissuade Joseph from his intended match, which would still enlarge their relation to meanness and poverty; concluding that, by a commission in the army, or some other genteel employment, he might soon put young Mr. Andrews on the foot of a gentleman; and, that being once done, his accomplishments might quickly gain him an alliance which would not be to their discredit."

Her nephew heartily embraced this proposal; and, finding Mr. Joseph with his wife, at his return to her chamber, he immediately began thus: "My love to my dear Pamela, brother, will extend to all her relations; nor shall I show them less respect than if I had married into the family of a duke. I hope I have given you some early testimonies of this, and shall continue to give you daily more. You will excuse me therefore, brother, if my concern for your interest makes me mention what may be, perhaps, disagreeable to you to hear: but I must insist upon it, that, if you have any value for my alliance or my friendship, you will decline any thoughts of engaging farther with a girl who is, as you are a relation of mine, so much beneath you. I know there may be at first some difficulty in your compliance, but that will daily diminish; and you will in the end sincerely thank me for my advice. I own, indeed, the girl is handsome; but beauty alone is a poor ingredient, and will make but an uncomfortable marriage."—"Sir," said Joseph, "I assure you her beauty is her least perfection; nor do I know a virtue which that young creature is not possest of."—"As to her virtues," answered Mr. Booby, "you can be yet but a slender judge of them; but, if she had never so many, you will find her equal in these among her superiors in birth and fortune, which now you are to esteem on a footing with yourself; at least I will take care they shall shortly be so, unless you prevent me by degrading yourself with such a match, a match I have hardly patience to think of, and which would break the hearts of your parents, who now rejoice in the expectation of seeing you make a figure in the world."—"I know not," replied Joseph, "that my parents have any power over my inclinations; nor am I obliged to sacrifice my happiness to their whim or ambition: besides, I shall be very sorry to see that the unexpected advancement of my sister should so suddenly inspire them with this wicked pride, and make them despise their equals. I am resolved on no account to quit my dear Fanny; no, though I could raise her as high above her present station as you have raised my sister."—"Your sister, as well as myself," said Booby, "are greatly obliged to you for the comparison: but, sir, she is not worthy to be compared in beauty to my Pamela; nor hath she half her merit. And besides, sir, as you civilly throw my marriage with your sister in my teeth, I must teach you the wide difference between us: my fortune enabled me to please myself; and it would have been as overgrown a folly in me to have omitted it as in you to do it."—"My fortune enables me to please myself likewise," said Joseph; "for all my pleasure is centered in Fanny; and whilst I have health I shall be able to support her with my labour in that station to which she was born, and with which she is content."—"Brother," said Pamela, "Mr. Booby advises you as a friend; and no doubt my papa and mamma will be of his opinion, and will have great reason to be angry with you for destroying what his goodness hath done, and throwing down our family again, after he hath raised it. It would become you better, brother, to pray for the assistance of grace against such a passion than to indulge it." —"Sure, sister, you are not in earnest; I am sure she is your equal, at least."—"She was my equal," answered Pamela; "but I am no longer Pamela Andrews; I am now this gentleman's lady, and, as such, am above her.—I hope I shall never behave with an unbecoming pride: but, at the same time, I shall always endeavour to know myself, and question not the assistance of grace to that purpose." They were now summoned to breakfast, and thus ended their discourse for the present, very little to the satisfaction of any of the parties.

Fanny was now walking in an avenue at some distance from the house, where Joseph had promised to take the first opportunity of coming to her. She had not a shilling in the world, and had subsisted ever since her return entirely on the charity of parson Adams. A young gentleman, attended by many servants, came up to her, and asked her if that was not the Lady Booby's house before him? This, indeed, he well knew;

but had framed the question for no other reason than to make her look up, and discover if her face was equal to the delicacy of her shape. He no sooner saw it than he was struck with amazement. He stopped his horse, and swore she was the most beautiful creature he ever beheld. Then, instantly alighting and delivering his horse to his servant, he rapt out half a dozen oaths that he would kiss her; to which she at first submitted, begging he would not be rude; but he was not satisfied with the civility of a salute, nor even with the rudest attack he could make on her lips, but caught her in his arms, and endeavoured to kiss her breasts, which with all her strength she resisted, and, as our spark was not of the Herculean race, with some difficulty prevented. The young gentleman, being soon out of breath in the struggle, quitted her, and, remounting his horse, called one of his servants to him, whom he ordered to stay behind with her, and make her any offers whatever to prevail on her to return home with him in the evening; and to assure her he would take her into keeping. He then rode on with his other servants, and arrived at the lady's house, to whom he was a distant relation, and was come to pay a visit.

The trusty fellow, who was employed in an office he had been long accustomed to, discharged his part with all the fidelity and dexterity imaginable, but to no purpose. She was entirely deaf to his offers, and rejected them with the utmost disdain. At last the pimp, who had perhaps more warm blood about him than his master, began to solicit for himself; he told her, though he was a servant, he was a man of some fortune, which he would make her mistress of; and this without any insult to her virtue, for that he would marry her. She answered, if his master himself, or the greatest lord in the land, would marry her, she would refuse him. At last, being weary with persuasions, and on fire with charms which would have almost kindled a flame in the bosom of an ancient philosopher or modern divine, he fastened his horse to the ground, and attacked her with much more force than the gentleman had exerted. Poor Fanny would not have been able to resist his rudeness a short time, but the deity who presides over chaste love sent her Joseph to her assistance. He no sooner came within sight, and perceived her struggling with a man, than, like a cannon-ball, or like lightning, or anything that is swifter, if anything be, he ran towards her, and, coming up just as the ravisher had torn her handkerchief from her breast, before his lips had touched that seat of innocence and bliss, he dealt him so lusty a blow in that part of his neck which a rope would have become with the utmost propriety, that the fellow staggered backwards, and, perceiving he had to do with something rougher than the little, tender, trembling hand of Fanny, he quitted her, and, turning about, saw his rival, with fire flashing from his eyes, again ready to assail him; and, indeed, before he could well defend himself, or return the first blow, he received a second, which, had it fallen on that part of the stomach to which it was directed, would have been probably the last he would have had any occasion for; but the ravisher, lifting up his hand, drove the blow upwards to his mouth, whence it dislodged three of his teeth; and now, not conceiving any extraordinary affection for the beauty of Joseph's person, nor being extremely pleased with this method of salutation, he collected all his force, and aimed a blow at Joseph's breast, which he artfully parried with one fist, so that it lost its force entirely in air; and, stepping one foot backward, he darted his fist so fiercely at his enemy, that, had he not caught it in his hand (for he was a boxer of no inferior fame), it must have tumbled him on the ground. And now the ravisher meditated another blow, which he aimed at that part of the breast where the heart is lodged; Joseph did not catch it as before, yet so prevented its aim that it fell directly on his nose, but with abated force. Joseph then, moving both fist and foot forwards at the same time, threw his head so dexterously into the stomach of the ravisher that he fell a lifeless lump on the field, where he lay many minutes breathless and motionless.

When Fanny saw her Joseph receive a blow in his face, and blood running in a stream from him, she began to tear her hair and invoke all human and divine power to his assistance. She was not, however, long under this affliction before Joseph, having conquered his enemy, ran to her, and assured her he was not hurt; she then instantly fell on her knees, and thanked God that he had made Joseph the means of her rescue, and at the same time preserved him from being injured in attempting it. She offered, with her handkerchief, to wipe his blood from his face; but he, seeing his rival attempting to recover his legs, turned to him, and asked him if he had enough? To which the other answered he had; for he believed he had fought with the devil instead of a man; and, loosening his horse, said he should not have attempted the wench if he had known she had been so well provided for.

Fanny now begged Joseph to return with her to parson

Adams, and to promise that he would leave her no more. These were propositions so agreeable to Joseph, that, had he heard them, he would have given an immediate assent; but indeed his eyes were now his only sense; for you may remember, reader, that the ravisher had tore her handkerchief from Fanny's neck, by which he had discovered such a sight, that Joseph hath declared all the statues he ever beheld were so much inferior to it in beauty, that it was more capable of converting a man into a statue than of being imitated by the greatest master of that art. This modest creature, whom no warmth in summer could ever induce to expose her charms to the wanton sun, a modesty to which, perhaps, they owed their inconceivable whiteness, had stood many minutes bare-necked in the presence of Joseph before her apprehension of his danger and the horror of seeing his blood would suffer her once to reflect on what concerned herself; till at last, when the cause of her concern had vanished, an admiration at his silence, together with observing the fixed position of his eyes, produced an idea in the lovely maid which brought more blood into her face than had flowed from Joseph's nostrils. The snowy hue of her bosom was likewise changed to vermilion at the instant when she clapped her handkerchief round her neck. Joseph saw the uneasiness she suffered, and immediately removed his eyes from an object, in surveying which he had felt the greatest delight which the organs of sight were capable of conveying to his soul; so great was his fear of offending her, and so truly did his passion for her deserve the noble name of love.

Fanny, being recovered from her confusion, which was almost equalled by what Joseph had felt from observing it, again mentioned her request; this was instantly and gladly complied with; and together they crossed two or three fields, which brought them to the habitation of Mr. Adams.

CHAPTER VIII

A DISCOURSE WHICH HAPPENED BETWEEN MR. ADAMS, MRS. ADAMS, JOSEPH, AND FANNY; WITH SOME BEHAVIOUR OF MR. ADAMS WHICH WILL BE CALLED BY SOME FEW READERS VERY LOW, ABSURD, AND UNNATURAL

THE parson and his wife had just ended a long dispute when the lovers came to the door. Indeed, this young couple had been the subject of the dispute; for Mrs. Adams was one of those prudent people who never do anything to injure their families, or, perhaps, one of those good mothers who would even stretch their conscience to serve their children. She had long entertained hopes of seeing her eldest daughter succeed Mrs. Slipslop, and of making her second son an exciseman by Lady Booby's interest. These were expectations she could not endure the thoughts of quitting, and was, therefore, very uneasy to see her husband so resolute to oppose the lady's intention in Fanny's affair. She told him, "It behoved every man to take the first care of his family; that he had a wife and six children, the maintaining and providing for whom would be business enough for him without intermeddling in other folks' affairs; that he had always preached up submission to superiors, and would do ill to give an example of the contrary behaviour in his own conduct; that if Lady Booby did wrong she must answer for it herself, and the sin would not lie at their door; that Fanny had been a servant, and bred up in the lady's own family, and consequently she must have known more of her than they did, and it was very improbable, if she had behaved herself well, that the lady would have been so bitterly her enemy; that perhaps he was too much inclined to think well of her because she was handsome, but handsome women were often no better than they should be; that G— made ugly women as well as handsome ones; and that if a woman had virtue it signified nothing whether she had beauty or no." For all which reasons she concluded he should oblige the lady, and stop the future publication of the banns. But all these excellent arguments had no effect on the parson, who persisted in doing his duty without regarding the consequence it might have on his worldly interest. He endeavoured to answer her as well as he could; to which she had just finished her reply (for she had always the last word everywhere but at church) when Joseph and Fanny entered their kitchen, where the parson and his wife then sat at breakfast over some bacon and cabbage. There was a coldness in the civility of Mrs. Adams which persons of accurate speculation might have observed, but escaped her present guests; indeed, it was a good deal covered by the heartiness of Adams, who no sooner heard that Fanny had neither eat nor drank that morning than he presented her a bone of bacon he had just been gnawing, being the only remains of his provision, and then ran nimbly to the tap, and produced a mug of small beer, which he called ale; however, it was the best in his house. Joseph, addressing himself to the parson, told him the discourse which had past between Squire Booby, his sister, and himself concerning Fanny; he then acquainted him with the dangers whence he had rescued her, and communicated some apprehensions on her account. He concluded that he should never have an easy moment till Fanny was absolutely his, and begged that he might be suffered to fetch a licence, saying he could easily borrow the money. The parson answered, That he had already given his sentiments concerning a licence, and that a very few days would make it unnecessary. "Joseph," says he, "I wish this haste doth not arise rather from your impatience than your fear; but, as it certainly springs from one of these causes, I will examine both. Of each of these therefore in their turn; and first for the first of these, namely, impatience. Now, child, I must inform you that, if in your purposed marriage with this young woman you have no intention but the indulgence of carnal appetites, you are guilty of a very heinous sin. Marriage was ordained for nobler purposes, as you will learn when you hear the service provided on that occasion read to you. Nay, perhaps, if you are a good lad, I, child, shall give you a sermon *gratis*, wherein I shall demonstrate how little regard ought to be had to the flesh on such occasions. The text will be Matthew the 5th, and part of the 28th verse —*Whosoever looketh on a woman, so as to lust after her*. The latter part I shall omit, as foreign to my purpose. Indeed, all such brutal lusts and affections are to be greatly subdued, if not totally eradicated, before the vessel can be said to be consecrated to honour. To marry with a view of gratifying those inclinations is a prostitution of that holy ceremony, and must entail a curse on all who so lightly undertake it. If, therefore, this haste arises from impatience, you are to correct, and not give way to it. Now, as to the second head which I proposed to speak to, namely, fear: it argues a diffidence, highly criminal, of that Power in which alone we should put our trust, seeing we may be well assured that he is able, not only to defeat the designs of our enemies, but even to turn their hearts. Instead of taking, therefore, any unjustifiable or desperate means to rid ourselves of fear, we should resort to prayer only on these occasions; and we may be then certain of obtaining what is best for us. When any accident threatens us we are not to despair, nor, when it overtakes us, to grieve; we must submit in all things to the will of Providence, and set our affections so much on nothing here that we cannot quit it without reluctance. You are a young man, and can know but little of this world; I am older, and have seen a great deal. All passions are criminal in their excess; and even love itself, if it is not subservient to our duty, may render us blind to it. Had Abraham so loved his son Isaac as to refuse the sacrifice required, is there any of us who would not condemn him? Joseph, I know your many good qualities, and value you for them; but, as I am to render an account of your soul, which is committed to my cure, I cannot see any fault without reminding you of it. You are too much inclined to passion, child, and have set your affections so absolutely on this young woman, that, if G— required her at your hands, I fear you would reluctantly part with her. Now, believe me, no Christian ought so to set his heart on any person or thing in this world, but that, whenever it shall be required or taken from him in any manner by Divine Providence, he may be able, peaceably, quietly, and contentedly, to resign it." At which words one came hastily in, and acquainted Mr. Adams that his youngest son was drowned. He stood silent a moment, and soon began to stamp about the room and deplore his loss with the bitterest agony. Joseph, who was overwhelmed with concern likewise, recovered himself sufficiently to endeavour to comfort the parson; in which attempt he used many arguments that he had at several times remembered out of his own discourses, both in private and public (for he was a great enemy to the passions, and preached nothing more than the conquest of them by reason and grace), but he was not at leisure now to hearken to his advice. "Child, child," said he, "do not go about impossibilities. Had it been any other of my children I could have borne it with patience; but my little prattler, the darling and comfort of my old age—the little wretch, to be snatched out of life just at his entrance into it; the sweetest, best-tempered boy, who never did a thing to offend me. It was but this morning I gave him his first lesson in *Quæ Genus*. This was the very book he learnt; poor child! it is of no further use to thee now. He would have made the best scholar, and have been an ornament to the Church;—such parts and such goodness never met in one so young." "And the handsomest lad too," says Mrs. Adams, recovering from a swoon in Fanny's arms. "My poor Jacky, shall I never see thee more?" cries the parson. "Yes, surely," says Joseph, "and in a better place; you will meet again, never to part more." I believe the parson did not hear these words, for he paid little regard to them, but went on lamenting, whilst the tears trickled down into his bosom. At last he cried out, "Where is my little darling?" and was sallying out, when to his great surprise and joy, in which I hope the reader will sympathise, he met his son in a wet condition indeed, but alive and running towards him. The person who brought the news of his misfortune had been a little too eager, as people sometimes are, from, I believe, no very good principle, to relate ill news; and, seeing him fall into the river, instead of running to his assistance, directly ran to acquaint his father of a fate which he had concluded to be inevitable, but whence the child was relieved by the same poor pedlar who had relieved his father before from a less distress. The parson's joy was now as extravagant as his grief had been before; he kissed and embraced his son a thousand times, and danced about the room like one frantic; but as soon as he discovered the face of his old friend the pedlar, and heard the fresh obligation he had to him, what were his sensations? not those which two courtiers feel in one another's embraces; not those with which a great man receives the vile treacherous engines of his wicked purposes, not those with which a worthless younger brother wishes his elder joy of a son, or a man congratulates his rival on his obtaining a mistress, a place, or an honour.—No, reader; he felt the ebullition, the overflowings of a full, honest, open heart, towards the person who had conferred a real obligation, and of which, if thou canst not conceive an idea within, I will not vainly endeavour to assist thee.

When these tumults were over, the parson, taking Joseph aside, proceeded thus—"No, Joseph, do not give too much way to thy passions, if thou dost expect happiness." The patience of Joseph, nor perhaps of Job, could bear no longer; he interrupted the parson, saying, "It was easier to give advice than take it; nor did he perceive he could so entirely conquer himself, when he apprehended he had lost his son, or when he found him recovered."—"Boy," replied Adams, raising his voice, "it doth not become green heads to advise grey hairs.—Thou art ignorant of the tenderness of fatherly affection; when thou art a father thou wilt be capable then only of knowing what a father can feel. No man is obliged to impossibilities; and the loss of a child is one of those great trials where our grief may be allowed to become immoderate."—"Well, sir," cries Joseph, "and if I love a mistress as well as you your child, surely her loss would grieve me equally."—"Yes, but such love is foolishness and wrong in itself, and ought to be conquered," answered Adams; "it savours too much of the flesh."—"Sure, sir," says

Joseph, "it is not sinful to love my wife, no, not even to doat on her to distraction!"—"Indeed but it is," says Adams. "Every man ought to love his wife, no doubt; we are commanded so to do; but we ought to love her with moderation and discretion."—"I am afraid I shall be guilty of some sin in spite of all my endeavours," says Joseph; "for I shall love without any moderation, I am sure."—"You talk foolishly and childishly," cries Adams.—"Indeed," says Mrs. Adams, who had listened to the latter part of their conversation, "you talk more foolishly yourself. I hope, my dear, you will never preach any such doctrine as that husbands can love their wives too well. If I knew you had such a sermon in the house I am sure I would burn it, and I declare, if I had not been convinced you had loved me as well as you could, I can answer for myself, I should have hated and despised you. Marry come up! Fine doctrine, indeed! A wife hath a right to insist on her husband's loving her as much as ever he can; and he is a sinful villain who doth not. Doth he not promise to love her, and to comfort her, and to cherish her, and all that? I am sure I remember it all as well as if I had repeated it over but yesterday, and shall never forget it. Besides, I am certain you do not preach as you practise; for you have been a loving and a cherishing husband to me; that's the truth on't; and why you should endeavour to put such wicked nonsense into this young man's head I cannot devise. Don't hearken to him, Mr. Joseph; be as good a husband as you are able, and love your wife with all your body and soul too." Here a violent rap at the door put an end to their discourse, and produced a scene which the reader will find in the next chapter.

CHAPTER IX

A VISIT WHICH THE POLITE LADY BOOBY AND HER POLITE FRIEND PAID TO THE PARSON

THE Lady Booby had no sooner had an account from the gentleman of his meeting a wonderful beauty near her house, and perceived the raptures with which he spoke of her, than, immediately concluding it must be Fanny, she began to meditate a design of bringing them better acquainted; and to entertain hopes that the fine clothes, presents, and promises of this youth, would prevail on her to abandon Joseph: she therefore proposed to her company a walk in the fields before dinner, when she led them towards Mr. Adams's house; and, as she approached it, told them if they pleased she would divert them with one of the most ridiculous sights they had ever seen, which was an old foolish parson, who, she said, laughing, kept a wife and six brats on a salary of about twenty pounds a year; adding, that there was not such another ragged family in the parish. They all readily agreed to this visit, and arrived whilst Mrs. Adams was declaiming as in the last chapter. Beau Didapper, which was the name of the young gentleman we have seen riding towards Lady Booby's, with his cane mimicked the rap of a London footman at the door. The people within, namely, Adams, his wife and three children, Joseph, Fanny, and the pedlar, were all thrown into confusion by this knock, but Adams went directly to the door, which being opened, the Lady Booby and her company walked in, and were received by the parson with about two hundred bows, and by his wife with as many curtsies; the latter telling the lady "She was ashamed to be seen in such a pickle, and that her house was in such a litter; but that if she had expected such an honour from her ladyship she should have found her in a better manner." The parson made no apologies, though he was in his half-cassock and a flannel night-cap. He said "They were heartily welcome to his poor cottage," and turning to Mr. Didapper, cried out, "*Non mea renidet in domo lacunar.*" The beau answered, "He did not understand Welsh;" at which the parson stared and made no reply.

Mr. Didapper, or beau Didapper, was a young gentleman of about four foot five inches in height. He wore his own hair, though the scarcity of it might have given him sufficient excuse for a periwig. His face was thin and pale; the shape of his body and legs none of the best, for he had very narrow shoulders and no calf; and his gait might more properly be called hopping than walking. The qualifications of his mind were well adapted to his person. We shall handle them first negatively. He was not entirely ignorant; for he could talk a little French and sing two or three Italian songs; he had lived too much in the world to be bashful, and too much at court to be proud: he seemed not much inclined to avarice, for he was profuse in his expenses; nor had he all the features of prodigality, for he never gave a shilling: no hater of women, for he always dangled after them; yet so little subject to lust, that he had, among those who knew him best, the character of great moderation in his pleasures; no drinker of wine; nor so addicted to passion but that a hot word or two from an adversary made him immediately cool.

Now, to give him only a dash or two on the affirmative side: though he was born to an immense fortune, he chose, for the pitiful and dirty consideration of a place of little consequence, to depend entirely on the will of a fellow whom they call a great man; who treated him with the utmost disrespect, and exacted of him a plenary obedience to his commands, which he implicitly submitted to, at the expense of his conscience, his honour, and of his country, in which he had himself so very large a share. And to finish his character; as he was entirely well satisfied with his own person and parts, so he was very apt to ridicule and laugh at any imperfection in another. Such was the little person, or rather thing, that hopped after Lady Booby into Mr. Adams's kitchen.

The parson and his company retreated from the chimney-side, where they had been seated, to give room to the lady and hers. Instead of returning any of the curtsies or extraordinary civility of Mrs. Adams, the lady, turning to Mr. Booby, cried out, "*Quelle Bête! Quel Animal!*" And presently after discovering Fanny (for she did not need the circumstance of her standing by Joseph to assure the identity of her person), she asked the beau "Whether he did not think her a pretty girl?" —"Begad, madam," answered he, "'tis the very same I met." "I did not imagine," replied the lady, "you had so good a taste."—"Because I never liked you, I warrant," cries the beau. "Ridiculous!" said she: "you know you was always my aversion." "I would never mention aversion," answered the beau, "with that face;[1] dear Lady Booby, wash your face before you mention aversion, I beseech you." He then laughed, and turned about to coquet it with Fanny.

Mrs. Adams had been all this time begging and praying the ladies to sit down, a favour which she at last obtained. The little boy to whom the accident had happened, still keeping his place by the fire, was chid by his mother for not being more mannerly: but Lady Booby took his part, and, commending his beauty, told the parson he was his very picture. She then, seeing a book in his hand, asked "If he could read?"—"Yes," cried Adams, "a little Latin, madam: he is just got into *Quæ Genus*."—"A fig for quere genius!" answered she; "let me hear him read a little English."—"*Lege, Dick, lege*," said Adams:

---

[1] Lest this should appear unnatural to some readers, we think proper to acquaint them, that it is taken verbatim from very polite conversation.

but the boy made no answer, till he saw the parson knit his brows, and then cried, "I don't understand you, father."—"How, boy!" says Adams; "what doth lego make in the imperative mood? Legito, doth it not?"—"Yes," answered Dick.—"And what besides?" says the father. "Lege," quoth the son, after some hesitation. "A good boy," says the father: "and now, child, what is the English of lego?"—To which the boy, after long puzzling, answered, he could not tell. "How!" cries Adams, in a passion;—"what, hath the water washed away your learning? Why, what is Latin for the English verb read? Consider before you speak." The child considered some time, and then the parson cried twice or thrice, "Le—, Le—." Dick answered, "Lego."—"Very well;—and then what is the English," says the parson, "of the verb lego?"—"To read," cried Dick.—"Very well," said the parson; "a good boy: you can do well if you will take pains.—I assure your ladyship he is not much above eight years old, and is out of his Propria quæ Maribus already.—Come, Dick, read to her ladyship;"—which she again desiring, in order to give the beau time and opportunity with Fanny, Dick began as in the following chapter.

CHAPTER X

THE HISTORY OF TWO FRIENDS, WHICH MAY AFFORD AN USEFUL LESSON TO ALL THOSE PERSONS WHO HAPPEN TO TAKE UP THEIR RESIDENCE IN MARRIED FAMILIES

"Leonard and Paul were two friends." — "Pronounce it Lennard, child," cried the parson.—"Pray, Mr. Adams," says Lady Booby, "let your son read without interruption." Dick then proceeded. "Lennard and Paul were two friends, who, having been educated together at the same school, commenced a friendship which they preserved a long time for each other. It was so deeply fixed in both their minds, that a long absence, during which they had maintained no correspondence, did not eradicate nor lessen it: but it revived in all its force at their first meeting, which was not till after fifteen years' absence, most of which time Lennard had spent in the East Indi-es."—"Pronounce it short, Indies," says Adams.—"Pray, sir, be quiet," says the lady.—The boy repeated—"in the East Indies, whilst Paul had served his king and country in the army. In which different services they had found such different success, that Lennard was now married, and retired with a fortune of thirty thousand pounds; and Paul was arrived to the degree of a lieutenant of foot; and was not worth a single shilling.

"The regiment in which Paul was stationed happened to be ordered into quarters within a small distance from the estate which Lennard had purchased, and where he was settled. This latter, who was now become a country gentleman, and a justice of peace, came to attend the quarter sessions in the town where his old friend was quartered, soon after his arrival. Some affair in which a soldier was concerned occasioned Paul to attend the justices. Manhood, and time, and the change of climate, had so much altered Lennard, that Paul did not immediately recollect the features of his old acquaintance: but it was otherwise with Lennard. He knew Paul the moment he saw him; nor could he contain himself from quitting the bench, and running hastily to embrace him. Paul stood at first a little surprised; but had soon sufficient information from his friend, whom he no sooner remembered than he returned his embrace with a passion which made many of the spectators laugh, and gave to some few a much higher and more agreeable sensation.

"Not to detain the reader with minute circumstances, Lennard insisted on his friend's returning with him to his house that evening; which request was complied with, and leave for a month's absence for Paul obtained of the commanding officer.

"If it was possible for any circumstance to give any addition to the happiness which Paul proposed in this visit, he received that additional pleasure by finding, on his arrival at his friend's house, that his lady was an old acquaintance which he had formerly contracted at his quarters, and who had always appeared to be of a most agreeable temper; a character she had ever maintained among her intimates, being of that number, every individual of which is called quite the best sort of woman in the world.

"But, good as this lady was, she was still a woman; that is to say, an angel, and not an angel."—"You must mistake, child," cries the parson, "for you read nonsense."—"It is so in the book," answered the son. Mr. Adams was then silenced by authority, and Dick proceeded—"For though her person was of that kind to which men attribute the name of angel, yet in her mind she was perfectly woman. Of which a great degree of obstinacy gave the most remarkable and perhaps most pernicious instance.

"A day or two passed after Paul's arrival before any instances of this appeared; but it was impossible to conceal it long. Both she and her husband soon lost all apprehension from their friend's presence, and fell to their disputes with as much vigour as ever. These were still pursued with the utmost ardour and eagerness, however trifling the causes were whence they first arose. Nay, however incredible it may seem, the little consequence of the matter in debate was frequently given as a reason for the fierceness of the contention, as thus: 'If you loved me, sure you would never dispute with me such a trifle as this.' The answer to which is very obvious; for the argument would hold equally on both sides, and was constantly retorted with some addition, as—'I am sure I have much more reason to say so, who am in the right.' During all these disputes, Paul always kept strict silence, and preserved an even countenance, without showing the least visible inclination to either party. One day, however, when madam had left the room in a violent fury, Lennard could not refrain from referring his cause to his friend. Was ever anything so unreasonable, says he, as this woman? What shall I do with her? I doat on her to distraction; nor have I any cause to complain of, more than this obstinacy in her temper; whatever she asserts, she will maintain against all the reason and conviction in the world. Pray give me your advice.—First, says Paul, I will give my opinion, which is, flatly, that you are in the wrong; for, supposing she is in the wrong, was the subject of your contention any ways material? What signified it whether you was married in a red or a yellow waistcoat? for that was your dispute. Now, suppose she was mistaken; as you love her you say so tenderly, and I believe she deserves it, would it not have been wiser to have yielded, though you certainly knew yourself in the right, than to give either her or yourself any uneasiness? For my own part, if ever I marry, I am resolved to enter into an agreement with my wife, that in all disputes (especially about trifles) that party who is most convinced they are right shall always surrender the victory; by which means we shall both be forward to give up the cause. I own, said Lennard, my dear friend, shaking him by the hand, there is great truth and reason in what you say; and I will for the future endeavour to follow your advice. They soon after broke up the conversation, and Lennard, going to his wife, asked her pardon, and told her his friend had convinced him he had been in the wrong. She immediately began a vast encomium on Paul, in which he seconded her, and both agreed he was the worthiest and wisest man upon earth. When

next they met, which was at supper, though she had promised
not to mention what her husband told her, she could not forbear
casting the kindest and most affectionate looks on Paul, and
asked him, with the sweetest voice, whether she should help
him to some potted woodcock? Potted partridge, my dear,
you mean, says the husband. My dear, says she, I ask your
friend if he will eat any potted woodcock; and I am sure I must
know, who potted it. I think I should know too, who shot them,
replied the husband, and I am convinced that I have not seen a
woodcock this year; however, though I know I am in the right,
I submit, and the potted partridge is potted woodcock if you
desire to have it so. It is equal to me, says she, whether it is
one or the other; but you would persuade one out of one's
senses; to be sure, you are always in the right in your own
opinion; but your friend, I believe, knows which he is eating.
Paul answered nothing, and the dispute continued, as usual, the
greatest part of the evening. The next morning the lady,
accidentally meeting Paul, and being convinced he was her
friend, and of her side, accosted him thus:—I am certain, sir,
you have long since wondered at the unreasonableness of my
husband. He is indeed, in other respects, a good sort of man,
but so positive, that no woman but one of my complying temper
could possibly live with him. Why, last night, now, was ever
any creature so unreasonable? I am certain you must condemn
him. Pray, answer me, was he not in the wrong? Paul, after
a short silence, spoke as follows: I am sorry, madam, that, as
good manners obliges me to answer against my will, so an
adherence to truth forces me to declare myself of a different
opinion. To be plain and honest, you was entirely in the wrong;
the cause I own not worth disputing, but the bird was undoubtedly a partridge. O sir! replyed the lady, I cannot
possibly help your taste. Madam, returned Paul, that is very
little material; for, had it been otherwise, a husband might have
expected submission.—Indeed! sir, says she, I assure you!—
Yes, madam, cryed he, he might, from a person of your excellent
understanding; and pardon me for saying, such a condescension
would have shown a superiority of sense even to your husband
himself.—But, dear sir, said she, why should I submit when I
am in the right?—For that very reason, answered he; it would
be the greatest instance of affection imaginable; for can anything be a greater object of our compassion than a person we
love in the wrong? Ay, but I should endeavour, said she, to
set him right. Pardon me, madam, answered Paul: I will

apply to your own experience if you ever found your arguments had that effect. The more our judgments err, the less we are willing to own it: for my own part, I have always observed the persons who maintain the worst side in any contest are the warmest. Why, says she, I must confess there is truth in what you say, and I will endeavour to practise it. The husband then coming in, Paul departed. And Lennard, approaching his wife with an air of good humour, told her he was sorry for their foolish dispute the last night; but he was now convinced of his error. She answered, smiling, she believed she owed his condescension to his complacence; that she was ashamed to think a word had passed on so silly an occasion, especially as she was satisfyed she had been mistaken. A little contention followed, but with the utmost good-will to each other, and was concluded by her asserting that Paul had thoroughly convinced her she had been in the wrong. Upon which they both united in the praises of their common friend.

"Paul now passed his time with great satisfaction, these disputes being much less frequent, as well as shorter than usual; but the devil, or some unlucky accident in which perhaps the devil had no hand, shortly put an end to his happiness. He was now eternally the private referee of every difference; in which, after having perfectly, as he thought, established the doctrine of submission, he never scrupled to assure both privately that they were in the right in every argument, as before he had followed the contrary method. One day a violent litigation happened in his absence, and both parties agreed to refer it to his decision. The husband professing himself sure the decision would be in his favour; the wife answered, he might be mistaken; for she believed his friend was convinced how seldom she was to blame; and that if he knew all——The husband replied, My dear, I have no desire of any retrospect; but I believe, if you knew all too, you would not imagine my friend so entirely on your side. Nay, says she, since you provoke me, I will mention one instance. You may remember our dispute about sending Jackey to school in cold weather, which point I gave up to you from mere compassion, knowing myself to be in the right; and Paul himself told me afterwards he thought me so. My dear, replied the husband, I will not scruple your veracity; but I assure you solemnly, on my applying to him, he gave it absolutely on my side, and said he would have acted in the same manner. They then proceeded to produce numberless other instances, in all which Paul had, on vows of secresy, given his opinion on both sides. In the conclusion, both believing each other, they fell severely on the treachery of Paul, and agreed that he had been the occasion of almost every dispute which had fallen out between them. They then became extremely loving, and so full of condescension on both sides, that they vyed with each other in censuring their own conduct, and jointly vented their indignation on Paul, whom the wife, fearing a bloody consequence, earnestly entreated her husband to suffer quietly to depart the next day, which was the time fixed for his return to quarters, and then drop his acquaintance.

"However ungenerous this behaviour in Lennard may be esteemed, his wife obtained a promise from him (though with difficulty) to follow her advice; but they both expressed such unusual coldness that day to Paul, that he, who was quick of apprehension, taking Lennard aside, pressed him so home, that he at last discovered the secret. Paul acknowledged the truth, but told him the design with which he had done it.—To which the other answered, he would have acted more friendly to have let him into the whole design; for that he might have assured himself of his secresy. Paul replyed, with some indignation, he had given him a sufficient proof how capable he was of concealing a secret from his wife. Lennard returned with some warmth—he had more reason to upbraid him, for that he had caused most of the quarrels between them by his strange conduct, and might (if they had not discovered the affair to each other) have been the occasion of their separation. Paul then said"——But something now happened which put a stop to Dick's reading, and of which we shall treat in the next chapter.

CHAPTER XI

IN WHICH THE HISTORY IS CONTINUED

JOSEPH ANDREWS had borne with great uneasiness the impertinence of beau Didapper to Fanny, who had been talking pretty freely to her, and offering her settlements; but the respect to the company had restrained him from interfering whilst the beau confined himself to the use of his tongue only; but the said beau, watching an opportunity whilst the ladies' eyes were disposed another way, offered a rudeness to her with his hands; which Joseph no sooner perceived than he presented him with so sound a box on the ear, that it conveyed him several paces from where he stood. The ladies immediately screamed out, rose from their chairs; and the beau, as soon as he recovered himself, drew his hanger: which Adams observing, snatched up the lid of a pot in his left hand, and, covering himself with it as with a shield, without any weapon of offence in his other hand, stept in before Joseph, and exposed himself to the enraged beau, who threatened such perdition and destruction, that it frighted the women, who were all got in a huddle together, out of their wits, even to hear his denunciations of vengeance. Joseph was of a different complexion, and begged Adams to let his rival come on; for he had a good cudgel in his hand, and did not fear him. Fanny now fainted into Mrs. Adams's arms, and the whole room was in confusion, when Mr. Booby, passing by Adams, who lay snug under the pot-lid, came up to Didapper, and insisted on his sheathing the hanger, promising he should have satisfaction; which Joseph declared he would give him, and fight him at any weapon whatever. The beau now sheathed his hanger, and taking out a pocket-glass, and vowing vengeance all the time, re-adjusted his hair; the parson deposited his shield; and Joseph, running to Fanny, soon brought her back to life. Lady Booby chid Joseph for his insult on Didapper; but he answered, he would have attacked an army in the same cause. "What cause?" said the lady. "Madam," answered Joseph, "he was rude to that young woman."—"What," says the lady, "I suppose he would have kissed the wench; and is a gentleman to be struck for such an offer? I must tell you, Joseph, these airs do not become you."—"Madam," said Mr. Booby, "I saw the whole affair, and I do not commend my brother; for I cannot perceive why he should take upon him to be this girl's champion."—"I can commend him," says Adams: "he is a brave lad; and it becomes any man to be the champion of the innocent; and he must be the basest coward who would not vindicate a woman with whom he is on the brink of marriage." —"Sir," says Mr. Booby, "my brother is not a proper match for such a young woman as this."—"No," says Lady Booby; "nor do you, Mr. Adams, act in your proper character by encouraging any such doings; and I am very much surprised you should concern yourself in it. I think your wife and family your properer care."—"Indeed, madam, your ladyship says very true," answered Mrs. Adams: "he talks a pack of nonsense, that the whole parish are his children. I am sure I don't understand what he means by it; it would make some women suspect he had gone astray, but I acquit him of that; I can read Scripture as well as he, and I never found that the parson was obliged to provide for other folks' children; and besides, he is but a poor curate, and hath little enough, as your ladyship knows, for me and mine."—"You say very well, Mrs. Adams," quoth the Lady Booby, who had not spoke a word to her before; "you seem to be a very sensible woman; and I assure you, your husband is acting a very foolish part, and opposing his own interest, seeing my nephew is violently set against this match: and indeed I can't blame him; it is by no means one suitable to our family." In this manner the lady proceeded with Mrs. Adams, whilst the beau hopped about the room, shaking his head, partly from pain and partly from anger; and Pamela was chiding Fanny for her assurance in aiming at such a match as her brother. Poor Fanny answered only with her tears, which had long since begun to wet her handkerchief; which Joseph perceiving, took her by the arm, and wrapping it in his carried her off, swearing he would own no relation to any one who was an enemy to her he loved more than all the world. He went out with Fanny under his left arm, brandishing a cudgel in his right, and neither Mr. Booby nor the beau thought proper to oppose him. Lady Booby and her company made a very short stay behind him; for the lady's bell now summoned them to dress; for which they had just time before dinner.

Adams seemed now very much dejected, which his wife perceiving, began to apply some matrimonial balsam. She told him he had reason to be concerned, for that he had probably ruined his family with his tricks almost; but perhaps he was grieved for the loss of his two children, Joseph and Fanny. His eldest daughter went on: "Indeed, father, it is very hard to bring strangers here to eat your children's bread out of their mouths. You have kept them since they came home; and, for anything I see to the contrary, may keep them a month longer; are you obliged to give her meat, tho'f she was never so handsome? But I don't see she is so much handsomer than other people. If people were to be kept for their beauty, she would scarce fare better than her neighbours, I believe. As for Mr. Joseph, I have nothing to say; he is a young man of honest principles, and will pay some time or other for what he hath; but for the girl—why doth she not return to her place she ran away from? I would not give such a vagabond slut a halfpenny though I had a million of money; no, though she was starving." "Indeed but I would," cries little Dick; "and, father, rather than poor Fanny shall be starved, I will give her all this bread and cheese"—(offering what he held in his hand). Adams smiled on the boy, and told him he rejoiced to see he was a Christian; and that if he had a halfpenny in his pocket, he would have given it him; telling him it was his duty to look upon all his neighbours as his brothers and sisters, and love them accordingly. "Yes, papa," says he, "I love her better than my sisters, for she is handsomer than any of them." "Is she so, saucebox?" says the sister, giving him a box on the ear; which the father would probably have resented, had not Joseph, Fanny, and the pedlar at that instant returned together. Adams bid his wife prepare some food for their dinner; she said, "Truly she could not, she had something else to do." Adams rebuked her for disputing his commands, and quoted many texts of Scripture to prove "That the husband is the head of the wife, and she is to submit and obey." The wife answered, "It was blasphemy to talk Scripture out of church; that such things were very proper to be said in the pulpit, but that it was pro- fane to talk them in common discourse." Joseph told Mr. Adams "He was not come with any design to give him or Mrs. Adams any trouble; but to desire the favour of all their company to the George (an ale-house in the parish), where he had bespoke a piece of bacon and greens for their dinner." Mrs. Adams, who was a very good sort of woman, only rather too strict in œconomies, readily accepted this invitation, as did the parson himself by her example; and away they all walked together, not omitting little Dick, to whom Joseph gave a shilling when he heard of his intended liberality to Fanny.

CHAPTER XII

WHERE THE GOOD-NATURED READER WILL SEE SOMETHING WHICH
WILL GIVE HIM NO GREAT PLEASURE

THE pedlar had been very inquisitive from the time he had first heard that the great house in this parish belonged to the Lady Booby, and had learnt that she was the widow of Sir Thomas, and that Sir Thomas had bought Fanny, at about the age of three or four years, of a travelling woman; and, now their homely but hearty meal was ended, he told Fanny he believed he could acquaint her with her parents. The whole company, especially she herself, started at this offer of the pedlar's. He then proceeded thus, while they all lent their strictest attention:—"Though I am now contented with this humble way of getting my livelihood, I was formerly a gentleman; for so all those of my profession are called. In a word, I was a drummer in an Irish regiment of foot. Whilst I was in this honourable station I attended an officer of our regiment into England a-recruiting. In our march from Bristol to Froome (for since the decay of the woollen trade the clothing towns have furnished the army with a great number of recruits) we overtook on the road a woman, who seemed to be about thirty years old or thereabouts, not very handsome, but well enough for a soldier. As we came up to her, she mended her pace, and falling into discourse with our ladies (for every man of the party, namely, a serjeant, two private men, and a drum, were provided with their woman except myself), she continued to travel on with us. I, perceiving she must fall to my lot, advanced presently to her, made love to her in our military way, and quickly succeeded to my wishes. We struck a bargain within a mile, and lived together as man and wife to her dying day." "I suppose," says Adams, interrupting him, "you were married with a licence; for I don't see how you could contrive to have the banns published while you were marching from place to place." "No, sir," said the pedlar, "we took a licence to go to bed together without any banns." "Ay! ay!" said the parson; "*ex necessitate*, a licence may be allowable enough; but surely, surely, the other is the more regular and eligible way." The pedlar proceeded thus: "She returned with me to our regiment, and removed with us from quarters to quarters, till at last, whilst we lay at Galloway, she fell ill of a fever and died. When she was on her death-bed she called me to her, and, crying bitterly, declared she could not depart this world without discovering a secret to me, which, she said, was the only sin which sat heavy on her heart. She said she had formerly travelled in a company of gypsies, who had made a practice of stealing away children; that for her own part, she had been only once guilty of the crime; which, she said, she lamented more than all the rest of her sins, since probably it might have occasioned the death of the parents; for, added she, it is almost impossible to describe the beauty of the young creature, which was about a year and a half old when I kidnapped it. We kept her (for she was a girl) above two years in our company, when I sold her myself, for three guineas, to Sir Thomas Booby, in Somersetshire. Now, you know whether there are any more of that name in this county." "Yes," says Adams, "there are several Boobys who are squires, but I believe no baronet now alive; besides, it answers so exactly in every point, there is no room for doubt; but you have forgot to tell us the parents from whom the child was stolen." "Their name," answered the pedlar, "was Andrews. They lived about thirty miles from the squire; and she told me that I might be sure to find them out by one circumstance; for that they had a daughter of a very strange name, Pamĕla, or Pamēla; some pronounced it one way, and some the other." Fanny, who had changed colour at the first mention of the name, now fainted away; Joseph turned pale, and poor Dicky began to roar; the parson fell on his knees, and ejaculated many thanks-givings that this discovery had been made before the dreadful sin of incest was committed; and the pedlar was struck with amazement, not being able to account for all this confusion; the cause of which was presently opened by the parson's daughter, who was the only unconcerned person (for the mother was chafing Fanny's temples, and taking the utmost care of her): and, indeed, Fanny was the only creature whom the daughter would not have pitied in her situation; wherein, though we compassionate her ourselves, we shall leave her for a little while, and pay a short visit to Lady Booby.

CHAPTER XIII

THE HISTORY, RETURNING TO THE LADY BOOBY, GIVES SOME
    ACCOUNT OF THE TERRIBLE CONFLICT IN HER BREAST
    BETWEEN LOVE AND PRIDE; WITH WHAT HAPPENED ON
    THE PRESENT DISCOVERY

THE lady sat down with her company to dinner, but eat nothing. As soon as her cloth was removed she whispered Pamela that she was taken a little ill, and desired her to entertain her husband and beau Didapper. She then went up into her chamber, sent for Slipslop, threw herself on the bed in the agonies of love, rage, and despair; nor could she conceal these boiling passions longer without bursting. Slipslop now approached her bed, and asked how her ladyship did; but, instead of revealing her disorder, as she intended, she entered into a long encomium on the beauty and virtues of Joseph Andrews; ending, at last, with expressing her concern that so much tenderness should be thrown away on so despicable an object as Fanny. Slipslop, well knowing how to humour her mistress's frenzy, proceeded to repeat, with exaggeration, if possible, all her mistress had said, and concluded with a wish that Joseph had been a gentleman, and that she could see her lady in the arms of such a husband. The lady then started from the bed, and, taking a turn or two across the room, cryed out, with a deep sigh, "Sure he would make any woman happy!" —"Your ladyship," says she, "would be the happiest woman in the world with him. A fig for custom and nonsense! What 'vails what people say? Shall I be afraid of eating sweetmeats because people may say I have a sweet tooth? If I had a mind to marry a man, all the world should not hinder me. Your ladyship hath no parents to tutelar your infections; besides, he is of your ladyship's family now, and as good a gentleman as any in the country; and why should not a woman follow her mind as well as man? Why should not your ladyship marry the brother as well as your nephew the sister? I am sure, if it was a fragrant crime, I would not persuade your ladyship to it."—"But, dear Slipslop," answered the lady, "if I could prevail on myself to commit such a weakness, there is that cursed Fanny in the way, whom the idiot—O how I hate and despise him!"—"She! a little ugly mynx," cries Slipslop; "leave her to me. I suppose your ladyship hath heard of Joseph's fitting with one of Mr. Didapper's servants about her; and his master hath ordered them to carry her away by force this evening. I'll take care they shall not want assistance. I was talking with this gentleman, who was below, just when your ladyship sent for me."—"Go back," says the Lady Booby, "this instant, for I expect Mr. Didapper will soon be going. Do all you can; for I am resolved this wench shall not be in our family: I will endeavour to return to the company; but let me know as soon as she is carried off." Slipslop went away; and her mistress began to arraign her own conduct in the following manner:—

"What am I doing? How do I suffer this passion to creep imperceptibly upon me? How many days are past since I could have submitted to ask myself the question?—Marry a footman! Distraction! Can I afterwards bear the eyes of my acquaintance? But I can retire from them; retire with one in whom I propose more happiness than the world without him can give me! Retire—to feed continually on beauties which my inflamed imagination sickens with eagerly gazing on; to

satisfy every appetite, every desire, with their utmost wish.
Ha! and do I doat thus on a footman? I despise, I detest my
passion.—Yet why? Is he not generous, gentle, kind?—Kind!
to whom? to the meanest wretch, a creature below my consideration. Doth he not—yes, he doth prefer her. Curse his
beauties, and the little low heart that possesses them; which
can basely descend to this despicable wench, and be ungratefully deaf to all the honours I do him. And can I then love
this monster? No, I will tear his image from my bosom, tread
on him, spurn him. I will have those pitiful charms, which
now I despise, mangled in my sight; for I will not suffer the
little jade I hate to riot in the beauties I contemn. No; though
I despise him myself, though I would spurn him from my feet,
was he to languish at them, no other should taste the happiness
I scorn. Why do I say happiness? To me it would be misery.
To sacrifice my reputation, my character, my rank in life, to
the indulgence of a mean and a vile appetite! How I detest
the thought! How much more exquisite is the pleasure resulting
from the reflection of virtue and prudence than the faint relish
of what flows from vice and folly! Whither did I suffer this
improper, this mad passion to hurry me, only by neglecting to
summon the aids of reason to my assistance? Reason, which
hath now set before me my desires in their proper colours, and
immediately helped me to expel them. Yes, I thank Heaven
and my pride, I have now perfectly conquered this unworthy
passion; and if there was no obstacle in its way, my pride would
disdain any pleasures which could be the consequence of so
base, so mean, so vulgar——" Slipslop returned at this instant
in a violent hurry, and with the utmost eagerness cryed out,
"O madam! I have strange news. Tom the footman is just
come from the George; where, it seems, Joseph and the rest of
them are a jinketting; and he says there is a strange man who
hath discovered that Fanny and Joseph are brother and sister."
—"How, Slipslop?" cries the lady, in a surprise.—"I had not
time, madam," cries Slipslop, "to enquire about particles, but
Tom says it is most certainly true."

This unexpected account entirely obliterated all those admirable reflections which the supreme power of reason had so
wisely made just before. In short, when despair, which had
more share in producing the resolutions of hatred we have seen
taken, began to retreat, the lady hesitated a moment, and then,
forgetting all the purport of her soliloquy, dismissed her woman
again, with orders to bid Tom attend her in the parlour, whither

she now hastened to acquaint Pamela with the news. Pamela said she could not believe it; for she had never heard that her mother had lost any child, or that she had ever had any more than Joseph and herself. The lady flew into a violent rage with her, and talked of upstarts and disowning relations who had so lately been on a level with her. Pamela made no answer; but her husband, taking up her cause, severely reprimanded his aunt for her behaviour to his wife: he told her, if it had been earlier in the evening she should not have staid a moment longer in her house; that he was convinced, if this young woman could be proved her sister, she would readily embrace her as such, and he himself would do the same. He then desired the fellow might be sent for, and the young woman with him, which Lady Booby immediately ordered; and, thinking proper to make some apology to Pamela for what she had said, it was readily accepted, and all things reconciled.

The pedlar now attended, as did Fanny and Joseph, who would not quit her; the parson likewise was induced, not only by curiosity, of which he had no small portion, but his duty, as he apprehended it, to follow them; for he continued all the way to exhort them, who were now breaking their hearts, to offer up thanksgivings, and be joyful for so miraculous an escape.

When they arrived at Booby-Hall they were presently called into the parlour, where the pedlar repeated the same story he had told before, and insisted on the truth of every circumstance; so that all who heard him were extremely well satisfied of the truth, except Pamela, who imagined, as she had never heard either of her parents mention such an accident, that it must be certainly false; and except the Lady Booby, who suspected the falsehood of the story from her ardent desire that it should be true; and Joseph, who feared its truth, from his earnest wishes that it might prove false.

Mr. Booby now desired them all to suspend their curiosity and absolute belief or disbelief till the next morning, when he expected old Mr. Andrews and his wife to fetch himself and Pamela home in his coach, and then they might be certain of certainly knowing the truth or falsehood of this relation; in which, he said, as there were many strong circumstances to induce their credit, so he could not perceive any interest the pedlar could have in inventing it, or in endeavouring to impose such a falsehood on them.

The Lady Booby, who was very little used to such company, entertained them all—viz. her nephew, his wife, her brother and sister, the beau, and the parson, with great good humour at her own table. As to the pedlar, she ordered him to be made as welcome as possible by her servants. All the company in the parlour, except the disappointed lovers, who sat sullen and silent, were full of mirth; for Mr. Booby had prevailed on Joseph to ask Mr. Didapper's pardon, with which he was perfectly satisfied. Many jokes passed between the beau and the parson, chiefly on each other's dress; these afforded much diversion to the company. Pamela chid her brother Joseph for the concern which he exprest at discovering a new sister. She said, if he loved Fanny as he ought, with a pure affection, he had no reason to lament being related to her.—Upon which Adams began to discourse on Platonic love; whence he made a quick transition to the joys in the next world, and concluded with strongly asserting that there was no such thing as pleasure in this. At which Pamela and her husband smiled on one another.

This happy pair proposing to retire (for no other person gave the least symptom of desiring rest), they all repaired to several beds provided for them in the same house; nor was Adams himself suffered to go home, it being a stormy night. Fanny indeed often begged she might go home with the parson; but her stay was so strongly insisted on, that she at last, by Joseph's advice, consented.

CHAPTER XIV

CONTAINING SEVERAL CURIOUS NIGHT-ADVENTURES, IN WHICH
MR. ADAMS FELL INTO MANY HAIR-BREADTH 'SCAPES, PARTLY
OWING TO HIS GOODNESS, AND PARTLY TO HIS INADVERTENCY

ABOUT an hour after they had all separated (it being now past three in the morning), beau Didapper, whose passion for Fanny permitted him not to close his eyes, but had employed his imagination in contrivances how to satisfy his desires, at last hit on a method by which he hoped to effect it. He had ordered his servant to bring him word where Fanny lay, and had received his information; he therefore arose, put on his breeches and nightgown, and stole softly along the gallery which led to her apartment; and, being come to the door, as he imagined it, he opened it with the least noise possible and entered the chamber. A savour now invaded his nostrils which he did not expect in the room of so sweet a young creature, and which might have probably had no good effect on a cooler lover. However, he groped out the bed with difficulty, for there was not a glimpse of light, and, opening the curtains, he whispered in Joseph's voice (for he was an excellent mimic), "Fanny, my angel! I am come to inform thee that I have discovered the falsehood of the story we last night heard. I am no longer thy brother, but thy lover; nor will I be delayed the enjoyment of thee one moment longer. You have sufficient assurances of my constancy not to doubt my marrying you, and it would be want of love to deny me the possession of thy charms."— So saying, he disencumbered himself from the little clothes he had on, and, leaping into bed, embraced his angel, as he conceived her, with great rapture. If he was surprised at receiving no answer, he was no less pleased to find his hug returned with equal ardour. He remained not long in this sweet confusion; for both he and his paramour presently discovered their error. Indeed it was no other than the accomplished Slipslop whom he had engaged; but, though she immediately knew the person whom she had mistaken for Joseph, he was at a loss to guess at the representative of Fanny. He had so little seen or taken notice of this gentlewoman, that light itself would have afforded him no assistance in his conjecture. Beau Didapper no sooner had perceived his mistake than he attempted to escape from the bed with much greater haste than he had made to it; but the watchful Slipslop prevented him. For that prudent woman, being disappointed of those delicious offerings which her fancy had promised her pleasure, resolved to make an immediate sacrifice to her virtue. Indeed she wanted an opportunity to heal some wounds, which her late conduct had, she feared, given her reputation; and, as she had a wonderful presence of mind, she conceived the person of the unfortunate beau to be luckily thrown in her way to restore her lady's opinion of her impregnable chastity. At that instant, therefore, when he offered to leap from the bed, she caught fast hold of his shirt, at the same time roaring out, "O thou villain! who hast attacked my chastity, and, I believe, ruined me in my sleep; I will swear a rape against thee, I will prosecute thee with the utmost vengeance." The beau attempted to get loose, but she held him fast, and when he struggled she cried out "Murder! murder! rape! robbery! ruin!" At which words, parson Adams, who lay in the next chamber, wakeful, and meditating on the pedlar's discovery, jumped out of bed, and, without staying to put a rag of clothes on, hastened into the apartment whence the cries proceeded. He made directly to the bed in the dark, where, laying hold of the beau's skin (for Slipslop had torn his shirt almost off), and finding his skin extremely soft, and hearing him in a low voice begging Slipslop to let him go, he no longer doubted but this was the young woman in danger of ravishing, and immediately falling on the bed, and laying hold on Slipslop's chin, where he found a rough beard, his belief was confirmed; he therefore rescued the beau, who presently made his escape, and then, turning towards Slipslop, received such a cuff on his chops, that, his wrath kindling instantly, he offered to return the favour so stoutly, that had poor Slipslop received the fist, which in the dark passed by her and fell on the pillow, she would most probably have given up the ghost. Adams, missing his blow, fell directly on Slipslop, who cuffed and scratched as well as she could; nor was he behindhand with her in his endeavours, but happily the darkness of the night befriended her. She then cried she was a woman; but Adams answered, she was rather the devil, and if she was he would grapple with him; and, being again irritated by another stroke on his chops, he gave her such a remembrance in the guts, that she began to roar loud enough to be heard all over the house. Adams then, seizing her by the hair (for her double-clout had fallen off in the scuffle), pinned her head down to the bolster, and then both called for lights together. The Lady Booby, who was as wakeful as any of her guests, had been alarmed from the beginning; and, being a woman of a bold spirit, she slipt on a nightgown, petticoat, and slippers, and taking a candle, which always burnt in her chamber, in her hand, she walked undauntedly to Slipslop's room; where she entered just at the instant as Adams had discovered, by the two mountains which Slipslop carried before her, that he was concerned with a female. He then concluded her to be a witch, and said he fancied those breasts gave suck to a legion of devils. Slipslop, seeing Lady Booby enter the room, cried help! or I am ravished, with a most audible voice: and Adams, perceiving the light, turned hastily, and saw the lady (as she did him) just as she came to the feet of the bed; nor did her modesty, when she found the naked condition of Adams, suffer her to approach farther. She then began to revile the parson as the wickedest of all men, and particularly railed at his impudence in chusing her house for the scene of his debaucheries, and her own woman for the object of his bestiality. Poor Adams had before discovered the countenance of his bedfellow, and, now first recollecting he was naked, he was no less confounded than Lady Booby herself, and immediately whipt under the bedclothes, whence the chaste Slipslop endeavoured in vain to shut him out. Then putting forth his head, on which, by way of ornament, he wore a flannel nightcap, he protested his innocence, and asked ten thousand pardons of Mrs. Slipslop for the blows he had struck her, vowing he had mistaken her for a witch. Lady Booby, then casting her eyes on the ground, observed something sparkle with great lustre, which, when she had taken it up, appeared to be a very fine pair of diamond buttons for the sleeves. A little farther she saw lie the sleeve itself of a shirt with laced ruffles. "Heyday!" says she, "what is the meaning of this?" "O, madam," says Slipslop, "I don't know what hath happened, I have been so terrified. Here may have been a dozen men in the room." "To whom belongs this laced shirt and jewels?" says the lady. "Undoubtedly," cries the parson, "to the young gentleman whom I mistook for a woman on coming into the room, whence proceeded all the subsequent mistakes; for if I had suspected him for a man, I would have seized him, had he been another Hercules, though, indeed, he seems rather to resemble Hylas." He then gave an account of the reason of his rising from bed, and the rest, till the lady came into the room; at which, and the figures of Slipslop and her gallant, whose heads only were visible at the opposite corners of the bed, she could not refrain from laughter; nor did Slipslop persist in accusing the parson of any motions towards a rape. The lady therefore desired him to return to his bed as soon as she was departed, and then ordering Slipslop to rise and attend her in her own room, she returned herself thither. When she was gone, Adams renewed his petitions for pardon to Mrs. Slipslop, who, with a most Christian temper, not only forgave, but began to move with much courtesy towards him, which he taking as a hint to begin, immediately quitted the bed, and made the best of his way towards his own; but unluckily, instead of turning to the right, he turned to the left, and went to the apartment where Fanny lay, who (as the reader may remember) had not slept a wink the preceding night, and who was so hagged out with what had happened to her in the day, that, notwithstanding all thoughts of her Joseph, she was fallen into so profound a sleep, that all the noise in the adjoining room had not been able to disturb her. Adams groped out the bed, and, turning the clothes down softly, a custom Mrs. Adams had long accustomed him to, crept in, and deposited his carcase on the bed-post, a place which that good woman had always assigned him.

As the cat or lap-dog of some lovely nymph, for whom ten thousand lovers languish, lies quietly by the side of the charming maid, and, ignorant of the scene of delight on which they repose, meditates the future capture of a mouse, or surprisal of a plate of bread and butter: so Adams lay by the side of Fanny, ignorant of the paradise to which he was so near; nor could the emanation of sweets which flowed from her breath overpower the fumes of tobacco which played in the parson's nostrils.   And now sleep had not overtaken the good man, when Joseph, who had secretly appointed Fanny to come to her at the break of day, rapped softly at the chamber-door, which when he had repeated twice, Adams cryed, "Come in, whoever you are."   Joseph thought he had mistaken the door, though she had given him the most exact directions; however, knowing his friend's voice, he opened it, and saw some female vestments lying on a chair.   Fanny waking at the same instant, and stretching out her hand on Adams's beard, she cried out,—"O heavens! where am I?" "Bless me! where am I?" said the parson.   Then Fanny screamed, Adams leapt out of bed, and Joseph stood, as the tragedians call it, like the statue of Surprise.   "How came she into my room?" cryed Adams.   "How came you into hers?" cryed Joseph, in an astonishment.   "I know nothing of the matter," answered Adams, "but that she is a vestal for me. As I am a Christian, I know not whether she is a man or woman. He is an infidel who doth not believe in witchcraft.   They as surely exist now as in the days of Saul.   My clothes are bewitched away too, and Fanny's brought into their place."   For he still insisted he was in his own apartment; but Fanny denied it vehemently, and said his attempting to persuade Joseph of such a falsehood convinced her of his wicked designs.   "How!" said Joseph in a rage, "hath he offered any rudeness to you?" She answered—She could not accuse him of any more than villanously stealing to bed to her, which she thought rudeness sufficient, and what no man would do without a wicked intention.

Joseph's great opinion of Adams was not easily to be staggered, and when he heard from Fanny that no harm had happened he grew a little cooler; yet still he was confounded, and, as he knew the house, and that the women's apartments were on this side Mrs. Slipslop's room, and the men's on the other, he was convinced that he was in Fanny's chamber.   Assuring Adams therefore of this truth, he begged him to give some account how he came there. Adams then, standing in his shirt, which did not offend Fanny, as the curtains of the bed were drawn, related all that had happened; and when he had ended Joseph told him,—It was plain he had mistaken by turning to the right instead of the left. "Odso!" cries Adams, "that's true: as sure as sixpence, you have hit on the very thing." He then traversed the room, rubbing his hands, and begged Fanny's pardon, assuring her he did not know whether she was man or woman. That innocent creature firmly believing all he said, told him she was no longer angry, and begged Joseph to conduct him into his own apartment, where he should stay himself till she had put her clothes on. Joseph and Adams accordingly departed, and the latter soon was convinced of the mistake he had committed; however, whilst he was dressing himself, he often asserted he believed in the power of witchcraft notwithstanding, and did not see how a Christian could deny it.

CHAPTER XV

THE ARRIVAL OF GAFFAR AND GAMMAR ANDREWS, WITH ANOTHER
    PERSON NOT MUCH EXPECTED; AND A PERFECT SOLUTION
    OF THE DIFFICULTIES RAISED BY THE PEDLAR

As soon as Fanny was drest Joseph returned to her, and they had a long conversation together, the conclusion of which was, that, if they found themselves to be really brother and sister, they vowed a perpetual celibacy, and to live together all their days, and indulge a Platonic friendship for each other.

The company were all very merry at breakfast, and Joseph and Fanny rather more chearful than the preceding night. The Lady Booby produced the diamond button, which the beau most readily owned, and alledged that he was very subject to walk in his sleep. Indeed, he was far from being ashamed of his amour, and rather endeavoured to insinuate that more than was really true had passed between him and the fair Slipslop.

Their tea was scarce over when news came of the arrival of old Mr. Andrews and his wife. They were immediately introduced, and kindly received by the Lady Booby, whose heart went now pit-a-pat, as did those of Joseph and Fanny. They felt, perhaps, little less anxiety in this interval than Œdipus himself, whilst his fate was revealing.

Mr. Booby first opened the cause by informing the old gentleman that he had a child in the company more than he knew of, and, taking Fanny by the hand, told him, this was that daughter of his who had been stolen away by gypsies in her infancy. Mr. Andrews, after expressing some astonishment, assured his honour that he had never lost a daughter by gypsies, nor ever had any other children than Joseph and Pamela. These words were a cordial to the two lovers; but had a different effect on Lady Booby. She ordered the pedlar to be called, who recounted his story as he had done before. At the end of which, old Mrs. Andrews, running to Fanny, embraced her, crying out, "She is, she is my child!" The company were all amazed at this disagreement between the man and his wife; and the blood had now forsaken the cheeks of the lovers, when the old woman, turning to her husband, who was more surprised than all the rest, and having a little recovered her own spirits, delivered herself as follows: "You may remember, my dear, when you went a serjeant to Gibraltar, you left me big with child; you stayed abroad, you know, upwards of three years. In your absence I was brought to bed, I verily believe, of this daughter, whom I am sure I have reason to remember, for I suckled her at this very breast till the day she was stolen from me. One afternoon, when the child was about a year, or a year and a half old, or thereabouts, two gypsy-women came to the door and offered to tell my fortune. One of them had a child in her lap. I showed them my hand, and desired to know if you was ever to come home again, which I remember as well as if it was but yesterday: they faithfully promised me you should —I left the girl in the cradle and went to draw them a cup of liquor, the best I had: when I returned with the pot (I am sure I was not absent longer than whilst I am telling it to you) the women were gone. I was afraid they had stolen something, and looked and looked, but to no purpose, and, Heaven knows, I had very little for them to steal. At last, hearing the child cry in the cradle, I went to take it up—but, O the living! how was I surprised to find, instead of my own girl that I had put into the cradle, who was as fine a fat thriving child as you shall see in a summer's day, a poor sickly boy, that did not seem to have an hour to live. I ran out, pulling my hair off and crying like any mad after the women, but never could hear a word of them from that day to this. When I came back the poor infant (which is our Joseph there, as stout as he now stands) lifted up its eyes upon me so piteously, that, to be sure, not-withstanding my passion, I could not find in my heart to do it any mischief. A neighbour of mine, happening to come in at the same time, and hearing the case, advised me to take care of this poor child, and God would perhaps one day restore me my own. Upon which I took the child up, and suckled it to be sure, all the world as if it had been born of my own natural body; and as true as I am alive, in a little time I loved the boy all to nothing as if it had been my own girl.—Well, as I was saying, times growing very hard, I having two children and nothing but my own work, which was little enough, God knows, to maintain them, was obliged to ask relief of the parish; but, instead of giving it me, they removed me, by justices' warrants, fifteen miles, to the place where I now live, where I had not been long settled before you came home. Joseph (for that was the name I gave him myself—the Lord knows whether he was baptized or no, or by what name), Joseph, I say, seemed to me about five years old when you returned; for I believe he is two or three years older than our daughter here (for I am thoroughly convinced she is the same); and when you saw him you said he was a chopping boy, without ever minding his age; and so I, seeing you did not suspect anything of the matter, thought I might e'en as well keep it to myself, for fear you should not love him as well as I did. And all this is veritably true, and I will take my oath of it before any justice in the kingdom."

The pedlar, who had been summoned by the order of Lady Booby, listened with the utmost attention to Gammar Andrews's story; and, when she had finished, asked her if the supposititious child had no mark on its breast? To which she answered, "Yes, he had as fine a strawberry as ever grew in a garden." This Joseph acknowledged, and, unbuttoning his coat, at the intercession of the company, showed to them. "Well," says Gaffar Andrews, who was a comical sly old fellow, and very likely desired to have no more children than he could keep, "you have proved, I think, very plainly, that this boy doth not belong to us; but how are you certain that the girl is ours?" The parson then brought the pedlar forward, and desired him to repeat the story which he had communicated to him the preceding day at the ale-house; which he complied with, and related what the reader, as well as Mr. Adams, hath seen before. He then confirmed, from his wife's report, all the circumstances of the exchange, and of the strawberry on Joseph's breast. At the repetition of the word strawberry, Adams, who had seen it without any emotion, started and cried, "Bless me! something comes into my head." But before he had time to bring anything out a servant called him forth. When he was gone the pedlar assured Joseph that his parents were persons of much greater circumstances than those he had hitherto mistaken for such; for that he had been stolen from a gentleman's house by those whom they call gypsies, and had been kept by them during a whole year, when, looking on him as in a dying condition, they had exchanged him for the other healthier child, in the manner before related. He said, As to the name of his father, his wife had either never known or forgot it; but that she had acquainted him he lived about forty miles from the place where the exchange had been made, and which way, promising to spare no pains in endeavouring with him to discover the place.

But Fortune, which seldom doth good or ill, or makes men happy or miserable, by halves, resolved to spare him this labour. The reader may please to recollect that Mr. Wilson had intended a journey to the west, in which he was to pass through Mr. Adams's parish, and had promised to call on him. He was now arrived at the Lady Booby's gates for that purpose, being directed thither from the parson's house, and had sent in the servant whom we have above seen call Mr. Adams forth. This had no sooner mentioned the discovery of a stolen child, and had uttered the word strawberry, than Mr. Wilson, with wildness in his looks, and the utmost eagerness in his words, begged to be showed into the room, where he entered without the least regard to any of the company but Joseph, and, embracing him with a complexion all pale and trembling, desired to see the mark on his breast; the parson followed him capering, rubbing his hands, and crying out, *Hic est quem quæris; inventus est, &c.* Joseph complied with the request of Mr. Wilson, who no sooner saw the mark than, abandoning himself to the most extravagant rapture of passion, he embraced Joseph with inexpressible ecstasy, and cried out in tears of joy, "I have discovered my son, I have him again in my arms!" Joseph was not sufficiently apprised yet to taste the same delight with his father (for so in reality he was), however, he returned some warmth to his embraces: but he no sooner perceived, from his father's account, the agreement of every circumstance, of person, time, and place, than he threw himself at his feet, and, embracing his knees, with tears begged his blessing, which was given with much affection, and received with such respect, mixed with such tenderness on both sides, that it affected all present; but none so much as Lady Booby, who left the room in an agony, which was but too much perceived, and not very charitably accounted for by some of the company.

CHAPTER XVI

BEING THE LAST, IN WHICH THIS TRUE HISTORY IS BROUGHT TO A HAPPY CONCLUSION

FANNY was very little behind her Joseph in the duty she exprest towards her parents, and the joy she evidenced in discovering them. Gammar Andrews kissed her, and said, She was heartily glad to see her; but for her part, she could never love any one better than Joseph. Gaffar Andrews testified no remarkable emotion: he blessed and kissed her, but complained bitterly that he wanted his pipe, not having had a whiff that morning.

Mr. Booby, who knew nothing of his aunt's fondness, imputed her abrupt departure to her pride, and disdain of the family into which he was married; he was therefore desirous to be gone with the utmost celerity; and now, having congratulated Mr. Wilson and Joseph on the discovery, he saluted Fanny, called her sister, and introduced her as such to Pamela, who behaved with great decency on the occasion.

He now sent a message to his aunt, who returned that she wished him a good journey, but was too disordered to see any company: he therefore prepared to set out, having invited Mr. Wilson to his house; and Pamela and Joseph both so insisted on his complying, that he at last consented, having first obtained a messenger from Mr. Booby to acquaint his wife with the news; which, as he knew it would render her completely happy, he could not prevail on himself to delay a moment in acquainting her with.

The company were ranged in this manner: the two old people, with their two daughters, rode in the coach; the squire, Mr. Wilson, Joseph, parson Adams, and the pedlar, proceeded on horseback.

In their way, Joseph informed his father of his intended match with Fanny; to which, though he expressed some reluctance at first, on the eagerness of his son's instances he consented; saying, if she was so good a creature as she appeared, and he described her, he thought the disadvantages of birth and fortune might be compensated. He however insisted on the match being deferred till he had seen his mother; in which, Joseph perceiving him positive, with great duty obeyed him, to the great delight of parson Adams, who by these means saw an opportunity of fulfilling the Church forms, and marrying his parishioners without a licence.

Mr. Adams, greatly exulting on this occasion (for such ceremonies were matters of no small moment with him), accidentally gave spurs to his horse, which the generous beast disdaining— for he was of high mettle, and had been used to more expert riders than the gentleman who at present bestrode him, for whose horsemanship he had perhaps some contempt—immediately ran away full speed, and played so many antic tricks that he tumbled the parson from his back; which Joseph perceiving, came to his relief.

This accident afforded infinite merriment to the servants, and no less frighted poor Fanny, who beheld him as he passed by the coach; but the mirth of the one and terror of the other were soon determined, when the parson declared he had received no damage.

The horse having freed himself from his unworthy rider, as he probably thought him, proceeded to make the best of his way; but was stopped by a gentleman and his servants, who were travelling the opposite way, and were now at a little distance from the coach. They soon met; and as one of the servants delivered Adams his horse, his master hailed him, and Adams, looking up, presently recollected he was the justice of peace before whom he and Fanny had made their appearance. The parson presently saluted him very kindly; and the justice informed him that he had found the fellow who attempted to swear against him and the young woman the very next day, and had committed him to Salisbury gaol, where he was charged with many robberies.

Many compliments having passed between the parson and the justice, the latter proceeded on his journey; and the former, having with some disdain refused Joseph's offer of changing horses, and declared he was as able a horseman as any in the kingdom, remounted his beast; and now the company again proceeded, and happily arrived at their journey's end, Mr. Adams, by good luck, rather than by good riding, escaping a second fall.

The company, arriving at Mr. Booby's house, were all received by him in the most courteous and entertained in the most splendid manner, after the custom of the old English hospitality, which is still preserved in some very few families in the remote parts of England. They all passed that day with the utmost satisfaction; it being perhaps impossible to find any set of people more solidly and sincerely happy. Joseph and Fanny found means to be alone upwards of two hours, which were the shortest but the sweetest imaginable.

In the morning Mr. Wilson proposed to his son to make a visit with him to his mother; which, notwithstanding his dutiful inclinations, and a longing desire he had to see her, a little concerned him, as he must be obliged to leave his Fanny; but the goodness of Mr. Booby relieved him; for he proposed to send his own coach and six for Mrs. Wilson, whom Pamela so very earnestly invited, that Mr. Wilson at length agreed with the entreaties of Mr. Booby and Joseph, and suffered the coach to go empty for his wife.

On Saturday night the coach returned with Mrs. Wilson, who added one more to this happy assembly. The reader may imagine much better and quicker too than I can describe the many embraces and tears of joy which succeeded her arrival. It is sufficient to say she was easily prevailed with to follow her husband's example in consenting to the match.

On Sunday Mr. Adams performed the service at the squire's parish church, the curate of which very kindly exchanged duty, and rode twenty miles to the Lady Booby's parish so to do; being particularly charged not to omit publishing the banns, being the third and last time.

At length the happy day arrived which was to put Joseph in the possession of all his wishes. He arose, and drest himself in a neat but plain suit of Mr. Booby's, which exactly fitted him; for he refused all finery; as did Fanny likewise, who could be prevailed on by Pamela to attire herself in nothing richer than a white dimity nightgown. Her shift indeed, which Pamela presented her, was of the finest kind, and had an edging of lace round the bosom. She likewise equipped her with a pair of fine white thread stockings, which were all she would accept; for she wore one of her own short round-eared caps, and over it a little straw hat, lined with cherry-coloured silk, and tied with a cherry-coloured ribbon. In this dress she came forth from her chamber, blushing and breathing sweets; and was by Joseph, whose eyes sparkled fire, led to church, the whole family attending, where Mr. Adams performed the ceremony; at which nothing was so remarkable as the extraordinary and unaffected modesty of Fanny. unless the true

Christian piety of Adams, who publickly rebuked Mr. Booby
and Pamela for laughing in so sacred a place, and on so
solemn an occasion.   Our parson would have done no less to
the highest prince on earth; for, though he paid all submission
and deference to his superiors in other matters, where the
least spice of religion intervened he immediately lost all respect of persons.   It was his maxim, that he was a servant of
the Highest, and could not, without departing from his duty,
give up the least article of his honour or of his cause to the
greatest earthly potentate.   Indeed, he always asserted that
Mr. Adams at church with his surplice on, and Mr. Adams
without that ornament in any other place, were two very
different persons.

When the church rites were over Joseph led his blooming
bride back to Mr. Booby's (for the distance was so very little
they did not think proper to use a coach); the whole company
attended them likewise on foot; and now a most magnificent
entertainment was provided, at which parson Adams demon-
strated an appetite surprising as well as surpassing every one
present.   Indeed the only persons who betrayed any deficiency
on this occasion were those on whose account the feast was
provided.   They pampered their imaginations with the much
more exquisite repast which the approach of night promised
them; the thoughts of which filled both their minds, though
with different sensations; the one all desire, while the other
had her wishes tempered with fears.

At length, after a day passed with the utmost merriment,
corrected by the strictest decency, in which, however, parson
Adams, being well filled with ale and pudding, had given a
loose to more facetiousness than was usual to him, the happy,
the blest moment arrived when Fanny retired with her mother,
her mother-in-law, and her sister.

She was soon undrest; for she had no jewels to deposit in
their caskets, nor fine laces to fold with the nicest exactness.
Undressing to her was properly discovering, not putting off,
ornaments; for, as all her charms were the gifts of nature, she
could divest herself of none.   How, reader, shall I give thee an
adequate idea of this lovely young creature? the bloom of roses
and lilies might a little illustrate her complexion, or their smell
her sweetness; but to comprehend her entirely, conceive youth,
health, bloom, neatness, and innocence, in her bridal bed; conceive all these in their utmost perfection, and you may place
the charming Fanny's picture before your eyes.

Joseph no sooner heard she was in bed than he fled with the utmost eagerness to her. A minute carried him into her arms, where we shall leave this happy couple to enjoy the private rewards of their constancy; rewards so great and sweet, that I apprehend Joseph neither envied the noblest duke, nor Fanny the finest duchess, that night.

The third day Mr. Wilson and his wife, with their son and daughter, returned home; where they now live together in a state of bliss scarce ever equalled. Mr. Booby hath, with unprecedented generosity, given Fanny a fortune of two thousand pounds, which Joseph hath laid out in a little estate in the same parish with his father, which he now occupies (his father having stocked it for him); and Fanny presides with most excellent management in his dairy; where, however, she is not at present very able to bustle much, being, as Mr. Wilson informs me in his last letter, extremely big with her first child.

Mr. Booby hath presented Mr. Adams with a living of one hundred and thirty pounds a year. He at first refused it, resolving not to quit his parishioners, with whom he had lived so long; but, on recollecting he might keep a curate at this living, he hath been lately inducted into it.

The pedlar, besides several handsome presents, both from Mr. Wilson and Mr. Booby, is, by the latter's interest, made an exciseman; a trust which he discharges with such justice, that he is greatly beloved in his neighbourhood.

As for the Lady Booby, she returned to London in a few days, where a young captain of dragoons, together with eternal parties at cards, soon obliterated the memory of Joseph.

Joseph remains blest with his Fanny, whom he doats on with the utmost tenderness, which is all returned on her side. The happiness of this couple is a perpetual fountain of pleasure to their fond parents; and, what is particularly remarkable, he declares he will imitate them in their retirement, nor will be prevailed on by any booksellers, or their authors, to make his appearance in high life.

BIOGRAPHY

xter, Richard (1615–91).
THE AUTOBIOGRAPHY OF RICHARD BAXTER. 868
swell, James (1740–95). *See* Johnson.
ntë, Charlotte (1816–55).
LIFE, 1857. By *Mrs Gaskell*. Introduction by *May Sinclair*. (*See also* Fiction.) 318
ns, Robert (1759–96).
LIFE, 1828. By *J. G. Lockhart* (1794–1854). With Introduction by *Prof. James Kinsley*, M.A., PH.D. (*See also* Poetry and Drama.) 156
on, Lord (1788–1824).
LETTERS. Edited by *R. G. Howarth*, B.LITT., and with an Introduction by *André Maurois*. (*See also* Poetry and Drama.) 931
ston, William (1845–1926).
A CHILD'S BOOK OF SAINTS, 1898. (*See also* Essays.) 61
lini, Benvenuto (1500–71).
THE LIFE OF BENVENUTO CELLINI, written by himself. Translated by *Anne Macdonell*. Introduction by *William Gaunt*. 51
wper, William (1731–1800).
SELECTED LETTERS. Edited, with Introduction, by *W. Hadley*, M.A. 774
(*See also* Poetry and Drama.)
kens, Charles (1812–70).
LIFE, 1874. By *John Forster* (1812–76). Introduction by *G. K. Chesterton*. 2 vols.
(*See also* Fiction.) 781–2
elyn, John (1620–1706).
DIARY. Edited by *William Bray*, 1819. Intro. by *G. W. E. Russell*. 2 vols. 220–1
x, George (1624–91).
JOURNAL, 1694. Revised by *Norman Penney*, with Account of Fox's last years. Introduction by *Rufus M. Jones*. 754
anklin, Benjamin (1706–90).
AUTOBIOGRAPHY, 1817. With Introduction and Account of Franklin's later life by *W. Macdonald*. Reset new edition (1949), with a newly compiled Index. 316
ethe, Johann Wolfgang von (1749–1832).
LIFE, 1855. By *G. H. Lewes* (1817–78). Introduction by *Havelock Ellis*. Index.
(*See also* Poetry and Drama.) 269
dson, William Henry (1841–1922).
FAR AWAY AND LONG AGO, 1918. Intro. by *John Galsworthy*. 956
nson, Samuel (1709–84).
LIVES OF THE ENGLISH POETS, 1781. Introduction by *Mrs L. Archer-Hind*. 2 vols.
(*See also* Essays, Fiction.) 770–1
BOSWELL'S LIFE OF JOHNSON, 1791. A new edition (1949), with Introduction by *S. C. Roberts*, M.A., LL.D., and a 30-page Index by Alan Dent. 2 vols. 1–2
ats, John (1795–1821).
LIFE AND LETTERS, 1848. By *Lord Houghton* (1809–85). Introduction by *Robert Lynd*. Note on the letters by Lewis Gibbs. (*See also* Poetry and Drama.) 801
mb, Charles (1775–1834).
LETTERS. New edition (1945) arranged from the Complete Annotated Edition of the Letters. 2 vols. (*See also* Essays and Belles-Lettres, Fiction.) 342–3
poleon Buonaparte (1769–1821).
HISTORY OF NAPOLEON BUONAPARTE, 1829. By *J. G. Lockhart* (1794–1854). 3
(*See also* Essays and Belles-Lettres.)
son, Horatio, Viscount (1758–1805).
LIFE, 1813. By *Robert Southey* (1774–1843). (*See also* Essays.) 52
tram, General Sir James (1803–63), 'the Bayard of India.'
LIFE, 1903. Deals with important passages in the history of India in the nineteenth century. By *L. J. Trotter* (1827–1912). 396
pys, Samuel (1633–1703).
DIARY. Newly edited (1953), with modernized spelling, by *John Warrington*, from the edition of Mynors Bright (1875–9). 3 vols. 53–5
tarch (46?–120).
LIVES OF THE NOBLE GREEKS AND ROMANS. Dryden's edition, 1683–6. Revised, with Introduction, by *A. H. Clough* (1819–61). 3 vols. 407–9
usseau, Jean Jacques (1712–78).
CONFESSIONS, 1782. 2 vols. Complete and unabridged English translation. New Introduction by *Prof. R. Niklaus*, B.A., PH.D., of Exeter University. 859–60
(*See also* Essays, Theology and Philosophy.)
ott, Sir Walter (1771–1832).
LOCKHART'S LIFE OF SCOTT. An abridgement by *J. G. Lockhart* himself from the original 7 volumes. New Introduction by *W. M. Parker*, M.A. 39

Swift, Jonathan (1667–1745).
> JOURNAL TO STELLA, 1710–13. Deciphered by *J. K. Moorhead*. Introduction by
> *Walter Scott*. Sir Walter Scott's essay 'Swift, Stella and Vanessa' is included.
> *(See also* Essays, Ficti)

Walpole, Horace (1717–97).
> SELECTED LETTERS. Edited, with Introduction, by *W. Hadley*, M.A.

Wellington, Arthur Wellesley, Duke of (1769–1852).
> LIFE, 1862. By *G. R. Gleig* (1796–1888).

CLASSICAL

Aeschylus (525–455 B.C.).
> PLAYS. Translated into English Verse by *G. M. Cookson*. New Introduction
> *John Warrington*, and notes on each play.

Aristophanes (450?–385? B.C.).
> THE COMEDIES. Translated by *J. Hookham Frere*, etc. Edited, with Introduct
> by *J. P. Maine* and *J. H. Frere*. 2 vols.   (*Vol. 1 temporarily out of print.*)

Aristotle (384–322 B.C.).
> POLITICS and THE ATHENIAN CONSTITUTION. Edited and translated by *J*
> *Warrington*.
> METAPHYSICS. Edited and translated by *John Warrington*. Introduction by
> *David Ross*, K.B.E., M.A., D.LITT.

Caesar, Julius (102?–44 B.C.).
> WAR COMMENTARIES. 'The Gallic Wars' and 'The Civil War.' Newly transla
> and edited by *John Warrington*.

Cicero, Marcus Tullius (106–43 B.C.).
> THE OFFICES (translated by *Thomas Cockman*, 1699); LAELIUS, ON FRIENDS
> CATO, ON OLD AGE; AND SELECT LETTERS (translated by *W. Melmoth*, 1753). W
> Note on Cicero's Character by De Quincey. Introduction by *John Warrington*.

Demetrius (fl. late first century A.D.). (*See under* Aristotle.)

Demosthenes (384–322 B.C.). (*See under* Oratory, p. 11.)

Epictetus (*b. c.* A.D. 60).
> MORAL DISCOURSES. THE ENCHIRIDION AND FRAGMENTS. Translated by *Eliza*
> *Carter* (1717–1806). Edited by *W. H. D. Rouse*, M.A.

Euripides (484?–407 B.C.).
> PLAYS. New Introduction by *John Warrington*. Translated by *A. S. Way*, D.I
> 2 vols.   63,

Herodotus (484?–425? B.C.).
> HISTORY. The 'History' deals with the period covering the Persian invasio
> Greece, 492–480 B.C. Rawlinson's Translation, additional notes and Introduct
> by *E. H. Blakeney*. 2 vols. (*Vol. II temporarily out of print.*)   40

Homer (? ninth century B.C.).
> ILIAD. New verse translation by *S. O. Andrew* and *Michael Oakley*.
> ODYSSEY. The new verse translation (first published 1953) by *S. O. And*
> Introduction by *John Warrington*.

Juvenal (*c.* A.D. 50–*c.* 130).
> SATIRES; with THE SATIRES OF PERSIUS. Introduction by *Prof. H. J. Rose*, N
> F.B.A. William Gifford Translation, 1802. Revised by *John Warrington*.

Lucretius (*c.* 99?–50? B.C.).
> ON THE NATURE OF THINGS. Metrical Translation by *W. E. Leonard*.

Ovid (43 B.C.–A.D. 18).
> SELECTED WORKS. Chosen by *J. C.* and *M. J. Thornton*. Selections from
> *Metamorphoses*, *Heroical Epistles*, the *Festivals*, the *Ibis*, and his epistles writte
> exile: also his *Art of Love*.

Persius (34–62). See Juvenal.

Plato (427–347 B.C.).
> THE REPUBLIC. Translated, with an Introduction, by *A. D. Lindsay*, C.B.E., L
> The greatest achievement of the Greek intellect in philosophy.
> SOCRATIC DISCOURSES OF PLATO AND XENOPHON. Introduction by *A. D. Lind*
> C.B.E., LL.D.
> THE LAWS. The last of Plato's dialogues is here printed in the A. E. Taylor (18
> 1945) Translation.

Sophocles (496?–406 B.C.).
> DRAMAS. This volume contains the seven surviving dramas.

Thucydides (*c.* 460–401 B.C.).
> HISTORY OF THE PELOPONNESIAN WAR. Translation by *Richard Crawley*. In
> duction by *John Warrington*. Index and five plans.

Virgil (70–19 B.C.).
> AENEID. Verse translation by *Michael Oakley*. Introduction by *E. M. Forster*.
> ECLOGUES AND GEORGICS. Verse Translation by *T. F. Royds*. The 'Eclogues' w
> inspired by Theocritus; the 'Georgics' describe a countryman's life.

Xenophon (430?–360? B.C.). (*See under* Plato.)

ESSAYS AND BELLES-LETTRES

athology of English Prose, from Bede to Stevenson. 675
acon, Francis, Lord Verulam (1561–1626).
    Essays, 1597–1626. Introduction by *Oliphant Smeaton*. Index of Quotations and Foreign Phrases and Glossary. (*See also* Theology and Philosophy.) 10
agehot, Walter (1826–77).
    Literary Studies, 1879. Introduction by *George Sampson*. 2 vols. 520–1
alloc, Hilaire (1870–1953).
    Stories, Essays and Poems. Edited with Introduction by *J. B. Morton*, c.b.e., the volume now contains a new selection from the *Sonnets*, *Verses* and celebrated *Epigrams*. 948
arke, Edmund (1729–97).
    Reflections on the Revolution in France (1790) and Other Essays. Introduction and Notes by *A. J. Grieve*, m.a. (*See also* Oratory.) 460
anton, William (1845–1926).
    The Invisible Playmate, 1894; W. V., Her Book, 1896; and In Memory of W. V., 1901. (*See also* Biography.) 566
arlyle, Thomas (1795–1881).
    Essays. Introduction by *J. R. Lowell*. 2 vols. Essays on men and affairs. 703–4
    Past and Present, 1843. New Introduction by *Douglas Jerrold*. 608
    Sartor Resartus, 1838; and Heroes and Hero-Worship, 1841. (*See also* History.) 278
astiglione, Baldassare (1478–1529).
    The Book of the Courtier, 1528. *Sir Thomas Hoby's* Translation, 1561. Introduction by *W. H. D. Rouse* and Notes by *Prof. W. B. Drayton Henderson*. 807
antury. A Century of English Essays, from Caxton to Belloc. 653
aesterfield, Philip Dormer Stanhope, Earl of (1694–1773).
    Letters to his Son; and Others. Introduction by *Prof. R. K. Root*. 823
aesterton, Gilbert Keith (1874–1936).
    Stories, Essays and Poems. Introduction by *Maisie Ward*. An 'omnibus' volume including four 'Father Brown' stories. 913
aleridge, Samuel Taylor (1772–1834).
    Biographia Literaria, 1817. Edited with a new Introduction by *George Watson*, m.a. Coleridge described the work as 'sketches of my literary life and opinions.' 11
    Shakespearean Criticism, 1849. Edited with a long Introduction by *Prof. T. M. Raysor* (1960), a distinguished Coleridge scholar of the University of Nebraska. 2 vols. (*See also* Poetry and Drama.) 162, 183
a la Mare, Walter (1873–1956).
    Stories, Essays and Poems. An anthology arranged by *Mildred Bozman*. 940
a Quincey, Thomas (1785–1859).
    Confessions of an English Opium-eater, 1822. Edited with Introduction by *Prof. J. E. Jordan* (1960). 223
akermann, Johann Peter (1792–1854).
    Conversations with Goethe, 1836–8. Translated by *John Oxenford*, 1850. Edited by *J. K. Moorhead*, with Introduction by *Havelock Ellis*. 851
    (*See also* Poetry and Drama, Biography.)
amerson, Ralph Waldo (1803–82).
    Essays, 1841–4. New Introduction by *Prof. Sherman Paul*. 12
aorio, John (1553?–1625). (*See* Montaigne.)
afillan, George (1813–78).
    A Gallery of Literary Portraits, 1845–54. 348
aay, Thomas (1716–71).
    Essays. (*See* Poetry.)
aamilton, Alexander (1757–1804), and Others.
    The Federalist, or the New Constitution, 1787–8. Introduction by *Prof. W. J. Ashley*. 519
aazlitt, William (1778–1830).
    Lectures on the English Comic Writers, 1819; and Miscellaneous Essays. Introduction by *W. E. Henley*. 411
    Lectures on the English Poets, 1818; and The Spirit of the Age, 1825. Introduction by *Catherine Macdonald Maclean*, m.a., d.litt., f.r.s.l. 459
    The Round Table and Characters of Shakespear's Plays, 1817–18. New Introduction by *Catherine Macdonald Maclean*. 65
    Table Talk, 1821–2, 1824. New Introduction by *Catherine Macdonald Maclean*. 321
aolmes, Oliver Wendell (1809–94).
    The Autocrat of the Breakfast-table, 1858. Introduction by *Van Wyck Brooks*. 66
aunt, Leigh (1784–1859).
    Selected Essays. 78 essays with Introduction by *J. B. Priestley*. 829
auxley, Aldous Leonard (*b.* 1894).
    Stories, Essays and Poems. 935
ahnson, Samuel (1709–84).
    The Rambler. Introduction by *S. C. Roberts*. (*See also* Biography, Fiction.) 994

Lamb, Charles (1775–1834).
    ESSAYS OF ELIA AND LAST ESSAYS OF ELIA, 1823–33. Introduction by *Augus*
    Birrell. Includes the first and the last Essays of Elia.
                             (See also Biography, Ficti◖
Landor, Walter Savage (1775–1864).
    IMAGINARY CONVERSATIONS, AND POEMS, 1824–9, 1853. Edited, with Introducti◖
    by *Havelock Ellis.*
Lawrence, David Herbert (1885–1930).
    STORIES, ESSAYS AND POEMS. Selected by *Desmond Hawkins.* Poetry, Essa
    Travel Sketches and Letters.
                                    (See also Ficti◖
Locke, John (1632–1704).
    AN ESSAY CONCERNING HUMAN UNDERSTANDING, 1690. Abridged and edited
    Raymond Wilburn, presenting the whole sweep of the work.
                         (See also Theology and Philosop◖
Lynd, Robert (1879–1949).
    ESSAYS ON LIFE AND LITERATURE. Introduction by *Desmond MacCarthy.*
Macaulay, Thomas Babington, Lord (1800–59).
    CRITICAL AND HISTORICAL ESSAYS, 1843. New Introduction by *Douglas Jerr*
    2 vols.   22
    MISCELLANEOUS ESSAYS, 1823–59; LAYS OF ANCIENT ROME, 1842; and MISC
    LANEOUS POEMS, 1812–47. Introduction by *Prof. G. M. Trevelyan,* O.M.
                                    (See also Histo◖
Machiavelli, Niccolò (1469–1527).
    THE PRINCE, 1513. New Introduction by *Prof. H. Butterfield,* M.A., HON. D.L◖
    Translated by *W. K. Marriott.*
Mazzini, Joseph (1805–72).
    THE DUTIES OF MAN (translated by *Miss E. Noyes*); and OTHER ESSAYS. N
    Introduction by *Dr Thomas Jones,* C.H., LL.D.
Milton, John (1608–74).
    PROSE WRITINGS. Introduction by *K. M. Burton,* M.A. The contents of this volu
    include 'Areopagitica,' 1644, and other important prose works.
                                    (See also Poetry, e◖
Mitford, Mary Russell (1787–1855).
    OUR VILLAGE, 1824–32. Edited, with an Introduction, by *Sir John Squire.* ◖
Modern Humour. An Anthology in Prose and Verse from over sixty authors.   ◖
Montaigne, Michel de (1533–92).
    ESSAYS, 1580–8. John Florio's version, 1603. Edited (from the third edition, 163
    with Intro. by *A. R. Waller,* 3 vols.   *(Vol. I temporarily out of print.)* 44◖
Napoleon Buonaparte (1769–1821).
    LETTERS. Some 300 of the most interesting of the Emperor's letters, cho
    and translated by *J. M. Thompson,* F.B.A., F.R.HIST.S. *(See also* Biography.) ◖
Nelson, Horatio, Viscount (1758–1805).
    NELSON'S LETTERS. Compiled by *Geoffrey Rawson.*   *(See also* Biography.) ◖
Newman, John Henry (1801–90).
    ON THE SCOPE AND NATURE OF UNIVERSITY EDUCATION; and CHRISTIANITY A
    SCIENTIFIC INVESTIGATION, 1852. Introduction by *Wilfrid Ward.*
                              (See also Theology and Philosop◖
Poe, Edgar Allan (1809–49).
    ESSAYS. (*See* Poetry.)
Quiller-Couch, Sir Arthur (1863–1944).
    CAMBRIDGE LECTURES, from 'Q.'s' well-known books *The Art of Reading,* 19
    The Art of Writing, 1916; *Studies in Literature,* 1918; and *Shakespeare's Workm*
    ship, 1918.   *(See also* Fiction.) ◖
Rousseau, Jean Jacques (1712–78).
    ÉMILE; OR, EDUCATION. Translated by *Barbara Foxley,* M.A. Intro. (1955) by *P*
    André Boutet de Monvel.   *(See also* Biography, Theology and Philosophy.) ◖
Ruskin, John (1819–1900).
    SESAME, AND LILIES, 1864; THE TWO PATHS, 1859; and THE KING OF THE GOLD
    RIVER; or THE BLACK BROTHERS, 1851. Introduction by *Sir Oliver Lodge.*   ◖
    THE SEVEN LAMPS OF ARCHITECTURE, 1849. With an Introduction (1956) by
    Arnold Lunn. Illustrated with 14 plates of engravings.
Sévigné, Marie de Rabutin-Chantal, Marquise de (1626–96).
    SELECTED LETTERS. Selected and translated by *H. T. Barnwell,* M.A.
Spectator, The, 1711–14. By Joseph Addison (1672–1719), Sir Richard Steele (16◖
    1729) and Others. Edited by *Prof. Gregory Smith.* New Introduction by *P. Smith*
    D.PHIL., M.P., and a Biographical and General Index by *Prof. Gregory Smith.* Re
    with minor revisions, 1945. 4 vols.   *(See also* Essays *under* Steele.) 164◖
Spencer, Herbert (1820–1903).
    ESSAYS ON EDUCATION, 1861. Introduction by *C. W. Eliot.*
Steele, Sir Richard (1672–1729).
    THE TATLER, 1709–11.   ◖
Sterne, Laurence (1713–68).
    A SENTIMENTAL JOURNEY THROUGH FRANCE AND ITALY, 1768; JOURNAL TO EL◖
    written in 1767; and LETTERS TO ELIZA, 1766–7. Introduction by *Daniel Geor*
                                       (See also Fiction.) ◖

venson, Robert Louis (1850–94).
VIRGINIBUS PUERISQUE, 1881; and FAMILIAR STUDIES OF MEN AND BOOKS, 1882.
    (*See also* Fiction, Poetry and Drama, Travel.) 765

ift, Jonathan (1667–1745).
A TALE OF A TUB, 1704; THE BATTLE OF THE BOOKS, 1704; and OTHER SATIRES.
Introduction by *Louis Melville*. (*See also* Biography, Fiction.) 347

innerton, Frank (*b.* 1884).
THE GEORGIAN LITERARY SCENE, 1935. A panorama, revised 1951, of English
writers (novelists, essayists, dramatists, poets) from 1919. 943

ackeray, William Makepeace (1811–63).
THE ENGLISH HUMORISTS, 1851; CHARITY AND HUMOUR, 1853; and THE FOUR
GEORGES, 1855. Introduction by *Walter Jerrold*. (*See also* Fiction.) 610

oreau, Henry David (1817–62).
WALDEN, OR LIFE IN THE WOODS, 1854. Introduction by *Prof. Basil Willey*. 281

ench, Richard Chevenix (1807–86).
ON THE STUDY OF WORDS, 1851; and ENGLISH PAST AND PRESENT, 1855. Introduction by *George Sampson*. 788

tler, Alexander Fraser (1747–1814).
ESSAY ON THE PRINCIPLES OF TRANSLATION, 1791. 168

alton, Izaak (1593–1683).
THE COMPLETE ANGLER, 1653. Introduction by *Andrew Lang*. 70

FICTION

nsworth, William Harrison (1805–82).
OLD SAINT PAUL'S, 1841. Introduction by *W. E. Axon*, LL.D. Great Fire of London. 522
ROOKWOOD, 1834. Introduction by *Frank Swinnerton*. Dick Turpin. 870
THE TOWER OF LONDON, 1840. Lady Jane Grey. 400
WINDSOR CASTLE, 1843. Intro. by *Ernest Rhys*. Henry VIII and Ann Boleyn. 709

nerican Short Stories of the Nineteenth Century. Edited, with an Introduction, by
John Cournos. Twenty stories from representative writers. 840

idersen, Hans Christian (1805–75).
FAIRY TALES AND STORIES. This represents a completely new selection and in the
Reginald Spink Translation. 4

isten, Jane (1775–1817). Each volume has an Introduction by *R. Brimley Johnson*.
EMMA, 1816. 24   PRIDE AND PREJUDICE, 1823. 22
MANSFIELD PARK, 1814. 23   SENSE AND SENSIBILITY, 1811. 21
NORTHANGER ABBEY, 1818; and PERSUASION, 1818. 25

alzac, Honoré de (1799–1850).
AT THE SIGN OF THE CAT AND RACKET, 1830; and OTHER STORIES. Translated by
Clara Bell. Introduction by *George Saintsbury*. 349
EUGÉNIE GRANDET, 1834. Translated by *Ellen Marriage*. New Introduction by
Prof. Marcel Girard. 169
OLD GORIOT, 1835. Translated by *Ellen Marriage*. New Introduction by *Prof.
Marcel Girard*. 170
THE WILD ASS'S SKIN, 1831. A youth makes a bargain with destiny. New Introduction
by *Prof. Marcel Girard*. 26

arbusse, Henri (1874–1935).
UNDER FIRE, THE STORY OF A SQUAD, 1916. Introduction by *Brian Rhys*. 798

eaconsfield, Benjamin Disraeli, Earl of (1804–81).
CONINGSBY, 1844. Introduction and Notes (with a Key to the Characters) by *B. N.
Langdon-Davies*. 535

ennett, Arnold (1867–1931).
THE OLD WIVES' TALE, 1908. The most durable novel of Bennett's. 919

lackmore, Richard Doddridge (1825–1900).
LORNA DOONE: A ROMANCE OF EXMOOR, 1869. Introduction by *Ernest Rhys*. 304

orrow, George (1803–81).
THE ROMANY RYE, 1857. Practically a sequel to *Lavengro*. (*See also* Travel.) 120

ronte, Anne (1820–49).
THE TENANT OF WILDFELL HALL and AGNES GREY. With a new Introduction by
Margaret Lane. 685

ronte, Charlotte (1816–55). For Mrs Gaskell's 'Life' *see* Biography.
JANE EYRE, 1847. Introduction by *Margaret Lane*. 287
THE PROFESSOR, 1857. Introduction by *Margaret Lane*. 417
SHIRLEY, 1849. Introduction by *Margaret Lane*. 288
VILLETTE, 1853. Introduction by *Margaret Lane*. 351

ronte, Emily (1818–48).
WUTHERING HEIGHTS, 1848; and POEMS. Introduction by *Margaret Lane*. 243

urney, Fanny (Madame Frances d'Arblay, 1753–1849).
EVELINA, 1778. Introduction by *Lewis Gibbs*. 352

utler, Samuel (1835–1902).
EREWHON, 1872 (revised 1901); and EREWHON REVISITED, 1901. Introduction by
Desmond MacCarthy. 881
THE WAY OF ALL FLESH, 1903. Introduction by *A. J. Hoppé*. 895

Collins, Wilkie (1824–89).
THE MOONSTONE, 1868. Introduction by *Dorothy L. Sayers*.
THE WOMAN IN WHITE, 1860. New Introduction by *Maurice Richardson*.
Conrad, Joseph (1857–1924).
LORD JIM, 1900. Characteristically set in the East Indies. Introduction by *R. Cunninghame Graham*.
THE NIGGER OF THE 'NARCISSUS,' 1897; TYPHOON, 1903; and THE SHADOW LI 1917. Introduction by *A. J. Hoppé*. Three of Conrad's best-known stories.
NOSTROMO, 1904. New edition of Conrad's greatest novel with an Introduction *Richard Curle.*
Cooper, James Fenimore (1789–1851).
THE LAST OF THE MOHICANS, 1826, A NARRATIVE OF 1757. With an Introduction *Ernest Rhys.*
THE PRAIRIE, 1827. The last of the 'Leatherstocking Tales.'
Craik, Mrs. *See* Mulock.
Daudet, Alphonse (1840–97).
TARTARIN OF TARASCON, 1872; and TARTARIN ON THE ALPS, 1885. Two li episodic novels, some of the funniest episodes ever written in French.
Defoe, Daniel (1661?–1731).
THE FORTUNES AND MISFORTUNES OF MOLL FLANDERS, 1722. Introduction *G. A. Aitken.* One of Defoe's greatest books, famous for its picture of low life.
JOURNAL OF THE PLAGUE YEAR, 1722. Introduction by *G. A. Aitken.*
LIFE, ADVENTURES AND PIRACIES OF THE FAMOUS CAPTAIN SINGLETON, 17 Introduction by *Edward Garnett.* A supposed record of a journey across Africa.
ROBINSON CRUSOE, 1719. Parts 1 and 2 complete. Introduction by *Guy N. Poco*
(*See also* Travel.)
De Rojas, Fernando (15th century).
CELESTINA: OR THE TRAGI-COMEDY OF CALISTO AND MELIBEA, attributed Fernando de Rojas. Translated, with an Introduction, by *Phyllis Hartnoll*, M. L. ÉS L. This is a new translation (1958).
Dickens, Charles (1812–70). Each of the following volumes of Dickens's works has Introduction by *G. K. Chesterton*:

BARNABY RUDGE, 1841.	76	LITTLE DORRIT, 1857.	
BLEAK HOUSE, 1852–3.	236	MARTIN CHUZZLEWIT, 1843–4.	
CHRISTMAS BOOKS, 1843–8.	239	NICHOLAS NICKLEBY, 1838–9.	
CHRISTMAS STORIES, 1850–67.	414	OLD CURIOSITY SHOP, 1841.	
DAVID COPPERFIELD, 1849–50.	242	OLIVER TWIST, 1838.	
DOMBEY AND SON, 1846–8.	240	OUR MUTUAL FRIEND, 1864–5.	
GREAT EXPECTATIONS, 1861.	234	PICKWICK PAPERS, 1836–7.	
HARD TIMES, 1854.	292	A TALE OF TWO CITIES, 1859.	

(*See also* Biograph
Disraeli, Benjamin. *See* Beaconsfield.
Dostoyevsky, Fyodor (1821–81).
THE BROTHERS KARAMAZOV, 1879–80. Translated by *Constance Garnett*. Int duction by *Edward Garnett*. 2 vols. 802
CRIME AND PUNISHMENT, 1866. *Constance Garnett* translation. 5
THE IDIOT, 1873. Translated by *Eva M. Martin*. New Introduction by *Rich Curle*. 6
LETTERS FROM THE UNDERWORLD, 1864; and OTHER TALES (THE GENTLE MAIDE THE LANDLADY). Translated, with Introduction, by *C. J. Hogarth*. 6
POOR FOLK, 1845; and THE GAMBLER, 1867. Translated, with Introduction, *C. J. Hogarth.* 7
THE POSSESSED, 1871. Translated by *Constance Garnett*. Introduction by *Niko Andreyev*, PH.D., M.A. 2 vols. 861
Dumas, Alexandre (1802–70).
THE BLACK TULIP, 1850. The brothers De Witt in Holland, 1672–5. New Int duction by *Prof. Marcel Girard.* 1
COUNT OF MONTE CRISTO, 1844. 2 vols. Napoleon's later phase. New Introduct by *Prof. Marcel Girard.* 393
MARGUERITE DE VALOIS, 1845. The Eve of St Bartholomew. 3
THE THREE MUSKETEERS, 1844. The France of Cardinal Richelieu.
Du Maurier, George Louis Palmella Busson (1834–96).
TRILBY, 1894. Illustrated by the author. Preface by *Sir Gerald Du Maurier. Tri* breathes the air of Paris in the eighties and is drawn largely from the author's ov experience. 8
Edgeworth, Maria (1767–1849).
CASTLE RACKRENT, 1800; and THE ABSENTEE, 1812. Introduction by *Pr Brander Matthews.* 4
Eliot, George (pseudonym of Mary Ann Evans, 1819–80).
ADAM BEDE, 1859. New Introduction by *Robert Speaight*.
MIDDLEMARCH, 1872. New Introduction by *Gerald Bullett*. 2 vols. 854
THE MILL ON THE FLOSS, 1860. Introduction by *Sir W. Robertson Nicoll*. 3
ROMOLA, 1863. Intro. by *Rudolph Dircks*. The Florence of Savonarola. 2
SILAS MARNER, THE WEAVER OF RAVELOE, 1861. Introduction by *A. Matheson*.

glish Short Stories. Thirty-six selected stories from Middle Ages to present time.
Introduction by *Richard Wilson*, B.A., D.LITT.   743

lding, Henry (1707–54). *George Saintsbury* has written an Introduction to the Everyman Fielding.
   AMELIA, 1751. 2 vols. Amelia is drawn from Fielding's first wife.   852–3
   JONATHAN WILD, 1743; and JOURNAL OF A VOYAGE TO LISBON, 1755. *Jonathan Wild* is a satire on false hero-worship; the *Journal* (published posthumously) narrates the incidents of Fielding's last voyage.   877
   JOSEPH ANDREWS, 1742. A skit on Richardson's *Pamela*.   467
   TOM JONES, 1749. 2 vols. The first great English novel of humour.   355–6

Flubert, Gustave (1821–80).
   MADAME BOVARY, 1857. Translated by *Eleanor Marx-Aveling*. Introduction by *George Saintsbury*.   808
   SALAMMBO, 1862. Translated by *J. C. Chartres*. Introduction by *Prof. F. C. Green*, M.A., PH.D. The war of the Mercenaries against Carthage.   869
   SENTIMENTAL EDUCATION, 1869. Modern translation, with Introduction and Notes by *Anthony Goldsmith*.   969

Forster, Edward Morgan (*b*. 1879).
   A PASSAGE TO INDIA, 1924. With an Introduction by *Peter Burra*.   972

Galsworthy, John (1867–1933).
   THE COUNTRY HOUSE.   917

Gaskell, Mrs Elizabeth (1810–65).
   CRANFORD, 1853. Introduction by *Frank Swinnerton*.   (*See also* Biography.) 83
   Ghost Stories. Introduction by *John Hampden*. Eighteen stories.   952

Gogol, Nikolay (1809–52).
   DEAD SOULS, 1842. Introduction by *Nikolay Andreyev*, PH.D., M.A.   726

Goldsmith, Oliver (1728–74).
   THE VICAR OF WAKEFIELD, 1766. Introduction by *J. M. Dent*.   295
   (*See also* Poetry.)

Goncharov, Ivan (1812–91).
   OBLOMOV, 1857. First complete English translation by *Natalie Duddington*. New Introduction by *Nikolay Andreyev*, PH.D., M.A.   878

Gorky, Maxim (pseudonym of Alexei Maximovitch Pieshkov, 1868–1936).
   THROUGH RUSSIA. Translated, with an Introduction, by *C. J. Hogarth*.   741

Grossmith, George (1847–1912), and Weedon (1853–1919).
   THE DIARY OF A NOBODY, 1894. With Weedon Grossmith's illustrations.   963

Hawthorne, Nathaniel (1804–64).
   THE HOUSE OF THE SEVEN GABLES, 1851. New Introduction by *Prof. Roy Harvey Pearce*.   176
   THE SCARLET LETTER: A ROMANCE, 1850. With new Introduction by *Prof. Roy Harvey Pearce*.   122
   TWICE-TOLD TALES, 1837–42. With a new Introduction by *Prof. Roy Harvey Pearce*.   531

Hugo, Victor Marie (1802–85).
   LES MISÉRABLES, 1862. Introduction by *Denis Saurat*.   2 vols. 363–4
   NOTRE DAME DE PARIS, 1831. Introduction by *Denis Saurat*.   422
   TOILERS OF THE SEA, 1866. Introduction by *Ernest Rhys*.   509

Huxley, Aldous.
   STORIES, ESSAYS AND POEMS. (*See under* Essays.)

James, Henry (1843–1916).
   THE AMBASSADORS, 1903. Introduction by *Frank Swinnerton*.   987
   THE TURN OF THE SCREW, 1898; and THE ASPERN PAPERS, 1888. Two famous short novels. Introduction by *Prof. Kenneth B. Murdock*, A.M., PH.D.   912

Jefferies, Richard (1848–87).
   AFTER LONDON, 1884; and AMARYLLIS AT THE FAIR, 1886. Introduction by *Richard Garnett*.   951

Jerome, Jerome K. (1859–1927).
   THREE MEN IN A BOAT and THREE MEN ON THE BUMMEL. Introduction by *D. C. Browning*, M.A., B.LITT.   118

Kingsley, Charles (1819–75).
   HEREWARD THE WAKE, 1866. Introduction by *Ernest Rhys*.   296
   WESTWARD HO!, 1855. Introduction by *Dr J. A. Williamson*, M.A.   20

Lamb, Charles (1775–1834), and Mary (1764–1847).
   TALES FROM SHAKESPEARE, 1807. Illustrated by *Arthur Rackham*.   8
   (*See also* Biography, Essays.)

Lawrence, David Herbert (1885–1930).
   THE WHITE PEACOCK, 1911.   (*See also* Essays.) 914

Loti, Pierre (1850–1923).
   ICELAND FISHERMAN, 1886. Translated by *W. P. Baines*.   920

Lover, Samuel (1797–1868).
   HANDY ANDY, 1842. Lover was a musician, portrait-painter, song-writer and actor who also wrote four novels of which this is generally accounted the best.   178

Lytton, Edward Bulwer, Baron (1803–73).
   THE LAST DAYS OF POMPEII, 1834. A romance of the first century A.D.   80

Mann, Thomas (1875–1955).
   STORIES AND EPISODES. Introduction by *Prof. Erich Heller* ,PH.D.   962

Manzoni, Alessandro (1785–1873).

THE BETROTHED (*I Promessi Sposi*, 1840, rev. ed.). Translated (1951) from
Italian by *Archibald Colquhoun*, who also adds a preface.

Marryat, Frederick (1792–1848).

MR MIDSHIPMAN EASY. New Introduction by *Oliver Warner*.

THE SETTLERS IN CANADA, 1844. Introduction by *Oliver Warner*.

Maugham, W. Somerset (*b.* 1874).

CAKES AND ALE, 1930. The finest novel of the author's inter-war period.

Maupassant, Guy de (1850–93).

SHORT STORIES. Translated by *Marjorie Laurie*. Intro. by *Gerald Gould*.

Melville, Herman (1819–91).

MOBY DICK, 1851. Intro. by *Prof. Sherman Paul*.

TYPEE, 1846; and BILLY BUDD (*published* 1924). South Seas adventures. N
Introduction by *Milton R. Stern*.

Meredith, George (1828–1909).

THE ORDEAL OF RICHARD FEVEREL, 1859. Introduction by *Robert Sencourt*.

Mickiewicz, Adam (1798–1855).

PAN TADEUSZ, 1834. Translated into English prose, with Introduction, by *Pr*
G. R. Noyes. Poland's epic of Napoleonic wars.

Modern Short Stories. Selected by *John Hadfield*. Twenty stories.

Moore, George (1852–1933).

ESTHER WATERS, 1894. The story of Esther Waters, the servant girl who 'we
wrong.' Introduction by *C. D. Medley*.

Mulock [Mrs Craik], Maria (1826–87).

JOHN HALIFAX, GENTLEMAN, 1856. Introduction by *J. Shaylor*.

Pater, Walter (1839–94).

MARIUS THE EPICUREAN, 1885. Introduction by *Osbert Burdett*.

Poe, Edgar Allan (1809–49).

TALES OF MYSTERY AND IMAGINATION. Introduction by *Padraic Colum*.
(*See also* Poetry and Dram

Priestley, J. B. (*b.* 1894).

ANGEL PAVEMENT, 1931. A finely conceived novel of London.

Quiller-Couch, Sir Arthur (1863–1944).

HETTY WESLEY, 1903. Introduction by the author. (*See also* Essays.) 8

Radcliffe, Mrs Ann (1764–1823).

THE MYSTERIES OF UDOLPHO, 1794. Intro. by *R. A. Freeman*. 2 vols. 865

Reade, Charles (1814–84).

THE CLOISTER AND THE HEARTH, 1861. Introduction by *Swinburne*.

Richardson, Samuel (1689–1761).

PAMELA, 1740. Introduction by *George Saintsbury*. 2 vols. 683

CLARISSA, 1747–8. Introduction by *Prof. W. L. Phelps*. 4 vols. 882

Russian Short Stories. Translated, with Introduction, by *Rochelle S. Townsend*. Stor
by Pushkin, Gogol, Tolstoy, Korolenko, Chehov, Chirikov, Andreyev, Kupr
Gorky, Sologub. 7

Scott, Sir Walter (1771–1832).

The following Waverley Novels each contain an Introduction, biographical a
bibliographical, based upon Lockhart's *Life*:

THE ANTIQUARY, 1816. Introduction by *W. M. Parker*, M.A.

THE BRIDE OF LAMMERMOOR, 1819. A romance of life in East Lothian, 1695. N
Introduction by *W. M. Parker*, M.A. 1

GUY MANNERING, 1815. A mystery story of the time of George III. New Intr
duction by *W. M. Parker*, M.A. 1

THE HEART OF MIDLOTHIAN, 1818. Period of the Porteous Riots, 1736. New Intr
duction by *W. M. Parker*, M.A. 1

IVANHOE, 1820. A romance of the days of Richard I.

KENILWORTH, 1821. The tragic story of Amy Robsart, in Elizabeth I's time. N
Preface and Glossary by *W. M. Parker*, M.A. 1

OLD MORTALITY, 1817. Battle of Bothwell Bridge, 1679. New Introduction
W. M. Parker, M.A. 1

QUENTIN DURWARD, 1823. A tale of adventures in fifteenth-century France. N
Introduction by *W. M. Parker*, M.A. 1

REDGAUNTLET, 1824. A tale of adventure in Cumberland, about 1763. New Intr
duction by *W. M. Parker*, M.A. 1

ROB ROY, 1818. A romance of the Rebellion of 1715. 1

THE TALISMAN, 1825. Richard Cœur-de-Lion and the Third Crusade, 1191. N
Preface by *W. M. Parker*, M.A. (*See also* Biography.) 1

Shchedrin (M. E. Saltykov, 1826–92).

THE GOLOVLYOV FAMILY. Translated by *Natalie Duddington*. Introduction
Edward Garnett. 9

Shelley, Mary Wollstonecraft (1797–1851).

FRANKENSTEIN, 1818. With Mary Shelley's own Preface. 6

Shorter Novels.

Vol. I: ELIZABETHAN. Introduction by *George Saintsbury* and Notes by *Phil*
Henderson. Contains: Deloney's 'Jack of Newberie' and 'Thomas of Reading
Nashe's 'The Unfortunate Traveller'; Green's 'Carde of Fancie.' 8

8

VOL. II: SEVENTEENTH CENTURY. Edited, with Introduction, by *Philip Henderson*.
Contains: Emanuel Ford's 'Ornatus and Artesia'; Aphra Behn's 'Oroonoko';
Neville's 'The Isle of Pines'; Congreve's 'Incognita.' 841
VOL. III: EIGHTEENTH CENTURY. Edited, with Introduction, by *Philip Henderson*.
Contains: Beckford's 'Vathek'; Horace Walpole's 'The Castle of Otranto'; Dr
Johnson' 'Rasselas.' 856
Sienkiewicz, Henryk (1846–1916).
QUO VADIS? 1896. Translated by *C. J. Hogarth*. Intro. by *Monica Gardner*. 970
TALES. Edited, with Introduction, by *Monica Gardner*. 871
Smollett, Tobias (1721–71).
THE EXPEDITION OF HUMPHRY CLINKER, 1771. Introduction by *Howard Mumford
Jones*, and 36 pages of Notes by *Charles Lee*. 975
PEREGRINE PICKLE, 1751. Introduction by *Walter Allen*. 2 vols. 838–9
RODERICK RANDOM, 1742. Introduction by *H. W. Hodges*. 790
Somerville, E. Œ. (1858–1949), and Ross, Martin (pseudonym of Violet Florence
Martin, 1862–1915).
EXPERIENCES OF AN IRISH R.M. Contains the authors' two books, *Some Experiences
of an Irish R.M.*, 1897, and *Further Experiences of an Irish R.M.*, 1908. 978
Stendhal (pseudonym of Henri Beyle, 1783–1842).
SCARLET AND BLACK, 1831. Translated by *C. K. Scott Moncrieff*. Introduction by
Prof. F. C. Green, M.A., DR.PHIL. 2 vols. 945–6
Sterne, Laurence (1713–68).
TRISTRAM SHANDY, 1760–7. Intro. by *George Saintsbury*. (*See also* Essays.) 617
Stevenson, Robert Louis (1850–94).
DR JEKYLL AND MR HYDE, 1886; THE MERRY MEN, 1887; WILL O' THE MILL,
1878; MARKHEIM, 1886; THRAWN JANET, 1881; OLALLA, 1885; THE TREASURE
OF FRANCHARD. Introduction by *M. R. Ridley*. 767
THE MASTER OF BALLANTRAE, 1869; WEIR OF HERMISTON, 1896. New Introduction
by *M. R. Ridley*. 764
ST IVES, 1898. Completed by Sir Arthur Quiller-Couch. Introduction (1958) by
M. R. Ridley. 904
TREASURE ISLAND, 1883; and KIDNAPPED, 1886. Introduction by *Sir Arthur
Quiller-Couch*. (*See also* Essays, Poetry, Travel.) 763
Story Book for Boys and Girls. Edited by *Guy Pocock* (1955). 934
Surtees, Robert Smith (1803–64).
JORROCKS'S JAUNTS AND JOLLITIES, 1838. 817
Swift, Jonathan (1667–1745).
GULLIVER'S TRAVELS, 1726. An unabridged edition; with an Introduction by *Sir
Harold Williams*, F.B.A., F.S.A., M.A. (*See also* Biography, Essays.) 60
Tales of Detection. Introduction by *Dorothy L. Sayers*. Nineteen stories, tracing the
development of the genuine detective story during the last hundred years. 928
Thackeray, William Makepeace (1811–63).
HENRY ESMOND, 1852. Introduction by *Walter Jerrold*. 73
THE NEWCOMES, 1853–5. 2 vols. Introduction by *Walter Jerrold*. 465–6
PENDENNIS, 1848–50. 2 vols. Introduction by *M. R. Ridley*, M.A. 425–6
VANITY FAIR, 1847–8. Introduction by *Hon. Whitelaw Reid*. 298
THE VIRGINIANS, 1857–9. 2 vols. Introduction by *Walter Jerrold*. 507–8
(*See also* Essays and Belles-Lettres.)
Tolstoy, Count Leo (1828–1910).
ANNA KARENINA, 1873–7. Translated by *Rochelle S. Townsend*. With Introduction
by *Nikolay Andreyev*, PH.D., M.A. 2 vols. 612–13
MASTER AND MAN, 1895; and OTHER PARABLES AND TALES. Introduction (1958)
by *Nikolay Andreyev*, PH.D., M.A. 469
WAR AND PEACE, 1864–9. Introduction by *Vicomte de Vogüé*. 3 vols. 525–7
Trollope, Anthony (1815–82).
THE WARDEN, 1855. The first of the 'Chronicles of Barset.' Introduction by
Kathleen Tillotson, M.A., B.LITT. 182
BARCHESTER TOWERS, 1857. The second of the 'Chronicles of Barset.' Introduction
(1956) on Anthony Trollope's 'Clergy' by *Michael Sadleir*. 30
DOCTOR THORNE, 1858. The third of the 'Chronicles of Barset.' 360
FRAMLEY PARSONAGE, 1861. The fourth of the 'Chronicles of Barset.' Introduction
by *Kathleen Tillotson*. 181
THE SMALL HOUSE AT ALLINGTON, 1864. The fifth of the 'Chronicles of Barset.' 361
THE LAST CHRONICLE OF BARSET, 1867. 2 vols. 391–2
Turgenev, Ivan (1818–83).
FATHERS AND SONS, 1862. Translated by *Dr Avril Pyman*. 742
SMOKE, 1867. A new translation, with Introduction, by *Natalie Duddington*. 988
VIRGIN SOIL, 1877. Translated by *Rochelle S. Townsend*. 528
Twain, Mark (pseudonym of Samuel Langhorne Clemens, 1835–1910).
TOM SAWYER, 1876; and HUCKLEBERRY FINN, 1884. Introduction by *Christopher
Morley*. 976
Verne, Jules (1828–1905).
FIVE WEEKS IN A BALLOON, 1862, translated by *Arthur Chambers*; and AROUND
THE WORLD IN EIGHTY DAYS, translated by *P. Desages*. 779
TWENTY THOUSAND LEAGUES UNDER THE SEA, 1869. 319

Voltaire, François Marie Arouet de (1694–1778).
    CANDIDE, AND OTHER TALES. Smollett's translation, edited by *J. C. Thornton*. 936
                                          (*See also* History.)
Walpole, Hugh Seymour (1884–1941).
    MR PERRIN AND MR TRAILL, 1911. 918
Wells, Herbert George (1866–1946).
    ANN VERONICA, 1909. Introduction by *A. J. Hoppé*. 997
    THE WHEELS OF CHANCE, 1896; and THE TIME MACHINE, 1895. 915
Wilde, Oscar.
    THE PICTURE OF DORIAN GRAY, 1891. (*See* Poetry and Drama.)
Woolf, Virginia (1882–1941).
    TO THE LIGHTHOUSE, 1927. Introduction by *D. M. Hoare*, PH.D. 949
Zola, Émile (1840–1902).
    GERMINAL, 1885. Translated, with an Introduction, by *Havelock Ellis*. 897

HISTORY

Anglo-Saxon Chronicle. Translated and Edited by *G. N. Garmonsway*, F.R.HIST.SOC.
    Foreword by *Prof. Bruce Dickins*. 624
Bede, the Venerable (673–735).
    THE ECCLESIASTICAL HISTORY OF THE ENGLISH NATION. Translated by *John Stevens*, revised by *J. A. Giles*, with notes by *L. C. Jane*. Introduction by *Prof. David Knowles*, O.S.B., M.A., LITT.D., F.B.A., F.S.A. 479
Carlyle, Thomas (1795–1881).
    THE FRENCH REVOLUTION, 1837. Introduction by *Hilaire Belloc*. 2 vols. 31–2
                                (*See also* Biography, Essays.)
Chesterton, Cecil (1879–1918). A HISTORY OF THE U.S.A., 1917. Edited by *Prof. D. W. Brogan*, M.A. 965
Creasy, Sir Edward (1812–78).
    FIFTEEN DECISIVE BATTLES OF THE WORLD, FROM MARATHON TO WATERLOO, 1852. With Diagrams and Index. New Introduction by *Audrey Butler*, M.A. (OXON.). 300
Gibbon, Edward (1737–94).
    THE DECLINE AND FALL OF THE ROMAN EMPIRE, 1776–88. Notes by *Oliphant Smeaton*. Intro. by *Christopher Dawson*. Complete text in 6 vols. 434–6, 474–6
Green, John Richard (1837–83).
    A SHORT HISTORY OF THE ENGLISH PEOPLE, 1874. Introduction by *L. C. Jane*. English history from 607 to 1873. Continued by: 'A Political and Social Survey from 1815 to 1915,' by *R. P. Farley*, and revised to 1950. 727–8
Holinshed, Raphael (*d.* 1580?).
    HOLINSHED'S CHRONICLE AS USED IN SHAKESPEARE'S PLAYS, 1578. Introduction by *Prof. Allardyce Nicoll* and *Josephine Nicoll*. 800
Joinville, Jean de. See Villehardouin.
Lützow, Count Franz von (1849–1916).
    BOHEMIA: AN HISTORICAL SKETCH, 1896. Introduction by *President T. G. Masaryk*. H. A. Piehler covers events from 1879 to 1938. 432
Macaulay, Thomas Babington, Baron (1800–59).
    THE HISTORY OF ENGLAND. The complete text in four volumes, which together contain 2,450 pages. Introduction by *Douglas Jerrold*. 34–7
                                      (*See also* Essays.)
Maine, Sir Henry (1822–88).
    ANCIENT LAW, 1861. Introduction by *Prof. J. H. Morgan*. 734
Mommsen, Theodor (1817–1903).
    HISTORY OF ROME, 1856. Translated by *W. P. Dickson*, LL.D. Introduction by *Edward A. Freeman*. 4 vols. (Vols. III and IV only.) 544–5
Motley, John (1814–77).
    THE RISE OF THE DUTCH REPUBLIC, 1856. Intro. by *V. R. Reynolds*. 3 vols. 86–8
Paston Letters, The, 1418–1506. 2 vols. A selection. 752–3
Prescott, William Hickling (1796–1859).
    HISTORY OF THE CONQUEST OF MEXICO, 1843. 2 vols. 397–8
Stanley, Arthur (1815–81).
    LECTURES ON THE HISTORY OF THE EASTERN CHURCH, 1861. Introduction by *A. J. Grieve*, M.A. 251
Thierry, Augustin (1795–1856).
    THE NORMAN CONQUEST, 1825. Introduction by *J. A. Price*, B.A. 2 vols. (*Vol. I temporarily out of print.*) 198–9
Villehardouin, Geoffrey de (1160?–1213?), and **Joinville, Jean, Sire de** (1224–1317).
    MEMOIRS OF THE CRUSADES. Translated, with an Introduction, by *Sir Frank T. Marzials*. 333
Voltaire, François Marie Arouet de (1694–1778).
    THE AGE OF LOUIS XIV, 1751. Translation by *Martyn P. Pollack*.
                                    (*See also* Fiction.) 780

ORATORY

British Orations. The 1960 edition of this selection of British historical speeches contains selections from four of the most famous of Sir Winston Churchill's World War II speeches. 714

Burke, Edmund (1729–97).
    SPEECHES AND LETTERS ON AMERICAN AFFAIRS. New Introduction by the *Very Rev. Canon Peter McKevitt*, PH.D. (*See also* Essays and Belles-Lettres.) 340

Demosthenes (384–322 B.C.).
    THE CROWN, AND OTHER ORATIONS. Translated with an Appendix on Athenian economics by *C. Rann Kennedy.* Introduction by *John Warrington.* 546

Lincoln, Abraham (1809–65).
    SPEECHES AND LETTERS, 1832–65. A new selection edited with an Introduction by *Paul M. Angle.* Chronology of Lincoln's life and index. 206

POETRY AND DRAMA

Anglo-Saxon Poetry. English poetry between A.D. 650 and 1000, from 'Widsith' and 'Beowulf' to the battle-pieces of 'Brunanburh' and 'Maldon.' Selected and translated by *Prof. R. K. Gordon*, M.A. Reset, and revised by the translator, 1954. 794

Arnold, Matthew (1822–88).
    COMPLETE POEMS. Introduction by *R. A. Scott-James.* 334

Ballads, A Book of British. Introduction and Notes by *R. Brimley Johnson.* Ballads from the earliest times to those of Yeats and Kipling. 572

Beaumont, Francis (1584–1616), and **Fletcher, John** (1579–1625).
    SELECT PLAYS. Introduction by *Prof. G. P. Baker.* 'The Knight of the Burning Pestle,' 'The Maid's Tragedy,' 'A King and No King,' 'The Faithful Shepherdess.' 'The Wild Goose Chase,' 'Bonduca,' with a glossary. 506

Blake, William (1757–1827).
    POEMS AND PROPHECIES. Edited, with special Introduction, by *Max Plowman.* 792

Brontë, Emily.
    POEMS. (*See* Fiction.)

Browning, Robert (1812–89).
    POEMS AND PLAYS, 1833–64. With a new Introduction by *John Bryson*, M.A., dealing with the four-volume Everyman Browning set. 2 vols. Volume III, containing *The Ring and the Book*, Browning's long dramatic poem (No. 502), is temporarily out of print. 41–2
    POEMS, 1871–90. Introduction by *M. M. Bozman.* 964

Burns, Robert (1759–96).
    POEMS AND SONGS. A very full selection and a very accurate text of Burns's copious lyrical output. Edited and introduced by *Prof. James Kinsley*, M.A., PH.D. 94
    (*See also* Biography.)

Byron, George Gordon Noel, Lord (1788–1824).
    THE POETICAL AND DRAMATIC WORKS. 3 vols. Edited with a Preface by *Guy Pocock*
    (*See also* Biography.) 486–8

Century. A CENTURY OF HUMOROUS VERSE, 1850–1950. Edited by *Roger Lancelyn Green*, M.A., B.LITT. 813

Chaucer, Geoffrey (*c.* 1343–1400).
    CANTERBURY TALES. New standard text edited by *A. C. Cawley*, M.A., PH.D., based on the Ellesmere Manuscript, with an ingenious system of glosses, page by page. 307
    TROILUS AND CRISEYDE. Prepared by *John Warrington* from the Campsall Manuscript. 992

Coleridge, Samuel Taylor (1772–1834).
    THE GOLDEN BOOK. (*See also* Essays, etc.) 43

Cowper, William (1731–1800).
    POEMS. Intro. by *Hugh I'Anson Fausset.* (*See also* Biography.) 872

Dante Alighieri (1265–1321).
    THE DIVINE COMEDY, first printed 1472. H. F. Cary's Translation, 1805–14. Edited, with Notes and Index, by *Edmund Gardner.* Foreword by *Prof. Mario Praz.* 308

De la Mare, Walter (1873–1956). (*See* Essays.)

Donne, John (1573–1631).
    COMPLETE POEMS. Edited, with a revised Intro., by *Hugh I'Anson Fausset.* 867

Dryden, John (1631–1700).
    POEMS. Edited by *Bonamy Dobrée*, O.B.E., M.A. 910

Eighteenth-century Plays. Edited by *John Hampden.* Includes Gay's 'Beggar's Opera,' Addison's 'Cato,' Rowe's 'Jane Shore,' Fielding's 'Tragedy of Tragedies, or, Tom Thumb the Great,' Lillo's 'George Barnwell,' Colman and Garrick's 'Clandestine Marriage,' and Cumberland's 'West Indian.' 818

English Galaxy of Shorter Poems, The. Chosen and Edited by *Gerald Bullett.* 959

English Religious Verse. Edited by *G. Lacey May.* An anthology from the Middle Ages to the present day, including some 300 poems by 150 authors. 937

Everyman, and Medieval Miracle Plays. New edition edited by *A. C. Cawley*, M.A., PH.D. Forewords to individual plays. 381

Fitzgerald, Edward (1809–83). See 'Persian Poems.'

11

Fletcher, John (1579–1625). *See* Beaumont.

Ford, John (1586–1639). *See* Webster.

Goethe, Johann Wolfgang von (1749–1832).
FAUST. Both parts of the tragedy which are the core of Goethe's life-work, in the re-edited translation of *Sir Theodore Martin*. (*See also* Biography, Essays.) 335

Golden Book of Modern English Poetry, The. Edited by *Thomas Caldwell* and *Philip Henderson*, containing some 300 poems by 130 poets, from T. E. Brown to Stephen Spender and C. Day Lewis. 921

Golden Treasury of English Songs and Lyrics, The, 1861. Compiled by Francis Turner Palgrave (1824–97). Enlarged edition, containing 88-page supplement. 96

Golden Treasury of Longer Poems, The. Revised edition (1954) with new supplementary poems. An anthology ranging from Chaucer to Walter de la Mare. 746

Goldsmith, Oliver (1728–74).
POEMS AND PLAYS. Edited, with Introduction, by *Austin Dobson*. 415
(*See also* Fiction.)

Gray, Thomas (1716–71).
POEMS: WITH A SELECTION OF LETTERS AND ESSAYS. Introduction by *John Drinkwater*, and biographical notes by *Lewis Gibbs*. 628

Heine, Heinrich (c. 1797–1856).
PROSE AND POETRY. With Matthew Arnold's essay on Heine. 911

Ibsen, Henrik (1828–1906).
A DOLL'S HOUSE, 1879; THE WILD DUCK, 1884; and THE LADY FROM THE SEA, 1888. Translated by *R. Farquharson Sharp* and *Elanor Marx-Aveling*. 494
GHOSTS, 1881; THE WARRIORS AT HELGELAND, 1857; and AN ENEMY OF THE PEOPLE, 1882. Translated by *R. Farquharson Sharp*. 552
PEER GYNT, 1867. Translated by *R. Farquharson Sharp*. 747
THE PRETENDERS, 1864; PILLARS OF SOCIETY, 1877; and ROSMERSHOLM, 1887. Translated by *R. Farquharson Sharp*. 659

Ingoldsby Legends, or *Mirth and Marvels*, by 'Thomas Ingoldsby, Esq.' Edited by *D. C. Browning*, M.A., B.LITT. 185

International Modern Plays. August Strindberg's 'Lady Julie,' Gerhard Hauptmann's 'Hannele,' Brothers Čapek's 'The Life of the Insects,' Jean Cocteau's 'The Infernal Machine,' and Luigi Chiarelli's 'The Mask and the Face.' Introduction by *Anthony Dent*. 989

Jonson, Ben (1573–1637).
PLAYS. Introduction by *Prof. F. E. Schelling*. 2 vols. Complete collection. 489–90

Keats, John (1795–1821).
POEMS. Revised, reset edition (1944). Edited by *Gerald Bullett*. 101
(*See also* Biography.)

Kingsley, Charles (1819–75).
POEMS. With Introduction by *Ernest Rhys*. (*See also* Fiction.) 793

La Fontaine, Jean de (1621–95).
FABLES, 1668. Presented complete in the renowned Sir Edward Marsh translation. 991

'Langland, William' (1330 ?–1400 ?).
PIERS PLOWMAN, 1362. Translation into modern English by *Donald* and *Rachel Attwater*. 571

Lawrence, David Herbert (1885–1930). (*See* Essays.)

Lessing, Gotthold Ephraim (1729–81).
LAOCOÖN, 1766, AND OTHER WRITINGS. Introduction by *W. A. Steel*. Contents: 'Laocoön'; 'Minna von Barnhelm,' 1767, a comedy in five acts; and 'Nathan the Wise,' 1779, his philosophical drama. 843

Longfellow, Henry Wadsworth (1807–82).
POEMS, 1823–66. 382

Marlowe, Christopher (1564–93).
PLAYS AND POEMS. New edition with an Introduction by *M. R. Ridley*, M.A. 383

Milton, John (1608–74).
POEMS. New edition by *Prof. B. A. Wright*, M.A., based on Milton's editions and manuscripts. With a new Introduction by *Prof. Wright*. (*See also* Essays.) 384

Minor Elizabethan Drama. 2 vols. Vol. I. Tragedy. Norton and Sackville's 'Gorboduc,' Kyd's 'Spanish Tragedy,' Peele's 'David and Bethsabe,' and 'Arden of Feversham.' Vol. II. Comedy. Udall's 'Ralph Roister Doister,' Lyly's 'Endimion,' Peele's 'Old Wives' Tale,' Greene's 'Friar Bacon and Friar Bungay,' etc. Introduction by *Prof. A. Thorndike*. Glossary. 491–2

Minor Poets of the Seventeenth Century. The Poems of Thomas Carew, Sir John Suckling, Lord Herbert, Richard Lovelace. Edited and revised by *R. G. Howarth*, B.A., B.LITT., F.R.S.L. 873

Modern Plays. R. C. Sherriff's 'Journey's End,' W. Somerset Maugham's 'For Services Rendered,' Noel Coward's 'Hay Fever,' A. A. Milne's 'The Dover Road,' Arnold Bennett and Edward Knoblock's 'Milestones.' Introduction by *John Hadfield*. 942.

Molière, Jean Baptiste de (1622–73).
COMEDIES. Introduction by *Prof. F. C. Green*. 2 vols. 830–1

New Golden Treasury, The. Introduction by *Ernest Rhys*. A companion to Palgrave (q.v.), giving earlier lyrics than he did, and also later. 695

Omar Khayyám (d. 1123 ?). (*See under* Persian Poems.)

Palgrave, Francis Turner (1824–97). *See* 'Golden Treasury of English Songs and Lyrics, The.'   96

Persian Poems. Selected and edited by *Prof. A. J. Arberry*, M.A., LITT.D., F.B.A.   996

Poe, Edgar Allan (1809–49).
   POEMS AND ESSAYS. Introduction by *Andrew Lang.*   (*See also* Fiction.) 791

Poems of our Time. An Anthology edited by *Richard Church*, C.B.E., *M. M. Bozman* and *Edith Sitwell*, D.LITT., D.B.E. Nearly 400 poems by about 130 poets.   981

Pope, Alexander (1688–1744).
   COLLECTED POEMS. Edited with Intro. (1956) by *Prof. Bonamy Dobrée*, O.B.E., M.A.
760

Restoration Plays. Introduction by *Edmund Gosse.* Includes Dryden's 'All for Love,' Wycherley's 'The Country Wife,' Congreve's 'The Way of the World,' Otway's 'Venice Preserved,' Farquhar's 'Beaux-Stratagem,' Vanbrugh's 'Provoked Wife,' Etherege's 'Man of Mode.'   604

Rossetti, Dante Gabriel (1828–82).
   POEMS AND TRANSLATIONS. Introduction by *E. G. Gardner.*   627

Shakespeare, William (1564–1616).
   A Complete Edition, based on Clark and Wright's Cambridge text, and edited by *Oliphant Smeaton.* With biographical Introduction, Chronological Tables and full Glossary. 3 vols.
        Comedies, 153; Histories, Poems and Sonnets, 154; Tragedies, 155

Shelley, Percy Bysshe (1792–1822).
   POETICAL WORKS. Introduction by *A. H. Koszul.* 2 vols.   257–8

Sheridan, Richard Brinsley (1751–1816).
   COMPLETE PLAYS. Introduction and notes by *Lewis Gibbs.*   95

Silver Poets of the Sixteenth Century. Edited by *Gerald Bullett.* The works of Sir Thomas Wyatt (1503–42), Henry Howard, Earl of Surrey (1517?–47), Sir Philip Sidney (1554–86), Sir Walter Ralegh (1552–1618) and Sir John Davies (1569–1626.)   985

Spenser, Edmund (1552–99).
   THE FAERIE QUEENE. Introduction by *Prof. J. W. Hales*, and Glossary. 2 vols. The reliable Morris text and glossary are used for this edition.   443–4
   THE SHEPHERD'S CALENDAR, 1579; and OTHER POEMS. Introduction by *Philip Henderson.*   879

Stevenson, Robert Louis (1850–94).
   POEMS. A CHILD'S GARDEN OF VERSES, 1885; UNDERWOODS, 1887; SONGS OF TRAVEL, 1896; and BALLADS, 1890, Introduction by *Ernest Rhys.*   768
        (*See also* Essays, Fiction, Travel.)

Swinburne, Algernon Charles (1837–1909).
   POEMS AND PROSE. A selection, edited with an Intro. by *Richard Church.*   961

Synge, J. M. (1871–1909).
   PLAYS, POEMS AND PROSE. Introduction by *Michaél Mac Liammóir.*   968

Tchekhov, Anton (1860–1904).
   PLAYS AND STORIES. 'The Cherry Orchard,' 'The Seagull,' 'The Wood Demon,' 'Tatyana Riepin' and 'On the Harmfulness of Tobacco' are included, as well as 13 of his best stories. The translation is by *S. S. Koteliansky.* Introduction by *David Magarshack.*   941

Tennyson, Alfred, Lord (1809–92).
   POEMS. A comprehensive edition (1950), with an Introduction by *Mildred Bozman.* 2 vols.   44, 626

Twenty-four One-Act Plays. Enlarged edition, new Introduction by *John Hampden.* Contains plays by T. S. Eliot, Sean O'Casey, Laurence Housman, W. B. Yeats, James Bridie, Noel Coward, Lord Dunsany, Wolf Mankowitz and others.   947

Webster, John (1580?–1625?), and **Ford, John** (1586–1639).
   SELECTED PLAYS. Introduction by *Prof. G. B. Harrison*, M.A., PH.D. In one volume: 'The White Devil,' 'The Duchess of Malfi,' 'The Broken Heart,' ''Tis Pity She's a Whore.'   899

Whitman, Walt (1819–92).
   LEAVES OF GRASS, 1855–92. New edition (1947) by *Dr Emory Holloway.*   573

Wilde, Oscar (1854–1900).
   PLAYS, PROSE WRITINGS, AND POEMS. Edited, with Introduction, by *Hesketh Pearson.* Including the two plays, 'The Importance of Being Earnest' and 'Lady Windermere's Fan'; his novel, 'The Picture of Dorian Gray' the poem, 'The Ballad of Reading Gaol'; the essay, 'The Soul of Man,' etc.   858

Wordsworth, William (1770–1850).
   POEMS. Edited, with Introductory study, notes, bibliography and full index, by *Philip Wayne*, M.A.   203, 311, 998

REFERENCE

Reader's Guide to Everyman's Library. Compiled by *A. J. Hoppé.* This volume is a new compilation and gives in one alphabetical sequence the names of all the authors, titles and subjects in Everyman's Library and its supplementary series, Everyman's Reference Library and the Children's Illustrated Classics.   889

Many volumes formerly included in Everyman's Library reference section are now included in Everyman's Reference Library and are bound in larger format.

ROMANCE

Aucassin and Nicolette, with other Medieval Romances. Translated, with Introduction, by *Eugene Mason.* 497

Boccaccio, Giovanni (1313–75).
DECAMERON, 1471. Translated by *J. M. Rigg*, 1903. Introduction by *Edward Hutton*, 2 vols. Unabridged. 845–6

Bunyan, John (1628–88).
PILGRIM'S PROGRESS, Parts I and II, 1678–84. Reset edition. Introduction by *Prof. G. B. Harrison*, M.A., PH.D. *(See also* Theology and Philosophy.) 204

Cervantes, Saavedra Miguel de (1547–1616).
DON QUIXOTE DE LA MANCHA. Translated by *P. A. Motteux*. Notes by *J. G. Lockhart.* Introduction and supplementary Notes by *L. B. Walton*, M.A., B.LITT. 2 vols. 385–6

Chrétien de Troyes (fl. 12th cent.).
ARTHURIAN ROMANCES ('Erec et Enide'; 'Cligés'; 'Yvain' and 'Lancelot'). Translated into prose, with Introduction, notes and bibliography, by *William Wistar Comfort.* 698

Kalevala, or The Land of Heroes. Translated from the Finnish by W. F. Kirby. 2 vols. 259–60

Mabinogion, The. Translated with Introduction by *Thomas Jones*, M.A., D.LITT., and *Gwyn Jones*, M.A. 97

Malory, Sir Thomas (fl. 1400 ?–70).
LE MORTE D'ARTHUR. Introduction by *Sir John Rhys.* 2 vols. 45–6

Marie de France (12th century), LAYS OF, AND OTHER FRENCH LEGENDS. Eight of Marie's 'Lais' and two of the anonymous French love stories of the same period translated with an Introduction by *Eugene Mason.* 557

Njal's Saga. THE STORY OF BURNT NJAL (written about 1280–90). Translated from the Icelandic by *Sir G. W. Dasent* (1861). Introduction (1957) and Index by *Prof. Edward Turville-Petre*, M.A. 558

Rabelais, François (1494 ?–1553).
THE HEROIC DEEDS OF GARGANTUA AND PANTAGRUEL, 1532–5. Introduction by *D. B. Wyndham Lewis.* 2 vols. A complete unabridged edition of Urquhart and Motteux's translation, 1653–94. 826–7

SCIENCE

Boyle, Robert (1627–91).
THE SCEPTICAL CHYMIST, 1661. Introduction by *M. M. Pattison Muir.* 559

Darwin, Charles (1809–82).
THE ORIGIN OF SPECIES, 1859. The sixth edition embodies Darwin's final additions and revisions. New Introduction (1956) by *W. R. Thompson*, F.R.S. 811
(See also Travel and Topography.)

Eddington, Arthur Stanley (1882–1944).
THE NATURE OF THE PHYSICAL WORLD, 1928. Introduction by *Sir Edmund Whittaker*, F.R.S., O.M. 922

Euclid (fl. *c.* 330–*c.* 275 B.C.).
THE ELEMENTS OF EUCLID. Edited by *Isaac Todhunter*, with Introduction by *Sir Thomas L. Heath*, K.C.B., F.R.S. 891

Faraday, Michael (1791–1867).
EXPERIMENTAL RESEARCHES IN ELECTRICITY, 1839–55. With Plates and Diagrams, and an appreciation by *Prof. John Tyndall.* 576

Harvey, William (1578–1657).
THE CIRCULATION OF THE BLOOD. Introduction by *Ernest Parkyn.* 262

Howard, John (1726 ?–90).
THE STATE OF THE PRISONS, 1777. Intro. and Notes by *Kenneth Ruck.* 835

Marx, Karl (1818–83).
CAPITAL, 1867. Translated by *Eden* and *Cedar Paul.* 2 vols. Introduction by *Prof. G. D. H. Cole.* 848–9

Mill, John Stuart (1806–73). *See* Wollstonecraft.

Owen, Robert (1771–1858).
A NEW VIEW OF SOCIETY, 1813; and OTHER WRITINGS. Introduction by *G. D. H. Cole.* 799

Pearson, Karl (1857–1936).
THE GRAMMAR OF SCIENCE, 1892. 939

Ricardo, David (1772–1823).
THE PRINCIPLES OF POLITICAL ECONOMY AND TAXATION, 1817. Introduction by *Prof. Michael P. Fogarty*, M.A. 590

Smith, Adam (1723–90).
THE WEALTH OF NATIONS, 1766. Intro. by *Prof. Edwin Seligman.* 2 vols. 412–13

White, Gilbert (1720–93).
A NATURAL HISTORY OF SELBORNE, 1789. New edition (1949). Introduction and Notes by *R. M. Lockley.* 48

Wollstonecraft, Mary (1759–97), THE RIGHTS OF WOMAN, 1792; and Mill, John Stuart (1806–73), THE SUBJECTION OF WOMEN, 1869. New Introduction by *Pamela Frankau.* 825

THEOLOGY AND PHILOSOPHY

Ancient Hebrew Literature. Being the Old Testament and Apocrypha, arranged by *R. Bruce Taylor*. 4 vols. *Volumes I and IV only in print.* 253, 256

Bacon, Francis (1561–1626).
THE ADVANCEMENT OF LEARNING, 1605. Introduction, Notes, Index and Glossary, by *G. W. Kitchin*. (*See also* Essays.) 719

Berkeley, George (1685–1753).
A NEW THEORY OF VISION, 1709. Introduction by *A. D. Lindsay*, C.B.E., LL.D. 483

Browne, Sir Thomas (1605–82).
RELIGIO MEDICI, 1642. New Introduction by *Halliday Sutherland*, M.D., F.R.S.L. 92

Bunyan, John (1628–88).
GRACE ABOUNDING, 1666; and THE LIFE AND DEATH OF MR BADMAN, 1658. Introduction by *Prof. G. B. Harrison*, M.A., PH.D. (*See also* Romance.) 815

Chinese Philosophy in Classical Times. Covering the period 1500 B.C.–A.D. 100. Edited and translated, with Introduction and Notes. 973

Descartes, René (1596–1650).
A DISCOURSE ON METHOD, 1637; MEDITATIONS ON THE FIRST PHILOSOPHY, 1641; and PRINCIPLES OF PHILOSOPHY, 1644. Translated by *Prof. J. Veitch*. Introduction by *A. D. Lindsay*, C.B.E., LL.D. 570

Ellis, Havelock (1859–1939).
SELECTED ESSAYS. Sixteen essays, with an Introduction by *J. S. Collis.* 930

Gore, Charles (1853–1932).
THE PHILOSOPHY OF THE GOOD LIFE, 1930. 924

Hindu Scriptures. Edited by *Nicol Macnicol*, M.A., D.LITT., D.D. Foreword by *Rabindranath Tagore.* 944

Hobbes, Thomas (1588–1679).
LEVIATHAN, 1651. Introduction by *A. D. Lindsay*, C.B.E., LL.D. 691

Hooker, Richard (1554–1600).
OF THE LAWS OF ECCLESIASTICAL POLITY, 1597. Introduction by *G. C. Morris*, M.A. 201–2

Hume, David (1711–76).
A TREATISE OF HUMAN NATURE, 1739. Intro. by *A. D. Lindsay*, C.B.E., LL.D. 2 vols. 548–9

James, William (1842–1910).
PAPERS ON PHILOSOPHY. Introduction by *Prof. C. M. Bakewell.* 739

Kant, Immanuel (1724–1804).
CRITIQUE OF PURE REASON, 1781. With an Introduction by *A. D. Lindsay*, C.B.E., LL.D. Translated by *J. M. D. Meiklejohn.* 909

King Edward VI (1537–53).
THE FIRST (1549) AND SECOND (1552) PRAYER BOOKS. Introduction by *Bishop Gibson.* 448

Koran, The. Rodwell's Translation, 1861. Intro. by *Rev. G. Margoliouth*, M.A. 380

Law, William (1686–1761).
A SERIOUS CALL TO A DEVOUT AND HOLY LIFE, 1728. Introduction by *Prof. Norman Sykes*, F.B.A., M.A., D.PHIL. 91

Leibniz, Gottfried Wilhelm (1646–1716).
PHILOSOPHICAL WRITINGS. Selected and translated by *Mary Morris*, with an Introduction by *C. R. Morris*, M.A. 905

Locke, John (1632–1704).
TWO TREATISES OF CIVIL GOVERNMENT, 1690. Introduction by *Prof. W. S. Carpenter.* (*See also* Essays.) 751

Malthus, Thomas Robert (1766–1834).
AN ESSAY ON THE PRINCIPLE OF POPULATION, 1798. New Introduction by *Prof. Michael P. Fogarty*, M.A. 2 vols. 692–3

Mill, John Stuart (1806–73).
UTILITARIANISM, 1863; LIBERTY, 1859; and REPRESENTATIVE GOVERNMENT, 1861. Introduction by *A. D. Lindsay*, C.B.E., LL.D. (*See also* Science.) 482

More, Sir Thomas (1478–1535).
UTOPIA, 1516; and DIALOGUE OF COMFORT AGAINST TRIBULATION, 1553. Introduction by *John Warrington*. Revised edition (1951). 461

New Testament, The. 93

Newman, John Henry, Cardinal (1801–90).
APOLOGIA PRO VITA SUA, 1864. Introduction by *Sir John Shane Leslie.* 636
(*See also* Essays.)

Nietzsche, Friedrich Wilhelm (1844–1900).
THUS SPAKE ZARATHUSTRA, 1883–91. Translated by *Prof. A. Tille* and revised by *M. M. Bozman*. Introduction (1957) by *Prof. Roy Pascal*, M.A., D.LITT. 892

Paine, Thomas (1737–1809).
RIGHTS OF MAN, 1792. Introduction by *Arthur Seldon.* 718

Pascal, Blaise (1623–62).
PENSÉES, 1670. Translated by *John Warrington*. Introduction by *Louis Lafuma*. This translation is from Lafuma's second edition. 874

Ramayana and Mahabharata. Condensed into English verse by *Romesh Dutt*, C.I.E. 403

Robinson, Wade (1838–76).
THE PHILOSOPHY OF ATONEMENT, AND OTHER SERMONS, 1875. Introduction by
F. B. Meyer.   637
Rousseau, Jean Jacques (1712–78).
THE SOCIAL CONTRACT, 1762; and OTHER ESSAYS. Introduction by *G. D. H. Cole.*
(See also Biography, Essays.) 660
Saint Augustine (353–430).
CONFESSIONS. Dr Pusey's Translation, 1838, with Introduction by *A. H. Armstrong,* M.A.   200
THE CITY OF GOD. Complete text of John Healey's Elizabethan Translation, 1610.
Edited by *R. V. G. Tasker,* M.A., B.D., with an Introduction by *Sir Ernest Barker.*
2 vols.   982–3
Saint Francis (1182–1226).
THE LITTLE FLOWERS; THE MIRROR OF PERFECTION (by Leo of Assisi); and THE
LIFE OF ST FRANCIS (by St Bonaventura). Introduction by *Thomas Okey.*   485
Spinoza, Benedictus de (1632–77).
ETHICS, 1677; and ON THE CORRECTION OF THE UNDERSTANDING, 1687. Translated
by *Andrew Boyle.* New Introduction by *T. S. Gregory.*   481
Swedenborg, Emanuel (1688–1772).
THE TRUE CHRISTIAN RELIGION, 1771. New and unabridged translation by *F.
Bayley.* Introduction by *Dr Helen Keller.* 960 pages.   893
Thomas à Kempis (1380?–1471).
THE IMITATION OF CHRIST, 1471.   484
Thomas Aquinas (1225–74).
SELECTED WRITINGS. Selected and edited by *Father M. C. D'Arcy.*   953

TRAVEL AND TOPOGRAPHY

Borrow, George (1803–81).
THE BIBLE IN SPAIN, 1842. Introduction by *Edward Thomas.*   151
WILD WALES: the People, Language and Scenery, 1862. Introduction by *David
Jones,* C.B.E., the painter and Borrovian.   *(See also* Fiction.) 49
Boswell, James (1740–95).
JOURNAL OF A TOUR TO THE HEBRIDES WITH SAMUEL JOHNSON, 1786. Edited, with
a new Introduction, by *Lawrence F. Powell,* M.A., HON. D.LITT.   387
Calderón de la Barca, Mme (1804–82).
LIFE IN MEXICO, 1843. Introduction by *Manuel Romero De Terreros.*   664
Cobbett, William (1762–1835).
RURAL RIDES, 1830. Introduction by *Asa Briggs,* M.A., B.SC. 2 vols.   638–9
Cook, James (1728–79).
VOYAGES OF DISCOVERY. Edited by *John Barrow,* F.R.S., F.S.A. Introduction by
Guy Pocock, M.A.   99
Crèvecœur, J. Hector St John de (1735–1813).
LETTERS FROM AN AMERICAN FARMER, 1782. Intro. and Notes by *W. Barton Blake.*
640
Darwin, Charles (1809–82).
THE VOYAGE OF THE 'BEAGLE,' 1839.   *(See also* Science.) 104
Defoe, Daniel (1661?–1731).
A TOUR THROUGH ENGLAND AND WALES, 1724–6. Intro. by *G. D. H. Cole.* 2 vols.
(See also Fiction.) 820–1
Kinglake, Alexander (1809–91).
EOTHEN, 1844. Introduction by *Harold Spender.*   337
Lane, Edward William (1801–76).
MANNERS AND CUSTOMS OF THE MODERN EGYPTIANS, 1836. With a new Introduction
by *Moursi Saad el-Din,* of the Egyptian Ministry of Education.   315
Park, Mungo (1771–1806).
TRAVELS. Introduction (1954) by *Prof. Ronald Miller,* M.A., PH.D.   205
Polo, Marco (1254–1324).
TRAVELS. Introduction by *John Masefield.*   306
Portuguese Voyages, 1498–1663. Edited by *Charles David Ley.*   986
Stevenson, Robert Louis (1850–94).
AN INLAND VOYAGE, 1878; TRAVELS WITH A DONKEY, 1879; and THE SILVERADO
SQUATTERS, 1883. New Introduction by *M. R. Ridley,* M.A.   766
(See also Essays, Poetry, Fiction.)
Stow, John (1525?–1605).
THE SURVEY OF LONDON. The fullest account of Elizabethan London.   589
Wakefield, Edward Gibbon (1796–1862).
A LETTER FROM SYDNEY, AND OTHER WRITINGS ON COLONIZATION. Introduction
by *Prof. R. C. Mills.*   828
Waterton, Charles (1782–1865).
WANDERINGS IN SOUTH AMERICA, 1825. Introduction by *Edmund Selous.*   772